GUIDE TO FOOD STORAGE

Follow this guide for food storage, and you can be sure that what's in your freezer, refrigerator, and pantry is fresh-tasting and ready to use in recipes.

IN THE FREEZER
(At -10° to 0° F)

DAIRY
Cheese, hard	3 months
Cheese, soft	2 weeks
Egg substitute	6 months
Egg whites	6 months
Egg yolks	8 months
Ice cream, sherbet	1 month

FRUITS AND VEGETABLES
Commercially frozen fruits	1 year
Commercially frozen vegetables	8 to 12 months

MEATS, POULTRY, AND SEAFOOD
Beef, Lamb, and Veal
Ground, uncooked, and all cuts, cooked	3 months
Roasts and steaks, uncooked	9 months

Pork
Ground, uncooked, and all cuts, cooked	3 months
Roasts and chops, uncooked	6 months

Poultry
All cuts, cooked	1 month
Boneless or bone-in pieces, uncooked	6 months

Seafood
Bass, perch, trout, and shellfish	3 months
Cod, flounder, and halibut	6 months

IN THE REFRIGERATOR
(At 34° to 40° F)

DAIRY
Butter	4 months
Buttermilk	1 to 2 weeks
Cheese, commercial grated Parmesan	1 year
Cheese, block	3 to 4 weeks
Cream cheese, fat-free, light, and ⅓-less-fat	2 weeks
Egg substitute, opened	3 days
Fresh eggs in shell	1 month

MEATS, POULTRY, AND SEAFOOD
Beef, Lamb, Pork, and Veal
Ground and stew meat, uncooked	1 to 2 days
Roasts, uncooked	2 to 4 days
Steaks and chops, uncooked	3 to 5 days

Chicken, Turkey, and Seafood
All cuts, uncooked	1 to 2 days

FRUITS AND VEGETABLES
Apples, beets, cabbage, carrots, celery, citrus fruits, eggplant, and parsnips	2 to 3 weeks
Apricots, asparagus, berries, cauliflower, cucumbers, mushrooms, okra, peaches, pears, peas, peppers, plums, salad greens, and summer squash	2 to 4 days
Corn, husked	1 day

IN THE PANTRY
Keep these at room temperature for 6 to 12 months.

BAKING AND COOKING STAPLES
Baking powder
Biscuit and baking mix
Broth, canned
Cooking spray
Honey
Mayonnaise, fat-free, low-fat, and light (unopened)
Milk, canned evaporated fat-free
Milk, nonfat dry powder
Mustard, prepared (unopened)
Oils, olive and vegetable
Pasta, dried
Peanut butter
Rice, instant and regular
Salad dressings, bottled (unopened)
Seasoning sauces, bottled
Tuna, canned

FRUITS, LEGUMES, AND VEGETABLES
Fruits, canned
Legumes (beans, lentils, peas), dried or canned
Tomato products, canned
Vegetables, canned

Panini Margherita,
page 126

Loaded Nachos,
page 82

"Meaty" Meatless
Spaghetti with Fresh
Spinach,
page 75

Chocolate-Cappuccino
Meringue Cookies,
page 173

Weight Watchers®

ANNUAL RECIPES
for SUCCESS
2006

Oxmoor House®

©2005 by Oxmoor House, Inc.

Book Division of Southern Progress Corporation

P.O. Box 2262, Birmingham, Alabama 35201-2262

ISBN: 0-8487-3018-6

ISSN: 1526-1565

Printed in the United States of America

First Printing 2005

Be sure to check with your health-care provider before making any changes in your diet.
Weight Watchers® and **POINTS**® are registered trademarks of *Weight Watchers* International, Inc., and are used under license by Healthy Living, Inc.

OXMOOR HOUSE, INC.

Editor in Chief: Nancy Fitzpatrick Wyatt

Executive Editor: Katherine M. Eakin

Copy Chief: Allison Long Lowery

WeightWatchers® ANNUAL RECIPES FOR SUCCESS 2006

Editor: Alyson Moreland Haynes

Nutrition Editor: Holley Contri Johnson, M.S., R.D.

Successes Editor: Heather Averett

Copy Editor: Diane Rose

Editorial Assistants: Julie Boston, Brigette Gaucher

Designer: Donna Sophronia-Sims

Director, Test Kitchens: Elizabeth Tyler Luckett

Assistant Director, Test Kitchens: Julie Christopher

Test Kitchens Staff: Kristi Carter, Nicole Lee Faber, Kathleen Royal Phillips, Elise Weis, Kelley Self Wilton

Senior Photographer: Jim Bathie

Senior Photo Stylist: Kay E. Clarke

Photo Stylist: Amy Wilson

Publishing Systems Administrator: Rick Tucker

Director of Production: Laura Lockhart

Production Assistant: Faye Porter Bonner

To order additional copies of this publication or any others, call 1-205-765-6400.

For more books to enrich your life, visit **oxmoorhouse.com**

CONTRIBUTORS

Copy Editors: Lisa C. Bailey, Dolores Hydock

Successes Writer: Jan Walsh

Indexer: Mary Ann Laurens

Photographer: Lee Harrelson

Photo Stylist: Katie Stoddard

Recipe Development: Gretchen Brown, Katherine Cobbs, Caroline Grant, Ana Kelly, Joyce Lock, Jackie Mills, Carolyn Williams

Editorial Intern: Mary Catherine Shamblin

Test Kitchens Intern: Meg Kozinski

Nutrition Intern: Rachel Quinlivan

COVER: Blueberry-Lemon Muffins, page 26

CONTENTS

Welcome! Enjoy the foods you love, live a healthier lifestyle, and feel good about the new you.

WeightWatchers® *Annual Recipes for Success 2006* helps you make positive changes in your life that will help you lose weight and adopt a healthier lifestyle. To get you started and keep you motivated to succeed, this *Weight Watchers* book offers:

- Over 275 **great-tasting recipes**
- More than 45 **color photographs** of delicious recipes
- Step-by-step recipe instructions, how-to photography, prep and cook times, and **Test Kitchens Secrets**
- Five **Special-Occasion Menus** with a game plan for preparing each meal
- Four weeks of **7-Day Menu Planners** that incorporate many recipes from the cookbook plus some new ones, too
- Nine truly inspiring **Weight-Loss Success Stories** from people just like you

Our Recipes

All recipes in **WeightWatchers®** *Annual Recipes for Success 2006* are approved by our Test Kitchens experts. Each recipe is tested at least once—sometimes two or three times—to ensure that it's easy to prepare and tastes terrific. But we've also made sure that each recipe contains the healthiest ingredients. This year, we've paid particular attention to the power foods—the foods that research indicates pack the most nutritional punch of vitamins, minerals, and fiber. We've included information on why each food is important to a healthy diet, along with recipe suggestions that will help you incorporate these foods into your eating plan. The following are our top five power foods for 2006.

Top Five Power Foods

Dairy products: Dairy foods are excellent sources of calcium and protein. Better yet, low-fat dairy products have been shown to aid in weight loss. Fat-free milk, 1% low-fat milk, low-fat or fat-free yogurt, and reduced-fat cheese should be included in a healthy eating plan. For tasty ways to include dairy products in your diet, try **Peppermint White Hot Chocolate** (page 20) and **Mexican Pizza** (page 62).

Fats: It's important to know good fats from bad fats for healthy eating. Two fats, saturated fat and trans fat, have been linked to increased risks for heart disease and cancer. But monounsaturated and polyunsaturated fats have been shown to lower cholesterol and decrease the risk for certain diseases. Olive oil, canola oil, peanut oil, almonds, peanuts, and avocados are examples of monounsaturated fats. Find these ingredients throughout the recipes in this book, including **Avocado Salad** (page 120) and **Almond-Crusted Turkey Cutlets with Papaya-Orange Salsa** (page 107). Corn, soybean, safflower, and cottonseed oils are great sources of polyunsaturated fats, as is fish. And there's a whole chapter devoted to fish beginning on page 51. So enjoy the good fats in moderation and limit your intake of saturated and trans fats.

Fruits: Fruit contains many healing phytochemicals that aid in fighting disease, slow the aging process, and improve your overall health. Blueberries are the #1 fruit that provide the antioxidant power you need. So bake up a batch of **Blueberry-Lemon Muffins** (page 26) and enjoy one warm from the oven while you read more about the health benefits of blueberries on page 27.

Veggies: Low in calories and high in fiber, veggies play an important role in healthy weight-loss maintenance. Dark, leafy greens, such as spinach and Swiss chard, are the big hitters for nutrients. Spinach contains folic acid, vitamin A, potassium, magnesium, and lutein—a phytochemical that protects the eyes from harmful UV rays. Swiss chard contains fiber, iron, and potassium as well as vitamins A, C, E, and K. For dinner tonight, why not try **Spinach, Mushroom, and Feta Frittata** (page 73) or **Chicken and Swiss Chard Manicotti Crêpes** (page 97).

Whole grains: Whole grains contain fiber, which not only helps with digestion, but also helps you feel full—a benefit that can help you eat less and control your weight. Try to include barley, brown rice, bulgur, oatmeal, quinoa, wheat berries, and wild rice in your meals. Filling recipes that include grains are **Tabbouleh** (page 121), **Confetti Barley Pilaf** (page 148), and **Roasted Chicken with Wild Rice Soup** (page 163).

Real-Life Success Stories

You'll find inspiration from nine individuals as they share their weight-loss stories.

"Weight Watchers gave me consistency, not tricks."

(Read the rest of Tajuana Gordon's story on page 41.)

OUR FAVORITE RECIPES

First tested in our kitchens, these recipes are now our staff's family favorites at home.

Blueberry-Lemon Muffins, 4 *POINTS* value (page 26). These tender muffins are delicious for breakfast or as a snack. Or serve them with chicken salad for lunch.

Chocolate-Peanut Butter Cup Pie, 6 *POINTS* value (page 169). Chocolate ice cream, hot fudge, and peanut butter cups fill a chocolate cookie crust in this heavenly four-ingredient dessert.

Frozen Pumpkin Layer Cake, 7 *POINTS* value (page 40). Angel food cake is layered with sugared pecans, pumpkin butter, and ice cream in this delectable dessert that's drizzled with caramel topping.

Ooey-Gooey Brownies, 4 *POINTS* value (page 171). We savored each indulgent bite of these chocolate-frosted, fudgy squares.

"Meaty" Meatless Spaghetti with Fresh Spinach, 8 *POINTS* value (page 75). Even meat-lovers will enjoy this Italian classic.

Polenta Triangles with Goat Cheese and Wild Mushrooms, 8 *POINTS* value (page 76). Upscale flavors make this recipe ideal for entertaining.

Chicken Tacos Verde, 5 *POINTS* value (page 98). Roasted tomatillos and Anaheim chiles are key flavor components in the green sauce that fills these soft tacos.

Green Beans in Vinaigrette with Feta, 1 *POINTS* value (page 144). Liven up any dinner plate with this colorful and tasty side.

Zucchini and Avocado Soup with Cucumber Salsa, 2 *POINTS* value (page 153). We loved the combination of flavors and textures in this chilled soup.

About Our Recipes

WeightWatchers® *Annual Recipes for Success 2006* gives you the nutrition facts you need to make your life easier. We've provided the following useful information with every recipe:

- A number calculated through the ***POINTS*®** Food System (a component of the ***POINTS*** Weight-Loss System) from *Weight Watchers* International, Inc.
- Diabetic exchange values for those who use them as a guide for planning meals
- A complete nutrient analysis per serving

POINTS FOOD SYSTEM

Every recipe in the book includes a number calculated using the ***POINTS*** Food System. Each food is given a ***POINTS*** value based on a formula that considers the calorie, fat, and fiber content of the food. Foods with more calories and fat receive high numbers, while fruits and vegetables receive low numbers. For more information about the *Weight Watchers* program and a meeting nearest you, call 1-800-651-6000 or visit online at www.weightwatchers.com.

DIABETIC EXCHANGES

Exchange values are provided for people with diabetes and for those who use them for calorie-controlled diets. All foods within a certain group contain approximately the same amount of nutrients and calories, so one serving of a food from a food group can be substituted or exchanged for one serving of any other item on the list. The food groups are starch, fruit, milk, vegetable, meat, and fat. The exchange values are based on the *Exchange Lists for Meal Planning* developed by the American Diabetes Association and The American Dietetic Association.

NUTRIENT ANALYSIS

Each recipe has a complete list of nutrients, including calories, protein, fat, saturated fat, carbohydrates, dietary fiber, cholesterol, iron, sodium, and calcium. This information makes it easy for you to use the recipes in any weight-loss program that you may choose to follow. Measurements are abbreviated g (grams) and mg (milligrams). Numbers are based on these assumptions:

- Unless otherwise indicated, meat, poultry, and fish refer to skinned, boned, and cooked servings.
- When we give a range for an ingredient (3 to 3½ cups flour, for instance), we calculate using the lesser amount.
- Some alcohol calories evaporate during heating; the analysis reflects that.
- Only the amount of marinade absorbed by the food is used in calculation.
- Garnishes and optional ingredients are not included in an analysis.

Nutritional values used in our calculations either come from The Food Processor, Version 7.5 (ESHA Research) or are provided by food manufacturers.

Appetizers & Beverages

CREAMY ASIAN DIP

prep: 11 minutes • cook: 4 minutes
other: 1 hour

*You can make this party-pleasing dip
a day ahead and store it in the
refrigerator. Serve it with boiled shrimp
or an assortment of vegetables, such
as blanched sugar snap peas, bell
pepper strips, carrot sticks, cucumber
slices, and broccoli florets.*

½ cup light mayonnaise
¼ cup reduced-fat sour cream
(such as Breakstone's)
2 tablespoons chopped fresh basil
2 tablespoons low-sodium soy
sauce
1 tablespoon rice vinegar
2 teaspoons sesame seeds, toasted
1 teaspoon sugar
1 teaspoon minced fresh ginger
2 teaspoons sesame oil
½ teaspoon dry mustard
⅛ teaspoon ground red pepper
⅛ teaspoon salt
⅛ teaspoon freshly ground black
pepper

1. Combine all ingredients in a small
bowl; stir well. Cover and chill at
least 1 hour. **YIELD:** 8 servings (serving
size: 2 tablespoons).

POINTS value: 2; **Exchanges:** 1½ Fat
Per serving: CAL 81 (83% from fat); PRO 0.8g;
FAT 7.5g (sat 1.8g); CARB 2.7g; FIB 0.2g;
CHOL 9mg; IRON 0.2mg; SOD 295mg; CALC 16mg

HOMEMADE GREEN GODDESS DIP

prep: 7 minutes • other: 1 hour

*Serve this creamy dip with a platter
full of fresh vegetables. We
recommend baby carrots, cucumber
slices, grape tomatoes, red bell pepper
strips, and celery sticks. It also makes
a delicious dressing when spooned
over iceberg wedges.*

1 cup light mayonnaise
½ cup plain low-fat yogurt
1 tablespoon chopped fresh chives
1 tablespoon chopped fresh parsley
1 tablespoon chopped fresh
tarragon
1 tablespoon tarragon vinegar or
white wine vinegar
4 canned anchovy fillets, chopped
(about 1 tablespoon)
2 teaspoons fresh lemon juice
½ teaspoon salt
¼ teaspoon white pepper
¼ teaspoon minced garlic

1. Combine all ingredients in a
blender or food processor; process
1 to 2 minutes or until smooth and
herbs are finely chopped. Spoon dip
into a serving bowl. Serve chilled with
assorted fresh vegetables. **YIELD:** 12
servings (serving size: 2 tablespoons).

POINTS value: 2; **Exchanges:** 1½ Fat
Per serving: CAL 76 (81% from fat); PRO 1.0g;
FAT 6.9g (sat 1.1g); CARB 2.6g; FIB 0.1g;
CHOL 8mg; IRON 0.1mg; SOD 298mg; CALC 24mg

ROASTING VEGETABLES

To get the very best results when
you roast vegetables, here are a
few things to keep in mind.
• Cut vegetables into uniform-
size pieces so they will cook
evenly.
• Spread out the pieces of food
in a single layer in the roasting
pan. If they are piled up on the
pan, not all of the pieces will
get roasted.
• Stir once while the vegetables
are roasting so that all sides can
get evenly browned.
• Use very high heat (no lower
than 400°) to get the best flavor.

ROASTED VEGGIE DIP

prep: 10 minutes • cook: 37 minutes

2 cups sliced zucchini (about
2 small)
1 cup sliced carrot (about
1 medium)
1 medium onion, cut into
¼-inch slices (about 1 cup)
1 medium red or yellow bell
pepper, sliced (about 1½ cups)
3 garlic cloves, peeled
Olive oil-flavored cooking spray
1 (8-ounce) tub whipped cream
cheese
½ teaspoon salt
¼ teaspoon ground red pepper
¼ teaspoon black pepper
3 tablespoons shredded fresh
Parmesan cheese
48 melba toast rounds

1. Preheat oven to 475°.

2. Place first 5 ingredients in a shallow roasting pan coated with cooking spray. Coat vegetables with cooking spray; toss well. Bake at 475° for 35 minutes or until browned, stirring occasionally. Cool slightly; coarsely chop.

3. Preheat broiler.

4. Combine whipped cream cheese and next 3 ingredients in a medium bowl. Stir in roasted vegetables. Spoon into a 1-quart dish. Sprinkle with Parmesan cheese, and broil 2 minutes or until cheese is melted. Serve immediately with melba toast rounds. YIELD: 24 servings (serving size: 2 tablespoons dip and 2 melba toast rounds).

POINTS value: 1; Exchanges: 1 Vegetable, 1 Fat
Per serving: CAL 68 (49% from fat); PRO 2.1g; FAT 3.8g (sat 2.3g); CARB 6.7g; FIB 0.9g; CHOL 11mg; IRON 0.4mg; SOD 132mg; CALC 27mg

BABA GHANOUSH

prep: 8 minutes • cook: 1 hour
other: 1 hour

Eggplant, garlic, and tahini are key ingredients in this Middle Eastern puree. Serve it as either a spread for sandwiches or as a dip with vegetables or pita bread.

1	large eggplant (about 2 pounds)
¼	cup chopped fresh parsley
2	garlic cloves, peeled and halved
¼	cup fresh lemon juice (about 2 lemons)
2	tablespoons tahini (sesame-seed paste)
1	tablespoon extravirgin olive oil
½	teaspoon salt
⅛	teaspoon ground cumin

1. Preheat oven to 400°.

2. Pierce eggplant several times with a fork; place on a foil-lined baking sheet. Bake at 400° for 1 hour or until tender. Cool slightly. Cut eggplant in half lengthwise, and place, cut sides down, in a colander; drain 30 minutes. Scrape out eggplant pulp; discard shell.

3. Place parsley and garlic in a food processor; pulse 6 to 7 times until minced. Add eggplant pulp, lemon juice, and remaining ingredients; process until smooth. Spoon into a bowl; cover and let stand at room temperature 30 minutes to allow flavors to blend. YIELD: 9 servings (serving size: ¼ cup).

POINTS value: 1; Exchanges: 1 Vegetable, 1 Fat
Per serving: CAL 61 (46% from fat); PRO 1.7g; FAT 3.5g (sat 0.5g); CARB 7.4g; FIB 0.3g; CHOL 0mg; IRON 0.5mg; SOD 136mg; CALC 18mg

MEXICAN BEAN DIP

prep: 9 minutes • cook: 6 minutes
other: 5 minutes

2	(15.5-ounce) cans pink or pinto beans, rinsed and drained
1	(10-ounce) can diced tomatoes and green chiles, undrained
1	teaspoon olive oil
⅔	cup chopped onion
1	garlic clove, minced
¼	teaspoon salt
¼	teaspoon ground cumin
¼	cup reduced-fat sour cream
¼	cup (1 ounce) shredded Monterey Jack cheese
1	tablespoon chopped fresh cilantro
6	ounces baked tortilla chips (about 120 chips)

1. Place half of beans in a bowl; mash with a fork or potato masher. Stir in remaining whole beans. Drain tomatoes, reserving ¼ cup liquid.

2. Heat oil in a medium cast-iron or nonstick skillet over medium-high heat. Add onion and garlic; sauté 2 minutes or until tender. Add beans, tomatoes, ¼ cup reserved tomato liquid, salt, and cumin; cook 3 minutes or until thoroughly heated, stirring constantly. Remove from heat, and let stand 2 minutes. Stir in sour cream.

3. Sprinkle cheese evenly over bean mixture; cover and let stand 3 minutes or until cheese melts. Sprinkle with cilantro, and serve warm with chips. YIELD: 12 servings (serving size: ¼ cup dip and 10 chips).

POINTS value: 2; Exchanges: ½ Starch, ½ Fat
Per serving: CAL 123 (19% from fat); PRO 4.4g; FAT 2.6g (sat 1.0g); CARB 21.4g; FIB 3.6g; CHOL 5mg; IRON 1.0mg; SOD 343mg; CALC 72mg

KEEPING HERBS FRESH

- To keep herbs fresh for up to 1 week, trim about ¼ inch from the stem, and rinse with cold water. Loosely wrap herbs in a damp paper towel, and seal in a zip-top plastic bag filled with air. Refrigerate. Check herbs daily, as some of them lose their flavor after a couple of days.

- Place herbs stem-down in a glass with water (let water cover about 1 inch of the stem ends); change the water every other day. Most herbs will keep for up to 1 week this way.

SEEDING AND DICING AN AVOCADO

1. Cut into the avocado all the way around using a sharp knife. You'll hit the large seed in the center, so don't expect to be able to cut all the way through the fruit. Once you've cut around it, twist both sides, and pull the halves apart. Take the knife and whack the seed; pull up to remove the seed, which will be stuck on the knife blade.
2. Using a table knife, score the flesh

of each avocado half in a checkerboard pattern to dice the avocado. Gently run the knife blade between the flesh and the peel to loosen the diced pieces of avocado.

YIELD: 16 servings (serving size: 2 tablespoons spread and 2 melba toast rounds).

POINTS value: 1; **Exchanges:** ½ Starch, ½ Lean Meat
Per serving: CAL 68 (25% from fat); PRO 6.6g; FAT 1.8g (sat 0.4g); CARB 5.8g; FIB 0.9g; CHOL 14mg; IRON 0.3mg; SOD 172mg; CALC 16mg

KALAMATA HUMMUS

prep: 7 minutes

1   (15.5-ounce) can chickpeas (garbanzo beans), undrained
¼   cup chopped green onions
3   tablespoons finely chopped pitted kalamata olives
2   teaspoons olive oil
2   teaspoons fresh lemon juice
¼   teaspoon salt
⅛   teaspoon ground cumin
⅛   teaspoon freshly ground black pepper
2   (6-inch) pitas, each cut into 8 wedges

1. Drain chickpeas; set aside 3 tablespoons liquid and 1 cup chickpeas. Reserve remaining chickpeas and liquid for another use.
2. Place chickpeas, reserved liquid, and next 7 ingredients in a food processor; process 2 minutes or until very smooth. Serve immediately, or cover and chill at least 1 hour. Serve with pita wedges. YIELD: 8 servings (serving size: 2 tablespoons hummus and 2 pita wedges).

POINTS value: 2; **Exchanges:** 1 Starch, ½ Fat
Per serving: CAL 92 (19% from fat); PRO 3.0g; FAT 2.0g (sat 0.3g); CARB 15.7g; FIB 1.9g; CHOL 0mg; IRON 1.0mg; SOD 272mg; CALC 28mg

BLACK BEAN-AVOCADO SALSA

prep: 15 minutes

Branch out beyond tortilla chips when you serve this salsa. Try it spooned over burgers and grilled chicken, or pair it with grilled shrimp or steak and warm flour tortillas for soft tacos.

2   cups diced peeled avocado (about 2 small)
⅓   cup chopped red onion
2   tablespoons fresh lime juice
¼   teaspoon salt
1   (15-ounce) can black beans, rinsed and drained

1. Combine all ingredients in a bowl, and toss gently. Serve immediately, or cover and chill up to 2 hours. YIELD: 12 servings (serving size: about ¼ cup).

POINTS value: 1; **Exchanges:** ½ Starch, ½ Vegetable
Per serving: CAL 56 (54% from fat); PRO 1.5g; FAT 3.8g (sat 0.6g); CARB 5.7g; FIB 2.5g; CHOL 0mg; IRON 0.6mg; SOD 89mg; CALC 12mg

SMOKED TROUT SPREAD

prep: 10 minutes • other: 1 hour

This easy make-ahead spread is ideal for entertaining.

1   (8-ounce) package smoked trout (such as Ducktrap)
1   (8-ounce) block fat-free cream cheese, softened
2   tablespoons finely chopped red onion
1   tablespoon fresh lemon juice
2   teaspoons extravirgin olive oil
1   teaspoon prepared horseradish
1   teaspoon Dijon mustard
⅛   teaspoon salt
2   drops hot sauce (such as Tabasco)
32   melba toast rounds

1. Flake trout with a fork; discard any skin and bones.
2. Place fish and cream cheese in a food processor; process until smooth. Spoon into a bowl. Add onion and next 6 ingredients, stirring until well blended. Cover and chill at least 1 hour. Serve with melba toast rounds.

ARTICHOKE AND SWEET GARLIC BRUSCHETTA

prep: 14 minutes • cook: 10 minutes
other: 15 minutes

Look for bottled garlic in jars in the produce section of your local supermarket. It's slightly sweet and mellow in flavor compared to minced fresh garlic. White balsamic vinegar is used when the flavor of balsamic vinegar is desired but the dark color is not. It's ideal for use in salads, pasta dishes, and sauces for fish and poultry.

1   (9-ounce) package frozen artichoke hearts
½   cup (2 ounces) shredded part-skim mozzarella cheese
2   tablespoons grated fresh Parmesan cheese
1   tablespoon bottled chopped garlic
1   tablespoon fresh lemon juice
1   tablespoon olive oil
2   teaspoons white balsamic vinegar or white wine vinegar
¼   teaspoon salt
¼   teaspoon freshly ground black pepper
8   (½-inch-thick) slices diagonally cut Italian bread (about 8 ounces)

1. Preheat broiler.
2. Cook artichokes according to package directions; cool and coarsely chop. Combine artichokes and next 8 ingredients in a bowl; stir well.
3. Place bread slices on a baking sheet; broil 2 minutes on each side or until lightly toasted. Divide artichoke mixture evenly among bread slices. Broil 1 minute or until cheese melts. YIELD: 8 servings (serving size: 1 bruschetta).

POINTS value: 3; **Exchanges:** 1 Starch, ½ High-Fat Meat
Per serving: CAL 134 (30% from fat); PRO 5.6g; FAT 4.5g (sat 1.4g); CARB 17.7g; FIB 2.7g; CHOL 5mg; IRON 1.1mg; SOD 307mg; CALC 89mg

GOAT CHEESE BRUSCHETTA

prep: 15 minutes • cook: 11 minutes

¼   cup (2 ounces) goat cheese, softened
¼   cup (2 ounces) tub-style light cream cheese with chives and onion
¼   teaspoon freshly ground black pepper
16 (½-inch-thick) slices diagonally cut French bread baguette
Olive oil-flavored cooking spray
4   garlic cloves, halved
¾   cup marinara sauce
1   tablespoon tomato paste with Italian herbs
2   tablespoons thinly sliced fresh basil

1. Preheat oven to 400°.
2. Combine first 3 ingredients in a small bowl; mash with a fork until well blended and smooth.
3. Coat both sides of bread slices with cooking spray; rub each side of bread with garlic halves. Place bread in a single layer on a foil-lined baking sheet. Bake at 400° for 6 minutes or until lightly toasted. Turn slices over, and spread about 1½ teaspoons cheese mixture on each slice. Bake at 400° for 5 minutes or until cheese mixture is warm.

4. While bruschetta bakes, heat marinara sauce and tomato paste in a small saucepan over medium heat. Spoon about 1½ teaspoons sauce down center of each bruschetta; sprinkle with basil. Serve immediately. YIELD: 16 servings (serving size: 1 bruschetta).

POINTS value: 1; **Exchange:** ½ Starch
Per serving: CAL 50 (33% from fat); PRO 2.0g; FAT 1.8g (sat 1.0g); CARB 6.3g; FIB 0.5g; CHOL 3mg; IRON 0.4mg; SOD 144mg; CALC 21mg

CATALAN TOMATO BRUSCHETTA

prep: 10 minutes • cook: 4 minutes

8   (1-ounce) slices rustic white, sourdough, or French bread
4   garlic cloves, halved
4   small ripe tomatoes, each cut in half crosswise
1   tablespoon extravirgin olive oil
½   teaspoon kosher salt
¼   teaspoon freshly ground black pepper

1. Preheat grill or broiler.
2. Place bread slices on grill rack or baking sheet; grill or broil 2 to 3 minutes on each side or until lightly browned.
3. Rub 1 side of each bread slice with 1 garlic clove half and 1 tomato half (tomato pulp will rub off onto bread). Discard garlic and tomato peels. Drizzle oil evenly over bread slices; sprinkle evenly with salt and pepper. YIELD: 8 servings (serving size: 1 bruschetta).

POINTS value: 2; **Exchange:** 1 Starch
Per serving: CAL 86 (24% from fat); PRO 2.4g; FAT 2.5g (sat 0.2g); CARB 15.1g; FIB 1.7g; CHOL 0mg; IRON 0.6mg; SOD 260mg; CALC 19mg

GRILLED PITA WEDGES WITH CARAMELIZED ONIONS

prep: 9 minutes • cook: 30 minutes

The sweet flavor of caramelized onion pairs beautifully with Asiago cheese in this delectable appetizer.

2   teaspoons olive oil
1   medium onion, thinly sliced
1   teaspoon sugar
⅛   teaspoon salt
½   teaspoon chopped fresh thyme
⅓   cup fat-free ricotta cheese
¼   cup (1 ounce) shredded Asiago cheese
¼   teaspoon minced garlic
Dash of freshly ground black pepper
2   (6-inch) pitas
Cooking spray

1. Prepare grill.
2. Heat oil in a large nonstick skillet over medium heat. Add onion, sugar, and salt; sauté 3 minutes. Reduce heat to medium-low, and cook 20 minutes or until very golden brown, stirring frequently. Stir in ½ teaspoon thyme.
3. Combine ricotta cheese, Asiago cheese, garlic, and pepper; stir well. Set aside.
4. Coat pitas with cooking spray. Place on grill rack; cover and grill 2 minutes on each side or just until crisp. Remove pitas from grill. Spread cheese mixture evenly over warm pitas; top evenly with caramelized onion.
5. Cover grill rack with foil, and place pitas on foil. Cover and grill 2 minutes or until pitas are thoroughly heated. Cut each pita into 4 wedges, and serve immediately.
YIELD: 4 servings (serving size: 2 wedges).

*POINTS value: 3; **Exchanges:** 1½ Starch, 1 Fat **Per serving:** CAL 162 (26% from fat); PRO 6.6g; FAT 4.5g (sat 1.6g); CARB 22.6g; FIB 1.1g; CHOL 10mg; IRON 0.9mg; SOD 275mg; CALC 132mg*

MELON-MINT PINWHEELS

prep: 22 minutes

For a quick alternative, combine the cheese and mint leaves with 1 cup cubed cantaloupe, and toss gently.

¼   small firm ripe cantaloupe
3½ ounces Manchego or Romano cheese, thinly shaved
18 large mint leaves
6   lime wedges

1. Cut cantaloupe wedge in half lengthwise; remove rind from cantaloupe. Cut 18 long, thin strips from side edge of cantaloupe wedges using a vegetable peeler or cheese slicer. Reserve remaining cantaloupe for another use.
2. Divide cheese and mint leaves evenly among cantaloupe strips, placing cheese and mint at 1 end of each cantaloupe strip. Roll cantaloupe strips around cheese and mint, jelly-roll fashion, to create a pinwheel; secure with wooden picks. Arrange pinwheels on a platter, and serve with lime wedges. YIELD: 6 servings (serving size: 3 pinwheels).

*POINTS value: 2; **Exchanges:** ¼ Fruit, ½ High-Fat Meat **Per serving:** CAL 71 (57% from fat); PRO 5.4g; FAT 4.5g (sat 2.8g); CARB 2.3g; FIB 0.1g; CHOL 17mg; IRON 0.2mg; SOD 202mg; CALC 179mg*

HOW TO MAKE MELON PINWHEELS

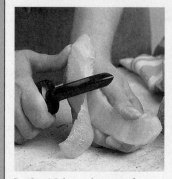

1. Cut 18 long, thin strips from side edge of peeled cantaloupe wedges using a vegetable peeler.

2. Divide cheese and mint leaves evenly among cantaloupe strips, placing cheese and mint at 1 end of each cantaloupe strip. Roll cantaloupe strips around cheese and mint, jelly-roll fashion, to create a pinwheel.

CAPRESE SKEWERS

(pictured on page 21)
prep: 15 minutes

Insalata Caprese is a simply prepared Italian salad made from vine-ripened tomatoes, fresh mozzarella, fresh basil, and olive oil. We've taken similar ingredients and threaded them onto wooden skewers to create these bursting-with-flavor handheld appetizers.

30   grape or cherry tomatoes
30   fresh basil leaves
4   ounces part–skim mozzarella cheese, cut into 30 (½-inch) cubes
2   tablespoons balsamic vinegar
1   tablespoon extravirgin olive oil
½   teaspoon kosher salt
¼   teaspoon freshly ground black pepper

1. Thread tomatoes, basil leaves, and mozzarella cheese cubes alternately onto 10 (6-inch) wooden skewers. Place skewers on a serving platter.
2. Combine vinegar and oil in a small bowl; stir well with a whisk. Drizzle vinegar mixture evenly over skewers, and sprinkle with salt and pepper. Serve immediately, or cover and chill until ready to serve. YIELD: 10 servings (serving size: 1 skewer).

POINTS value: 1; **Exchanges:** 1 Vegetable, ½ Lean Meat
Per serving: CAL 58 (57% from fat); PRO 3.5g; FAT 3.7g (sat 1.6g); CARB 3.0g; FIB 0.7g; CHOL 6mg; IRON 0.3mg; SOD 157mg; CALC 91mg

STUFFED POTATO SKINS

(pictured on page 21)
prep: 15 minutes • cook: 1 hour and 16 minutes • other: 30 minutes

4   (8-ounce) baking potatoes
3   slices precooked bacon (such as Armour Ready Crisp)
Butter-flavored cooking spray
½   teaspoon freshly ground black pepper
¼   teaspoon salt
1   cup (4 ounces) preshredded reduced-fat colby-Jack cheese
⅓   cup refrigerated light ranch dressing

1. Preheat oven to 425°.
2. Pierce potatoes with a fork (do not wrap in foil). Bake potatoes at 425° for 1 hour or until tender. Cool potatoes 30 minutes.
3. Meanwhile, heat bacon slices according to package directions until crisp; crumble bacon. Set aside.
4. Cut potatoes lengthwise into 4 wedges. Scoop out as much potato pulp as possible without tearing potato skins. Reserve potato pulp for another use.
5. Arrange potato skins on a foil-lined baking sheet. Coat both sides of potato skins with cooking spray; sprinkle evenly with pepper and salt. Bake at 425° for 13 minutes or until lightly browned. Sprinkle skins evenly with bacon and cheese; bake an additional 3 minutes or until cheese melts. Serve immediately with dressing. YIELD: 16 servings (serving size: 1 potato skin and 1 teaspoon dressing).

POINTS value: 1; **Exchanges:** ½ Starch, ½ Fat
Per serving: CAL 55 (46% from fat); PRO 2.5g; FAT 2.7g (sat 1.1g); CARB 4.6g; FIB 0.3g; CHOL 6mg; IRON 0.3mg; SOD 144mg; CALC 52mg

CRABMEAT SEVICHE

prep: 31 minutes • other: 30 minutes

*Traditional seviche consists of raw fish marinated in lime juice, onions, tomatoes, and chiles. The acid in the lime juice firms the flesh of the fish and turns it opaque. We used crabmeat instead of fish and added more vegetables for an upscale appetizer that makes an impressive presentation when served in a small wide-mouthed glass. For a light meal with a **POINTS** value of 3, serve ¾ cup seviche stuffed in a tomato or on a bed of salad greens.*

½   cup finely chopped red onion
½   cup chopped plum tomato (about 2)
½   cup diced seeded peeled cucumber
⅓   cup chopped fresh cilantro
⅓   cup fresh lime juice (about 3 limes)
¼   cup chopped green onions
¼   cup orange juice
¼   cup ketchup
2   teaspoons hot sauce
1   jalapeño pepper, seeded and minced
1   pound lump crabmeat, shell pieces removed

1. Combine first 10 ingredients in a bowl; toss well. Carefully fold in crabmeat so as not to break up crab pieces. Cover and chill at least 30 minutes. YIELD: 6 servings (serving size: about ½ cup).

POINTS value: 2; **Exchanges:** 1 Vegetable, 2 Very Lean Meat
Per serving: CAL 108 (13% from fat); PRO 16.0g; FAT 1.6g (sat 0.2g); CARB 7.5g; FIB 0.8g; CHOL 76mg; IRON 1.0mg; SOD 326mg; CALC 94mg

EASY PICKLED SHRIMP

prep: 13 minutes • cook: 4 minutes
other: 24 hours

The key to success with this recipe is not overcooking the shrimp. As the shrimp marinate, the vinegar and lemon continue to firm the texture or "cook" the shrimp. Leftovers can be refrigerated in the marinade up to 2 days and will become even tastier with time. Serve with crusty bread to soak up the flavorful juices, if desired.

2   teaspoons olive oil
36 peeled and deveined medium
    shrimp (about 1 pound)
2   garlic cloves, minced
½   cup thinly sliced green bell
    pepper strips
1   medium red onion, quartered
    and thinly sliced crosswise
½   lemon, thinly sliced
1½ cups water
½   cup white vinegar
1   tablespoon Old Bay seasoning
2   tablespoons fresh lemon juice
1   teaspoon pickling spice
½   teaspoon crushed red pepper
¼   teaspoon salt
3   bay leaves

1. Heat oil in a large nonstick skillet over medium-high heat. Add shrimp and garlic; sauté 3 minutes or until shrimp begin to turn pink. Place shrimp in an 11 x 7-inch baking dish. Top evenly with bell pepper, onion, and lemon slices.
2. Combine water and next 7 ingredients in a small bowl; pour evenly over shrimp. Cover and marinate shrimp at least 24 hours. Remove shrimp from marinade with a slotted spoon, and serve with wooden picks.

YIELD: 6 servings (serving size: 6 shrimp).

POINTS value: 2; **Exchanges:** 2 Very Lean Meat
Per serving: CAL 92 (24% from fat); PRO 15.7g; FAT 2.4g (sat 0.4g); CARB 1.3g; FIB 0.1g; CHOL 146mg; IRON 2.3mg; SOD 377mg; CALC 32mg

APRICOT-CURRY GLAZED SHRIMP SKEWERS

prep: 27 minutes • cook: 4 minutes

Served on mini skewers, this appetizer is the ideal finger food for a party. Or you can use longer skewers and serve this as a main dish for three people. A main-dish serving has a POINTS value of 5. Complete the meal with steamed rice and sugar snap peas.

24 large shrimp (about 1⅓ pounds)
½   cup apricot preserves
2   tablespoons light stick butter,
    melted
1   tablespoon Dijon mustard
2   teaspoons curry powder
1½ teaspoons rice vinegar
¼   teaspoon garlic powder
⅛   teaspoon salt
⅛   teaspoon ground red pepper
⅛   teaspoon freshly ground black
    pepper
Cooking spray

1. Prepare grill or broiler.
2. Peel and devein shrimp, leaving tails intact.
3. Combine preserves and next 8 ingredients in a medium bowl; stir well. Reserve ½ cup preserves mixture to serve as a dip with shrimp skewers. Add shrimp to remaining preserves mixture in bowl; toss well to coat.

4. Thread 3 shrimp onto each of 8 (6-inch) skewers. Place skewers on a grill rack or broiler pan coated with cooking spray; cook 2 minutes on each side or until shrimp are done. Serve immediately with reserved ½ cup preserves mixture. YIELD: 8 servings (serving size: 1 skewer and 1 tablespoon glaze).
Note: If using wooden skewers, soak them in water 30 minutes before grilling or broiling.

POINTS value: 3; **Exchanges:** 1 Fruit, 2 Very Lean Meat
Per serving: CAL 123 (17% from fat); PRO 12.6g; FAT 2.4g (sat 1.2g); CARB 13.6g; FIB 0.4g; CHOL 117mg; IRON 2.2mg; SOD 239mg; CALC 33mg

BUYING SHRIMP

To save prep time, instead of peeling and deveining shrimp yourself, you can buy peeled and deveined raw shrimp at the seafood counter of most supermarkets. The chart below shows how much peeled and deveined shrimp to buy when the recipe calls for unpeeled shrimp.

Unpeeled Raw Shrimp		Peeled and Deveined Raw Shrimp
⅔ pound	=	½ pound
1 pound	=	¾ pound
1⅓ pounds	=	1 pound
2 pounds	=	1½ pounds
2⅔ pounds	=	2 pounds
4 pounds	=	3 pounds

HOISIN-GLAZED MINI MEATBALLS

prep: 20 minutes • cook: 25 minutes

Freeze unbaked meatballs on a baking sheet. Place frozen meatballs in a zip-top plastic bag; freeze up to 1 month. Thaw meatballs, and bake as directed.

1 pound ground beef, extralean
½ cup finely chopped green bell pepper
¼ cup quick-cooking oats
¼ cup finely chopped onion
3 tablespoons low-sodium soy sauce
¼ teaspoon salt
1 large egg
Cooking spray
¼ cup apricot fruit spread (such as Smucker's Simply Fruit)
3 tablespoons hoisin sauce
1 tablespoon apple cider vinegar
⅛ to ¼ teaspoon crushed red pepper

1. Preheat oven to 350°.
2. Combine first 7 ingredients in a medium bowl. Shape into 32 balls. Place meatballs on a foil-lined broiler pan coated with cooking spray. Bake at 350° for 25 minutes or until done.
3. Meanwhile, combine apricot fruit spread and next 3 ingredients in a medium saucepan; stir well. Place over medium-high heat, and cook 2 minutes or until thoroughly heated, stirring frequently. Remove from heat; add meatballs, tossing to coat. Serve immediately. YIELD: 32 servings (serving size: 1 meatball).

POINTS value: 1; **Exchange:** 1 Very Lean Meat
Per serving: CAL 39 (36% from fat); PRO 3.4g; FAT 1.5g (sat 0.6g); CARB 2.7g; FIB 0.2g; CHOL 12mg; IRON 0.4mg; SOD 105mg; CALC 3mg

ANTIPASTO

prep: 12 minutes • other: 30 minutes

Traditionally served "before the food," this classic appetizer makes an elegant but easy start to just about any Italian meal.

1 (12-ounce) bottle roasted red bell peppers, drained and cut into 1-inch-wide strips
1 (8-ounce) jar whole mushrooms, drained
2 (6-ounce) jars marinated quartered artichoke hearts, undrained
2 tablespoons chopped fresh basil
1 teaspoon minced garlic
½ teaspoon freshly ground black pepper
8 (½-ounce) slices prosciutto or capocollo
8 (½-ounce) slices turkey salami
8 (¾-ounce) slices light provolone or part-skim mozzarella cheese

1. Combine first 6 ingredients in a bowl; toss well. Cover; let stand 30 minutes, or chill overnight.
2. Arrange prosciutto, salami, and cheese around outside edge of a large serving platter. Spoon bell pepper mixture onto center of platter.
YIELD: 8 servings (serving size: 1 slice prosciutto, 1 slice salami, 1 slice cheese, and about ⅔ cup bell pepper mixture).

POINTS value: 3; **Exchanges:** 1 Vegetable, 2 Lean Meat, ½ Fat
Per serving: CAL 161 (46% from fat); PRO 15.2g; FAT 8.6g (sat 2.6g); CARB 8.0g; FIB 2.2g; CHOL 24mg; IRON 0.7mg; SOD 905mg; CALC 170mg

BUFFALO CHICKEN SKEWERS

prep: 24 minutes • cook: 6 minutes

1 pound chicken breast tenders (9 tenders)
¼ cup hot sauce (such as Frank's Red Hot)
3 tablespoons light stick butter, melted
1 tablespoon ketchup
¼ teaspoon salt
Cooking spray
18 (4-inch) celery sticks
¾ cup refrigerated light blue cheese dressing (such as Marie's)

1. Preheat broiler.
2. Place each chicken tender between 2 sheets of heavy-duty plastic wrap; pound to ¼-inch thickness using a meat mallet or rolling pin. Cut each tender in half crosswise.
3. Combine hot sauce, butter, and ketchup in a medium bowl; reserve 3 tablespoons mixture, and set aside. Add chicken to remaining mixture in bowl; toss well. Thread 1 piece of chicken onto each of 18 (6-inch) skewers. Sprinkle evenly with salt.
4. Cover a large baking sheet with foil, and coat with cooking spray. Place skewers on prepared pan, and broil 3 minutes on each side or until done. Brush with reserved 3 tablespoons hot sauce mixture. Serve with celery and dressing. YIELD: 18 servings (serving size: 1 skewer, 1 celery stick, and 2 teaspoons dressing).
Note: If using wooden skewers, soak them in water 30 minutes before broiling.

POINTS value: 1; **Exchanges:** 1 Very Lean Meat, ½ Fat
Per serving: CAL 54 (33% from fat); PRO 6.0g; FAT 1.9g (sat 0.8g); CARB 2.9g; FIB 0.3g; CHOL 18mg; IRON 0.3mg; SOD 162mg; CALC 5mg

PEPPERMINT WHITE HOT CHOCOLATE

(pictured on page 22)
prep: 8 minutes • cook: 8 minutes

4   cups 1% low-fat milk
7   hard peppermint candies,
     crushed
½   cup white chocolate chips
½   teaspoon pure peppermint
     extract
4   hard peppermint candies
1   tablespoon light-colored corn
     syrup
6   tablespoons frozen fat-free
     whipped topping, thawed

1. Cook milk in a heavy saucepan over medium heat until warm (do not boil). Add 7 crushed peppermint candies, stirring until candies dissolve. Add white chocolate, stirring with a whisk until chocolate melts. Cook until tiny bubbles form around edge of pan (do not boil), stirring constantly with a whisk. Remove from heat; stir in extract.
2. Coarsely crush 2 peppermint candies; set aside. Finely crush remaining 2 peppermint candies. Coat rims of 6 mugs with corn syrup. Place 2 finely crushed peppermint candies in a saucer; dip rim of each mug in candies to coat.
3. Pour ⅔ cup hot chocolate into each mug; top each serving with 1 tablespoon whipped topping. Sprinkle 2 coarsely crushed candies evenly over topping. YIELD: 6 servings.

POINTS value: 5; **Exchanges:** 2 Starch, 1 Fat
Per serving: CAL 199 (28% from fat); PRO 6.2g;
FAT 6.3g (sat 3.8g); CARB 29.4g; FIB 0.0g;
CHOL 7mg; IRON 0.1mg; SOD 105mg; CALC 228mg

LIME-MINT SPARKLERS

prep: 5 minutes

This refreshing beverage is fashioned after the mojito, a Cuban cocktail made with rum, freshly squeezed lime juice, sprigs of mint, sugar, and club soda. If you want to serve it in the spirit of tradition, add 1½ ounces of rum to each serving. Make the presentation special by rubbing the rims of martini glasses with a lime wedge and inverting the glasses onto a shallow plate of salt or sugar to coat. Serve the beverage over crushed ice in the prepared glasses with sprigs of fresh mint and lime wedges. The rum cocktail has a POINTS value of 3 per serving.

1   (1-liter) bottle sparkling water
     (such as Perrier), chilled
1   (6-ounce) can frozen limeade
     concentrate, undiluted
⅓   cup minced fresh mint
Crushed ice

1. Combine sparkling water, limeade, and mint in a large pitcher; stir until concentrate thaws and mixture is well blended. Serve over crushed ice. YIELD: 6 servings (serving size: 1 cup).

POINTS value: 1; **Exchange:** ½ Starch
Per serving: CAL 57 (0% from fat); PRO 0.1g;
FAT 0.0g (sat 0.0g); CARB 14.1g; FIB 0.2g;
CHOL 0mg; IRON 0.1mg; SOD 5mg; CALC 30mg

RHUBARB-STRAWBERRY FLOAT

prep: 6 minutes • cook: 14 minutes
other: 1 hour

Serve this float the old-fashioned way—with a straw and a spoon.

½   pound frozen chopped rhubarb
     (about 1½ cups)
1   cup water
4   packets sugar substitute with
     aspartame (such as Equal)
1   cup strawberry low-fat ice
     cream (such as Healthy
     Choice)

1. Combine rhubarb and water in a medium saucepan. Bring to a boil; cover, reduce heat, and simmer 10 minutes. Strain rhubarb through a sieve into a bowl; discard solids. Add sugar substitute to rhubarb liquid; stir well to dissolve. Cover and chill at least 1 hour.
2. Spoon ½ cup ice cream into each of 2 glasses. Pour ½ cup rhubarb liquid over ice cream in each glass. YIELD: 2 servings.

POINTS value: 2; **Exchanges:** ½ Fruit, 1 Low-Fat Milk
Per serving: CAL 141 (14% from fat); PRO 2.7g;
FAT 2.1g (sat 1.0g); CARB 27.5g; FIB 3.0g;
CHOL 0mg; IRON 0.3mg; SOD 37mg; CALC 320mg

Caprese Skewers,
page 17

Stuffed Potato Skins,
page 17

Peppermint White
Hot Chocolate,
page 20

Refrigerator Sweet
Potato Rolls,
page 30

Gingerbread Scones with
Lemon Glaze,
page 28

Breads

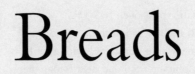

SPICY CHEDDAR DROP BISCUITS

prep: 12 minutes • cook: 10 minutes

If you have a timid palate, simply omit the ground red pepper.

1   cup low-fat baking mix (such as Bisquick)
1   cup (4 ounces) shredded light Cheddar cheese with jalapeño peppers (such as Cabot)
½   teaspoon garlic powder, divided
¼   teaspoon salt
¼   teaspoon ground red pepper, divided
½   cup low-fat buttermilk
Cooking spray
2   tablespoons light stick butter, melted

1. Preheat oven to 425°.
2. Lightly spoon baking mix into a dry measuring cup; level with a knife. Combine baking mix, cheese, ¼ teaspoon garlic powder, salt, and ⅛ teaspoon ground red pepper in a medium bowl. Add buttermilk, stirring just until moist (dough will be stiff). Spoon dough evenly into 8 mounds on a baking sheet coated with cooking spray. Bake at 425° for 10 minutes or until golden.
3. Combine remaining ¼ teaspoon garlic powder, remaining ⅛ teaspoon ground red pepper, and butter; brush over hot biscuits. Serve immediately.
YIELD: 8 servings (serving size: 1 biscuit).

POINTS value: 3; **Exchanges:** 1 Starch, 1 Fat
Per serving: CAL 111 (37% from fat); PRO 6.0g; FAT 4.7g (sat 2.7g); CARB 12.2g; FIB 0.2g; CHOL 13mg; IRON 0.6mg; SOD 367mg; CALC 135mg

PUMPKIN-WALNUT BISCUITS

prep: 17 minutes • cook: 26 minutes

2¼   cups all-purpose flour
⅓   cup yellow cornmeal
2   tablespoons light brown sugar
1   tablespoon baking powder
½   teaspoon salt
½   teaspoon ground cinnamon
⅓   cup chilled butter, cut into small pieces
¼   cup finely chopped walnuts, toasted
¾   cup canned unsweetened pumpkin
¾   cup fat-free milk
Cooking spray

1. Preheat oven to 400°.
2. Lightly spoon flour into dry measuring cups; level with a knife. Combine flour and next 5 ingredients in a bowl. Cut in butter with a pastry blender or 2 knives until mixture resembles coarse meal. Stir in walnuts.
3. Combine pumpkin and milk in a small bowl; stir well with a whisk. Add to flour mixture, stirring just until moist.
4. Turn dough out onto a heavily floured surface; knead lightly 5 times with floured hands. Pat dough into a 9-inch square; cut dough into 16 square biscuits. Place biscuits on a baking sheet coated with cooking spray.
5. Bake at 400° for 23 minutes or until lightly browned. Serve warm.
YIELD: 16 servings (serving size: 1 biscuit).

POINTS value: 3; **Exchanges:** 1 Starch, 1 Fat
Per serving: CAL 134 (34% from fat); PRO 3.1g; FAT 5.1g (sat 2.0g); CARB 19.2g; FIB 1.0g; CHOL 10mg; IRON 1.3mg; SOD 225mg; CALC 71mg

BLUEBERRY-LEMON MUFFINS

(pictured on cover)
prep: 22 minutes • cook: 20 minutes
other: 30 minutes

Traditional blueberry muffins get a twist of lemon and a sweet glaze to earn top scores from our Test Kitchens.

2   cups all-purpose flour
⅔   cup granulated sugar
1½   teaspoons baking powder
½   teaspoon baking soda
¼   teaspoon salt
1   cup fresh blueberries
1   tablespoon grated lemon rind, divided
¾   cup low-fat buttermilk
3   tablespoons butter, melted
1   tablespoon fresh lemon juice, divided
1   large egg, lightly beaten
Cooking spray
½   cup powdered sugar

1. Preheat oven to 400°.
2. Lightly spoon flour into dry measuring cups; level with a knife. Combine flour and next 4 ingredients in a medium bowl; stir well with a whisk. Add blueberries and 2 teaspoons lemon rind; toss gently. Make a well in center of mixture.
3. Combine buttermilk, butter, 1 teaspoon lemon juice, and egg in a bowl; stir well with a whisk. Add to flour mixture, stirring just until moist. Spoon batter into 12 muffin cups coated with cooking spray.
4. Bake at 400° for 17 to 18 minutes or until golden brown. Remove muffins from pan immediately; cool on a wire rack.

5. Combine powdered sugar, remaining 1 teaspoon lemon rind, and remaining 2 teaspoons lemon juice in a small bowl; stir until smooth. Drizzle glaze evenly over muffins. YIELD: 12 servings (serving size: 1 muffin).

POINTS value: 4; **Exchanges:** 2 Starch, ½ Fat
Per serving: CAL 184 (18% from fat); PRO 3.4g; FAT 3.7g (sat 1.7g); CARB 34.8g; FIB 0.9g; CHOL 26mg; IRON 1.2mg; SOD 206mg; CALC 57mg

---

GOT BLUE?

Blueberries have always been a natural source of nutrients and a sweet summer treat. The news on blueberries gets even better, though. Ranked first among the top twenty foods for antioxidant capacity by the USDA, blueberries contain plant compounds that provide anti-aging and cardiovascular benefits and help maintain urinary tract health. Antioxidants protect against cell damage that can lead to Alzheimer's, cancer, and heart disease.

In addition, these little berries are low in calories, high in fiber, and virtually fat-free, so they're great to use in all sorts of recipes. Although available year-round, it's best to buy blueberries when they are in season because they're less expensive. You can then freeze them for later use. Look for firm berries with a silvery frost, and discard any that are shriveled and moldy. Don't wash them until you are ready to use them, and store them in the refrigerator for up to 5 days.

ORANGE-GINGER CORN MUFFINS

prep: 10 minutes • cook: 18 minutes

1⅓ cups self-rising flour
⅔ cup self-rising yellow cornmeal
¼ cup sugar
¼ teaspoon baking soda
1 cup low-fat buttermilk
¼ cup egg substitute
¼ cup unsweetened applesauce
¼ cup orange marmalade
2 tablespoons canola or vegetable oil
1 teaspoon grated fresh ginger
1 teaspoon grated orange rind
Cooking spray

1. Preheat oven to 400°.
2. Lightly spoon flour and cornmeal into dry measuring cups; level with a knife. Combine flour, cornmeal, sugar, and baking soda in a medium bowl; stir well with a whisk. Combine buttermilk and next 6 ingredients in a bowl; stir well with a whisk. Add to flour mixture, stirring just until moist. Spoon batter into 12 muffin cups coated with cooking spray.
3. Bake at 400° for 18 minutes or until muffins spring back when touched lightly in center. Remove muffins from pan immediately; place on a wire rack. YIELD: 12 servings (serving size: 1 muffin).

POINTS value: 3; **Exchanges:** 1½ Starch, ½ Fat
Per serving: CAL 137 (17% from fat); PRO 3.2g; FAT 2.7g (sat 0.2g); CARB 25.4g; FIB 0.9g; CHOL 0mg; IRON 1.1mg; SOD 320mg; CALC 100mg

---

STICKY ORANGE ROLLS

prep: 15 minutes • cook: 27 minutes

As these rolls bake, a sweet brown-sugar syrup forms on the bottom of the pan. Then these gooey rolls are drizzled with an orange-flavored glaze.

1 (11-ounce) can refrigerated French bread dough
2 tablespoons light stick butter, melted
½ cup packed light brown sugar
1½ teaspoons ground cinnamon
2 teaspoons grated orange rind
Cooking spray
½ cup powdered sugar
1 tablespoon orange juice
¼ teaspoon vanilla extract

1. Preheat oven to 350°.
2. Remove dough from package, place on a lightly floured work surface, and carefully unroll dough.
3. Brush butter evenly over dough; sprinkle with brown sugar, cinnamon, and orange rind. Starting with a long edge, roll up, jelly-roll fashion; pinch seam to seal (do not seal ends of roll). Using a serrated knife, cut roll evenly into 12 slices. Place slices, cut sides down, in an 8-inch square baking pan coated with cooking spray.
4. Bake at 350° for 27 minutes or until tops are lightly browned. Place a plate upside down on top of pan; invert onto plate.
5. Combine powdered sugar, orange juice, and vanilla in a small bowl; drizzle over rolls. YIELD: 12 servings (serving size: 1 roll).

POINTS value: 3; **Exchanges:** 1½ Starch
Per serving: CAL 129 (12% from fat); PRO 2.6g; FAT 1.7g (sat 0.9g); CARB 26.3g; FIB 0.2g; CHOL 3mg; IRON 0.8mg; SOD 178mg; CALC 11mg

CHOCOLATE CHIP MINI SCONES

prep: 16 minutes • cook: 12 minutes

These scones freeze well and can be served at room temperature or reheated in a conventional oven.

3   tablespoons sugar, divided
⅛   teaspoon ground cinnamon
2   cups self-rising flour
¼   cup chilled butter, cut into small pieces
½   cup semisweet chocolate minichips
¾   cup low-fat buttermilk
Cooking spray

1. Preheat oven to 400°.
2. Combine 2 tablespoons sugar and cinnamon in a small bowl; set aside.
3. Lightly spoon flour into dry measuring cups; level with a knife. Combine flour and remaining 1 tablespoon sugar in a large bowl. Cut in butter with a pastry blender or 2 knives until mixture resembles coarse meal. Stir in minichips. Add buttermilk, stirring just until moist.
4. Turn dough out onto a lightly floured surface; knead lightly 4 to 5 times with floured hands. Pat dough out to ½-inch thickness; cut with a 1½-inch round cutter. Place on a baking sheet coated with cooking spray. Spray tops of scones lightly with cooking spray; sprinkle with cinnamon-sugar. Bake at 400° for 12 minutes or until golden. Serve warm. YIELD: 28 servings (serving size: 1 scone).

POINTS value: 1; **Exchanges:** ½ Starch, ½ Fat
Per serving: CAL 66 (35% from fat); PRO 1.2g; FAT 2.6g (sat 1.4g); CARB 9.9g; FIB 0.3g; CHOL 5mg; IRON 0.5mg; SOD 122mg; CALC 38mg

GINGERBREAD SCONES WITH LEMON GLAZE

(pictured on page 24)
prep: 13 minutes • cook: 10 minutes

2   cups all-purpose flour
¼   cup granulated sugar
2   teaspoons baking powder
1   teaspoon ground ginger
1   teaspoon ground cinnamon
¼   teaspoon salt
¼   teaspoon ground nutmeg
⅓   cup chilled butter, cut into small pieces
¼   cup sweetened dried cranberries
⅓   cup 1% low-fat milk
3   tablespoons molasses
Cooking spray
⅓   cup powdered sugar
1   tablespoon fresh lemon juice

1. Preheat oven to 425°.
2. Lightly spoon flour into dry measuring cups; level with a knife. Combine flour and next 6 ingredients in a large bowl; cut in butter with a pastry blender or 2 knives until mixture resembles coarse meal. Stir in cranberries. Add milk and molasses, stirring with a fork (mixture will be very crumbly).
3. Turn dough out onto an unfloured surface, and knead until dry ingredients are moist. Pat dough into a 7-inch circle; cut into 8 wedges. Place wedges on a baking sheet coated with cooking spray. Bake at 425° for 10 minutes or until bottoms are lightly browned.
4. While scones bake, combine powdered sugar and lemon juice in a small bowl; stir well. Drizzle glaze over warm scones. Serve warm. YIELD: 8 servings (serving size: 1 scone).

Note: Cut scones with a sharp chef's knife coated with cooking spray.

POINTS value: 6; **Exchanges:** 2½ Starch, 1½ Fat
Per serving: CAL 265 (27% from fat); PRO 3.7g; FAT 8.0g (sat 3.9g); CARB 45.3g; FIB 1.2g; CHOL 20mg; IRON 2.0mg; SOD 258mg; CALC 106mg

CHERRY WHEAT PANCAKES

prep: 7 minutes • cook: 13 minutes

⅔   cup all-purpose flour
⅓   cup whole wheat flour
1   tablespoon granulated sugar
½   teaspoon baking soda
½   teaspoon ground cinnamon
¼   teaspoon salt
1   cup low-fat buttermilk
1   large egg, lightly beaten
1   tablespoon vegetable oil
⅔   cup chopped dried sweet cherries
Cooking spray
1½   teaspoons powdered sugar

1. Lightly spoon flours into dry measuring cups; level with a knife. Combine flours and next 4 ingredients in a large bowl; stir with a whisk. Combine buttermilk, egg, and oil; add to flour mixture, stirring until smooth. Stir in cherries.
2. Heat a nonstick griddle or nonstick skillet coated with cooking spray over medium-high heat. Spoon about ¼ cup batter for each pancake onto pan. Turn pancakes when tops are covered with bubbles and edges look cooked. Sprinkle with powdered sugar. YIELD: 10 servings (serving size: 1 pancake).

POINTS value: 2; **Exchanges:** 1 Starch, ½ Fruit
Per serving: CAL 117 (18% from fat); PRO 3.1g; FAT 2.3g (sat 0.4g); CARB 20.3g; FIB 1.8g; CHOL 22mg; IRON 0.8mg; SOD 156mg; CALC 45mg

APPLE-WHEAT GERM HOTCAKES

prep: 20 minutes • cook: 4 minutes per batch

These pancakes have a double dose of whole grains: whole wheat flour and crunchy wheat germ. Serve them with warmed applesauce and a dollop of sour cream, if desired.

⅔   cup whole wheat flour
⅓   cup all-purpose flour
1   teaspoon baking powder
½   teaspoon baking soda
¼   teaspoon salt
⅔   cup low-fat buttermilk
⅔   cup water
½   cup unsweetened chunky applesauce
2   tablespoons light brown sugar
2   tablespoons butter, melted
2   tablespoons apple butter
¼   teaspoon ground nutmeg
1   large egg
Cooking spray
¼   cup toasted wheat germ

1. Lightly spoon flours into dry measuring cups; level with a knife. Combine flours, baking powder, baking soda, and salt in a large bowl.
2. Combine buttermilk and next 7 ingredients in a bowl; stir well with a whisk. Add to flour mixture, stirring just until moist.
3. Heat a nonstick griddle or nonstick skillet lightly coated with cooking spray over medium heat. Spoon about ¼ cup batter for each pancake onto pan. Sprinkle each pancake with 1 teaspoon wheat germ. Turn hotcakes when tops are covered with bubbles and edges look cooked. YIELD: 6 servings (serving size: 2 pancakes).
Note: The temperature of the griddle or skillet needs to be kept at medium to medium-low because the wheat germ burns easily. If the wheat germ burns, wipe the griddle clean with a wet paper towel.

POINTS value: 3; **Exchanges:** 1½ Starch, 1 Fat
Per serving: CAL 177 (28% from fat); PRO 5.6g; FAT 5.6g (sat 2.5g); CARB 27.5g; FIB 2.7g; CHOL 46mg; IRON 1.5mg; SOD 355mg; CALC 94mg

DRIED FRUIT AND WALNUT ZUCCHINI BREAD

prep: 15 minutes • cook: 50 minutes
other: 1 hour and 30 minutes

1   cup packed dark brown sugar, divided
¼   cup chopped walnuts
1   teaspoon ground cinnamon, divided
2   cups all-purpose flour
1   tablespoon baking powder
1   teaspoon baking soda
½   teaspoon ground nutmeg
¼   teaspoon salt
¼   teaspoon ground allspice
1   cup packed shredded zucchini (about 1 large)
¾   cup low-fat buttermilk
½   cup golden raisins
2   tablespoons vegetable oil
1   tablespoon grated orange rind
1   teaspoon vanilla extract
2   large eggs, lightly beaten
Cooking spray

1. Preheat oven to 350°.
2. Combine 2 tablespoons brown sugar, walnuts, and ¼ teaspoon cinnamon in a small bowl. Set aside.
3. Lightly spoon flour into dry measuring cups; level with a knife. Combine flour, remaining brown sugar, remaining ¾ teaspoon cinnamon, baking powder, and next 4 ingredients in a large bowl; make a well in center of mixture.
4. Combine zucchini and next 6 ingredients in a medium bowl; add to flour mixture. Stir just until moist.
5. Spoon batter into an 8 x 4-inch loaf pan coated with cooking spray. Sprinkle walnut mixture evenly over batter.
6. Bake at 350° for 50 minutes or until a wooden pick inserted in center comes out almost clean. Cool 5 minutes in pan on a wire rack; remove from pan. Cool completely on wire rack. YIELD: 16 servings (serving size: 1 slice).

POINTS value: 3; **Exchanges:** 2 Starch
Per serving: CAL 169 (20% from fat); PRO 3.6g; FAT 3.8g (sat 0.7g); CARB 31.1g; FIB 1.0g; CHOL 27mg; IRON 1.4mg; SOD 235mg; CALC 89mg

QUICK BREAD TIPS

So called because it doesn't require stand time for yeast to rise, quick bread is a great item to assemble in fewer than 20 minutes, bake in less than an hour, and freeze for a later date. The key to a tender and low-fat quick bread is to avoid overmixing. The rule of thumb for quick-bread batters is to stir the ingredients about ten times. If you overmix, the flour's gluten will start to develop, which will toughen the final product.

FOCACCIA WITH ONIONS, FRESH HERBS, AND FETA

**prep: 23 minutes • cook: 45 minutes
other: 12 hours and 5 minutes**

Fresh herbs, crunchy walnuts, tangy feta cheese, and sweet onions come together in perfect harmony atop this flat bread.

1   (1-pound) loaf frozen bread dough
2   tablespoons olive oil, divided
2   cups vertically sliced yellow onion (about 1 large)
1   tablespoon sugar
1   teaspoon chopped fresh rosemary
1   teaspoon chopped fresh thyme
½   teaspoon salt
⅛   teaspoon freshly ground black pepper
Cooking spray
¼   cup coarsely chopped walnuts
½   cup (2 ounces) crumbled feta cheese

1. Thaw bread dough in refrigerator at least 12 hours.
2. Preheat oven to 400°.
3. Heat 1 tablespoon oil in a large nonstick skillet over medium heat. Add onion and sugar; cook 20 minutes or until golden brown, stirring occasionally. Remove from heat; stir in rosemary, thyme, salt, and pepper.
4. Place dough on a lightly floured surface; let rest 5 minutes. Pat or roll dough into a 14 x 8-inch rectangle (about ¼ inch thick). Place on a baking sheet coated with cooking spray. Brush dough with remaining 1 tablespoon oil. Spread onion mixture and walnuts evenly over dough, leaving a ½-inch border on all sides;

sprinkle evenly with cheese. Bake at 400° on bottom rack of oven for 25 minutes or until crust is golden. Cut into 12 pieces. YIELD: 12 servings (serving size: 1 piece).

POINTS value: 4; **Exchanges:** *1½ Starch, 1 Fat*
Per serving: *CAL 165 (36% from fat); PRO 5.6g; FAT 6.8g (sat 1.3g); CARB 22.1g; FIB 1.5g; CHOL 6mg; IRON 1.6mg; SOD 379mg; CALC 44mg*

REFRIGERATOR SWEET POTATO ROLLS

(pictured on page 23)
prep: 53 minutes • cook: 1 hour and 15 minutes • other: 8 hours and 45 minutes

2   medium sweet potatoes (about 2 pounds)
2   packages dry yeast (about 4½ teaspoons)
1   teaspoon brown sugar
½   cup warm water (100° to 110°)
¾   cup warm 2% reduced-fat milk (100° to 110°)
½   cup packed brown sugar
¼   cup butter, melted
2   teaspoons salt
½   teaspoon grated orange rind
1   large egg, lightly beaten
5   cups bread flour, divided
Cooking spray
1   tablespoon butter, melted
1   teaspoon grated orange rind
1   tablespoon fresh orange juice

1. Preheat oven to 450°.
2. Place sweet potatoes on a foil-lined baking sheet; bake at 450° for 1 hour or until tender. Cut potatoes in half lengthwise; cool to touch.
3. While potatoes cool, dissolve yeast and 1 teaspoon brown sugar in warm water in a large bowl; let stand

5 minutes. Add milk and next 4 ingredients, stirring until sugar dissolves. Add egg; stir well.
4. Peel and mash sweet potatoes with a fork until smooth. Stir 1½ cups potato into yeast mixture. Reserve remaining potato for another use.
5. Lightly spoon flour into dry measuring cups; level with a knife. Add 2 cups flour to yeast mixture; stir until smooth. Gradually stir in enough remaining flour to form a soft dough. Turn dough out onto a lightly floured surface. Knead until smooth and elastic (about 8 minutes), adding just enough remaining flour to prevent dough from sticking.
6. Place dough in a large bowl coated with cooking spray, turning to coat top. Cover with plastic wrap, and let rise in refrigerator at least 8 hours or up to 3 days, punching dough down as necessary when dough rises to top of bowl.
7. Coat 3 (9-inch) round cake pans with cooking spray. With lightly floured hands, shape dough into 36 (1½-inch) balls. Place 12 balls in each pan, making sure balls do not touch. Cover and let rise in a warm place (85°), free from drafts, 45 minutes or until doubled in size. (Press two fingers into dough. If indentation remains, the dough has risen enough.)
8. Preheat oven to 375°.
9. Uncover rolls, and bake at 375° for 15 to 18 minutes or until golden.
10. Combine 1 tablespoon butter, 1 teaspoon orange rind, and 1 tablespoon orange juice. Brush over warm rolls in pan. Serve warm. YIELD: 36 servings (serving size: 1 roll).

POINTS value: 2; **Exchanges:** *1½ Starch*
Per serving: *CAL 111 (18% from fat); PRO 3.0g; FAT 2.2g (sat 1.0g); CARB 19.8g; FIB 0.9g; CHOL 10mg; IRON 1.1mg; SOD 152mg; CALC 17mg*

Desserts

ALMOND MERINGUES

prep: 19 minutes • cook: 2 hours and
10 minutes • other: 8 hours

*The secret to perfectly crisp meringue
cookies is to prepare them on a dry
day and resist opening the oven door
to peek at the cookies. Moisture in the
atmosphere and the slightest escape of
heat from the oven may cause the
cookies to be sticky.*

3   large egg whites
½   teaspoon almond extract
¼   teaspoon vanilla extract
⅛   teaspoon cream of tartar
⅛   teaspoon salt
¼   cup granulated sugar
¼   cup powdered sugar
2   tablespoons sliced almonds,
    crushed

1. Preheat oven to 225°.
2. Cover a large baking sheet with
parchment paper; set aside.
3. Combine first 5 ingredients in a
large bowl; beat with a mixer at high
speed until foamy. Gradually add
sugars, 1 tablespoon at a time, beating until stiff peaks form.
4. Drop egg white mixture by heap-
ing tablespoonfuls onto prepared
baking sheet. Sprinkle with almonds.
Bake at 225° for 2 hours and 10
minutes. Turn oven off; cool
meringues in closed oven at least 8
hours or until dry. Carefully remove
meringues from paper. Store in an
airtight container. YIELD: 14 servings
(serving size: 1 meringue).

POINTS value: 1; **Exchange:** ½ Starch
Per serving: CAL 32 (12% from fat); PRO 1.0g;
FAT 0.4g (sat 0.0g); CARB 5.9g; FIB 0.1g;
CHOL 0mg; IRON 0.0mg; SOD 33mg; CALC 3mg

LEMON-ANISE BISCOTTI WITH HAZELNUTS

prep: 20 minutes • cook: 1 hour and
6 minutes • other: 2 hours and 30 minutes

*Perfect for dunking in a hot cup of
coffee, these cookies get supercrisp
without the need for turning during
baking. The secret? The slices bake
while standing upright.*

½   cup hazelnuts
2   cups all-purpose flour
⅔   cup sugar
2   teaspoons aniseed, crushed
1½ teaspoons baking powder
2   teaspoons grated lemon rind
⅛   teaspoon salt
2   large eggs
2   teaspoons vanilla extract
Cooking spray
1   teaspoon water
1   large egg white, lightly beaten
1   (4-ounce) bar bittersweet
    chocolate, chopped (such as
    Ghirardelli)

1. Preheat oven to 350°.
2. Place hazelnuts on a baking sheet.
Bake at 350° for 12 minutes or until
toasted, stirring once. Turn nuts out
onto a towel. Roll up towel; rub off
skins. Finely chop nuts.
3. Lightly spoon flour into dry
measuring cups; level with a knife.
Combine flour and next 5 ingredients
in a large bowl; stir in 6 tablespoons
hazelnuts. Combine 2 eggs and
vanilla in a small bowl; stir with a
whisk until well blended. Add egg
mixture to flour mixture (mixture
will be very crumbly).
4. Knead dough in bowl with wet
hands until dry ingredients are moist.
Turn dough out onto a baking sheet

coated with cooking spray. Shape
dough into 2 (14 x 1½-inch) logs.
Combine water and egg white;
brush evenly over logs, and sprinkle
with remaining 2 tablespoons nuts.
Bake at 350° for 24 minutes.
5. Reduce oven temperature to
300°. Cut logs diagonally into
¼-inch-thick slices with a serrated
knife. Carefully stand cookies on
edge on ungreased baking sheets.
Bake at 300° for 30 minutes or until
dry but not browned. Remove
cookies from pans; cool on wire racks.
6. Place chocolate in a small, shallow
dish. Microwave at HIGH 30 seconds
or until almost melted, stirring until
smooth. Dip 1 side of each cookie
lightly in chocolate to coat in a thin
layer, shaking gently to remove
excess chocolate. Place cookies on
wax paper; let chocolate dry for at
least 2 hours. YIELD: 45 biscotti (serving size: 1 biscotto).

POINTS value: 1; **Exchanges:** ½ Starch, ½ Fat
Per serving: CAL 60 (31% from fat); PRO 1.4g;
FAT 2.1g (sat 0.7g); CARB 9.0g; FIB 0.5g;
CHOL 10mg; IRON 0.4mg; SOD 27mg; CALC 14mg

HEALTHIER COOKIES

There are actually health benefits to making your sweet treats.
Using fresh, whole ingredients
eliminates the worry of trans fats.
Trans fats are vegetable oils
injected with hydrogen, a pres-
surized gas that changes the liquid
oil into a solid. Trans fats are
used in making margarine and
shortening, and they have been
associated with an increased
risk of coronary heart disease.

PEANUT BUTTER-CHOCOLATE COOKIES

1. Roll peanut butter dough and chocolate dough each into 76 (½-inch) balls.

2. Gently roll together 1 chocolate dough ball and 1 peanut butter dough ball.

3. Place balls 2 inches apart on baking sheets.

4. Flatten cookies with the bottom of a glass.

PEANUT BUTTER-CHOCOLATE COOKIES

(pictured on page 42)

prep: 48 minutes • cook: 8 minutes per batch • other: 1 hour plus an additional 11 minutes per batch

½   cup butter, softened
½   cup granulated sugar
½   cup packed light brown sugar
1   teaspoon vanilla extract
1   large egg, lightly beaten
⅓   cup natural-style peanut butter (such as Smucker's)
1½ cups all-purpose flour
½   teaspoon baking soda
⅛   teaspoon salt
¼   cup unsweetened cocoa
Cooking spray

1. Beat butter and sugars with a mixer at medium speed until well blended. Add vanilla and egg; beat well. Add peanut butter; beat until blended. Divide butter mixture evenly between 2 bowls.

2. Lightly spoon flour into dry measuring cups; level with a knife. Combine flour, baking soda, and salt. Spoon half of flour mixture into 1 bowl of butter mixture; stir until well blended.

3. Stir cocoa into remaining flour mixture; add to remaining bowl of butter mixture, stirring until well blended. Cover both bowls of dough, and chill at least 1 hour.

4. Preheat oven to 375°.

5. Roll peanut butter dough into 76 (½-inch) balls. Roll chocolate dough into 76 (½-inch) balls. Gently roll together 1 chocolate dough ball and 1 peanut butter dough ball. Place balls 2 inches apart on baking sheets coated with cooking spray. Flatten cookies with the bottom of a glass. Bake at 375° for 8 minutes. Cool 1 to 2 minutes on pans. Remove from pans; cool completely on wire racks. YIELD: 76 cookies (serving size: 1 cookie).

POINTS value: 1; **Exchange:** ½ Starch
Per serving: CAL 38 (42% from fat); PRO 0.7g; FAT 1.9g (sat 0.7g); CARB 5.0g; FIB 0.2g; CHOL 6mg; IRON 0.2mg; SOD 25mg; CALC 3mg

FRESH BLUEBERRY-MANGO DESSERT

prep: 15 minutes • cook: 4 minutes

Because this fresh summer-fruit dessert feeds a crowd and can be made ahead, it's ideal to serve at your next backyard gathering. Serve it in cups with spoons, or as a sauce for angel food cake or vanilla light ice cream.

⅔ cup packed light brown sugar
1 cup water
2½ tablespoons cornstarch
1 teaspoon grated lime rind
2 tablespoons fresh lime juice
4 cups fresh blueberries
2 cups cubed peeled ripe mango (about 1½ mangoes)
2 teaspoons vanilla extract

1. Combine first 5 ingredients in a medium saucepan; stir well with a whisk. Add blueberries and mango; bring to a boil, and cook 1 minute or until thick, stirring constantly. Remove from heat; stir in vanilla. Serve warm, or cover and chill. YIELD: 10 servings (serving size: ½ cup).

POINTS value: 2; Exchanges: 1 Starch, 1 Fruit
Per serving: CAL 139 (2% from fat); PRO 0.8g; FAT 0.4g (sat 0.1g); CARB 35.3g; FIB 2.6g; CHOL 0mg; IRON 0.5mg; SOD 8mg; CALC 23mg

CARAMELIZED PEARS WITH SPICED ICE CREAM

(pictured on page 45)
prep: 18 minutes • cook: 53 minutes
other: 2 hours and 5 minutes

Spiced ice cream gently melts over warm and tender vanilla-poached pears. To make the dessert ahead, bake the pears, and refrigerate them before broiling. When you're ready to serve dessert, sprinkle the pears with sugar, and broil—perfect for easy entertaining.

1½ cups vanilla reduced-fat ice cream, softened
¼ teaspoon ground allspice or ground cinnamon
3 ripe Bosc pears
Cooking spray
1 teaspoon lemon juice
1 tablespoon butter, melted
1 cup pear nectar
1 (3-inch) piece vanilla bean, split lengthwise
2 tablespoons honey
¼ cup Riesling or other slightly sweet white wine or pear nectar
1 tablespoon sugar
2 tablespoons sliced almonds, toasted

1. Combine ice cream and allspice in a freezer-safe container; stir well. Cover; freeze 2 hours or until firm.
2. Preheat oven to 375°.
3. Peel and core pears; cut each pear in half lengthwise, leaving stems intact. Place pears, cut sides down, in a 13 x 9-inch baking dish coated with cooking spray. Brush pear halves with lemon juice; drizzle with melted butter.
4. Place pear nectar in a small saucepan. Scrape seeds from vanilla bean; add seeds and bean to nectar. Stir in honey. Bring to a boil, stirring occasionally. Pour boiling mixture over pears. Cover loosely with foil; bake at 375° for 35 minutes, basting frequently with cooking liquid. Uncover; turn pears over. Stir in wine. Bake, uncovered, 10 minutes, basting occasionally with cooking liquid. Remove pears from oven.
5. Preheat broiler.
6. While broiler preheats, discard vanilla bean. Turn pears, cut sides down, and sprinkle with sugar. Broil 3 to 5 minutes or until sugar is caramelized (add additional pear nectar, as needed, if liquid boils away). Remove pears from oven; let stand 5 minutes. Place pear halves in each of 6 dessert dishes; drizzle cooking liquid evenly over each pear. Top each pear half with ¼ cup ice cream, and sprinkle each with 1 teaspoon almonds. YIELD: 6 servings.

POINTS value: 3; Exchanges: ½ Starch, ½ Fruit, 1 Fat
Per serving: CAL 175 (19% from fat); PRO 2.3g; FAT 4.0g (sat 1.5g); CARB 34.9g; FIB 3.2g; CHOL 8mg; IRON 0.3mg; SOD 42mg; CALC 66mg

---

MANGO MADNESS

Although still considered exotic, the mango is widely available throughout the United States and is great to slice and eat alone or to use in recipes from sweet to savory. Mangos have a smooth, bright yellow flesh that is wonderfully sweet, and they pack a nutritional punch. One mango (sliced, raw) equals about 1 cup and contains 107 calories, 0.5g total fat, and 3.0g fiber. Mangoes are also a good source of beta carotene, Vitamin A, and Vitamin C. For information on how to cut a mango, see page 38.

STRAWBERRY CHEESECAKE PARFAITS

prep: 26 minutes • cook: 5 minutes

Enjoy all of the flavor and creaminess of strawberry cheesecake in less than 30 minutes. Prepare these layered parfaits before dinner, and they'll be ready to serve at the end of the meal.

1½   cups chopped fresh strawberries (about ¾ pound)
1   tablespoon granulated sugar
¾   cup (6 ounces) ⅓-less-fat cream cheese
3   tablespoons brown sugar, divided
2½   tablespoons reduced-fat sour cream (such as Breakstone's)
1   tablespoon fat-free milk
½   teaspoon vanilla extract
½   cup graham cracker crumbs
¼   cup frozen fat-free whipped topping, thawed
4   teaspoons sliced almonds, toasted

1. Combine strawberries and granulated sugar in a bowl; stir well. Let stand 15 minutes.
2. While strawberries stand, place cream cheese in a medium bowl; beat with a mixer at medium speed until smooth. Add 2 tablespoons brown sugar, sour cream, milk, and vanilla; beat until well blended.
3. Combine remaining 1 tablespoon brown sugar and graham cracker crumbs in a small bowl; stir well.
4. Spoon 2 tablespoons cream cheese mixture into each of 4 (8-ounce) parfait glasses. Top each with 1 tablespoon graham cracker crumb mixture and about 2 tablespoons strawberries. Repeat procedure once.

Top each parfait with 1 tablespoon whipped topping, 1 tablespoon strawberries, and 1 teaspoon almonds. Serve immediately, or cover and chill. YIELD: 4 servings (serving size: 1 parfait).

POINTS value: 6; **Exchanges:** 2 Starch, 2 Fat
Per serving: CAL 245 (45% from fat); PRO 6.7g; FAT 12.5g (sat 1.0g); CARB 26.9g; FIB 1.8g; CHOL 35mg; IRON 0.8mg; SOD 77mg; CALC 73mg

HAZELNUT CRÈME BRÛLÉES

prep: 10 minutes • cook: 1 hour and 9 minutes • other: 5 hours

Once you shatter the caramelized sugar shell and sink your spoon into the cool, silky-smooth custard, you'll see why this recipe received our Test Kitchens' highest rating. Work quickly and pour the caramelized sugar into a paper-thin layer over the chilled brûlées.

1½   cups 2% reduced-fat milk
¾   cup nonfat dry milk
½   cup fat-free hazelnut liquid nondairy coffee creamer (such as Coffee-mate)
1   teaspoon vanilla extract
⅛   teaspoon salt
4   large egg yolks
2   tablespoons Frangelico (hazelnut-flavored liqueur) or fat-free hazelnut liquid nondairy coffee creamer
¼   cup sugar
1   tablespoon water

1. Preheat oven to 300°.
2. Combine first 5 ingredients in a bowl; stir well with a whisk. Place egg yolks in a medium bowl; stir with a whisk until smooth.

Gradually whisk milk mixture into egg yolks. Stir in liqueur. Divide mixture evenly among 5 (4-ounce) ramekins or custard cups. Place ramekins in a 13 x 9-inch baking pan; add hot water to pan to a depth of 1 inch.
3. Bake at 300° for 1 hour or until center barely moves when ramekin is touched. Remove ramekins from pan, and cool completely on a wire rack. Cover ramekins, and chill at least 4 hours or overnight.
4. Place sugar and water in a small, heavy saucepan over medium-high heat; cook 9 to 10 minutes or until golden. Immediately pour caramelized sugar evenly over cold custards to form a paper-thin layer on tops of custards. Serve immediately. YIELD: 5 servings (serving size: 1 crème brûlée).

POINTS value: 4; **Exchanges:** 1 Starch, 1 Low-Fat Milk
Per serving: CAL 198 (23% from fat); PRO 8.6g; FAT 4.9g (sat 2.1g); CARB 27.6g; FIB 0.0g; CHOL 169mg; IRON 0.5mg; SOD 164mg; CALC 255mg

GREAT BRÛLÉE

The water bath insulates and protects the custards from the heat of the oven so they cook slowly and evenly. The depth of the water should be half the height of the custard containers, and the pan must be large enough so that the containers don't touch.

Plan to serve the crème brûlées within an hour after pouring the caramelized sugar on top of the custards. Otherwise, the hard sugar shells will start to dissolve into the custards.

PUMPKIN BREAD PUDDING

**prep: 14 minutes • cook: 35 minutes
other: 30 minutes**

8½   cups (1-inch cubed) French
      bread (about 10 ounces)
1   cup 1% low-fat milk
½   cup granulated sugar
½   cup evaporated fat-free milk
½   cup packed light brown sugar
1½   teaspoons pumpkin pie spice
1   teaspoon vanilla extract
1   (15-ounce) can unsweetened
      pumpkin
3   large eggs, lightly beaten
Cooking spray
3   cups vanilla fat-free, no sugar
      added ice cream

1. Preheat oven to 350°.
2. Place bread cubes in a large bowl.
Combine milk and next 7 ingredients
in a large bowl, stirring well with a
whisk. Pour pumpkin mixture over
bread cubes, folding mixture gently
to coat bread cubes; let stand 15
minutes.
3. Spoon bread cube mixture into a
13 x 9-inch baking dish coated with
cooking spray.
4. Bake at 350° for 35 minutes or
until pudding is set. Remove from
oven; let let stand 15 minutes. Serve
warm with ice cream. YIELD: 12
servings (serving size: ½ cup bread
pudding and ¼ cup vanilla ice
cream).

POINTS value: 4; **Exchanges:** 1 Starch, 1½ Fat-Free
Milk
Per serving: CAL 209 (10% from fat); PRO 7.4g;
FAT 2.3g (sat 0.7g); CARB 40.7g; FIB 1.8g;
CHOL 55mg; IRON 1.7mg; SOD 221mg;
CALC 146mg

FUDGY CHOCOLATE
CHIP PANCAKES

(pictured on page 44)
**prep: 8 minutes • cook: 3 minutes
per batch**

*Served hot off the griddle, these
fudge-topped chocolate chip pancakes
satisfy a sweet tooth as well as
a slice of frosted layer cake does.*

1   cup all-purpose flour
¼   cup cocoa
2   tablespoons sugar
1   teaspoon baking powder
¼   teaspoon baking soda
⅛   teaspoon salt
1   cup low-fat buttermilk
1   tablespoon vegetable oil
1   large egg, lightly beaten
⅓   cup semisweet chocolate chips
Cooking spray
9   tablespoons fat-free hot fudge
      topping
9   tablespoons frozen fat-free
      whipped topping, thawed
9   tablespoons fresh raspberries

1. Lightly spoon flour into a dry
measuring cup; level with a knife.
Lightly spoon cocoa into a dry
measuring cup; level with a knife.
Combine flour, cocoa, and next 4
ingredients in a large bowl; stir with
a whisk. Combine buttermilk, oil,
and egg; add to flour mixture,
stirring until well blended. Stir in
chocolate chips.
2. Spoon ¼ cup batter for each pancake onto a medium nonstick skillet
coated with cooking spray (chocolate
will burn if pan is too hot). Turn
pancakes when tops are covered
with bubbles and edges look cooked.

3. Microwave hot fudge topping
according to package directions. Cut
each pancake in half, and top with
fudge topping, whipped topping,
and raspberries. Serve immediately.
YIELD: 9 servings (serving size: 1 pancake, 1 tablespoon fudge topping,
1 tablespoon whipped topping,
and 1 tablespoon raspberries).

POINTS value: 4; **Exchanges:** 2 Starch, ½ Fruit, 1 Fat
Per serving: CAL 202 (22% from fat); PRO 5.2g;
FAT 5.2g (sat 2.3g); CARB 36.9g; FIB 2.8g;
CHOL 25mg; IRON 1.6mg; SOD 197mg;
CALC 92mg

COOL HOTCAKES

To have dessert ready in only
minutes, prepare these pancakes ahead, and freeze. For
best results, place each cooked
pancake between layers of wax
paper, and seal in a plastic
zip-top freezer bag or airtight
container. When you're ready
to serve, remove the desired
number of pancakes from the
freezer, and microwave them
on HIGH for 30 seconds or
until warm.

BLUEBERRY CLAFOUTI

prep: 8 minutes • cook: 41 minutes
other: 15 minutes

Clafouti (kla-foo-TEE) is one of the easiest French desserts to prepare. Make it by topping a layer of fresh fruit with batter and baking; the resulting texture is between that of a pudding and a cake. The keys to a successful clafouti are minimal use of flour and a hot oven in which to cook it quickly.

2   cups fresh blueberries
Cooking spray
¾   cup all-purpose flour
2   cups 1% low-fat milk
½   cup granulated sugar
2   tablespoons butter, melted
⅛   teaspoon salt
3   large eggs
1   (6-inch) vanilla bean, split
      lengthwise, or 1 tablespoon
      vanilla extract
2   tablespoons sliced almonds
1   tablespoon powdered sugar

1. Preheat oven to 375°.
2. Place blueberries in an 8-inch square baking dish coated with cooking spray.
3. Lightly spoon flour into dry measuring cups; level with a knife. Combine flour, milk, and next 4 ingredients in a bowl; stir with a whisk until well blended. Scrape seeds from vanilla bean, and stir seeds into milk mixture. Discard bean, or reserve for another use. Let milk mixture stand 5 minutes. Pour milk mixture over fruit; sprinkle with almonds.
4. Bake at 375° for 41 minutes or until clafouti is set to the touch in center. Let stand 10 minutes. Sprinkle with powdered sugar just before serving. **YIELD:** 8 servings (serving size: 1 square).

POINTS value: 4; **Exchanges:** 2 Starch, 1 Fat
Per serving: CAL 202 (28% from fat); PRO 6.2g; FAT 6.3g (sat 2.5g); CARB 31.0g; FIB 1.3g; CHOL 89mg; IRON 1.0mg; SOD 115mg; CALC 94mg

CARAMEL-APPLE GALETTE

(pictured on page 47)
prep: 21 minutes • cook: 25 minutes

For a fitting end to a hearty autumn meal, serve this free-form French tart. Golden-colored turbinado sugar is coarse raw sugar. It makes the pastry glisten and adds crunch and a slight molasses flavor to the dessert. You can substitute 2 teaspoons granulated sugar.

Cooking spray
½   (15-ounce) package refrigerated
      pie dough (such as Pillsbury)
3   medium Granny Smith apples
      (about 1 pound), peeled, cored,
      and cut into ¼-inch-thick
      wedges (about 4 cups)
⅓   cup granulated sugar
1   tablespoon all-purpose
      flour
2   teaspoons fresh lemon juice
1   teaspoon vanilla extract
¼   teaspoon salt
¼   teaspoon ground cinnamon
1   teaspoon water
1   large egg white, lightly beaten
1   tablespoon turbinado sugar
⅓   cup fat-free caramel topping

1. Preheat oven to 425°.
2. Line a large baking sheet with parchment paper; coat paper with cooking spray. Roll dough into a 13-inch circle on prepared parchment.
3. Combine apples and next 6 ingredients in a large bowl; toss well. Place apple mixture in center of dough, leaving a 3-inch border (apples will be piled high on dough). Fold edges of dough toward center, pressing gently to seal (dough will only partially cover apple mixture). Combine water and egg white; brush over edges of dough, and sprinkle galette with turbinado sugar.
4. Bake at 425° for 25 minutes or until golden brown (filling may leak slightly during cooking). Drizzle with caramel topping, and serve warm. **YIELD:** 8 servings (serving size: 1 slice).

POINTS value: 5; **Exchanges:** 1½ Starch, 1 Fruit, 1½ Fat
Per serving: CAL 233 (27% from fat); PRO 1.7g; FAT 7.0g (sat 3.0g); CARB 40.8g; FIB 0.8g; CHOL 5mg; IRON 0.1mg; SOD 216mg; CALC 5mg

VANILLA BASICS

Usually you want the real thing: a whole vanilla bean. Sometimes just the extract will suffice, but the trick is to know when to spend time and money on a bean. For lightly cooked sauces and syrups, when "proof" of real vanilla is necessary for presentation, and to flavor coffee, opt for whole beans. When baking or cooking, extract is best because the vanilla will be exposed to heat for long periods of time.

To use whole vanilla beans, take a small knife with a tip, and cut the bean in half lengthwise. Then scrape the seeds out with the knife blade, or push them out of the vanilla bean with your thumbnail.

HOW TO CUT A MANGO

With the peel still on, stand the mango up so that the stem end points toward you. With a sharp knife, cut straight down about an inch to one side of the stem, just grazing the side of the pit. Repeat on the other side of the fruit, and trim off the flesh left around the pit.

For mango chunks, hold a mango half in the palm of your hand, and carefully score the flesh in square cross-sections, cutting to, but not through, the skin. Turn the mango inside out, and cut the chunks from the skin.

For mango slices, hold a mango half in the palm of your hand, and carefully slice the flesh, cutting to, but not through, the skin. Run a knife across the bottom of the slices next to the peel to remove the slices.

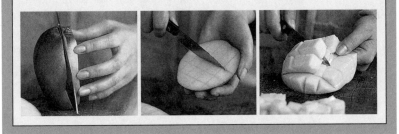

FRESH MANGO PIE

(pictured on page 44)
prep: 24 minutes • other: 4 hours and 10 minutes

Delicious, sweet ripe mangoes are the key to this recipe. Purchase the mangoes 3 to 4 days ahead, and let them ripen on the kitchen counter. Mangoes are ripe when they yield slightly to gentle pressure.

1   (0.3-ounce) package sugar-free peach-flavored gelatin
¾   cup mango nectar, divided
½   teaspoon grated lime rind
4   cups sliced peeled ripe mango (about 4 medium mangoes)
1   (6-ounce) shortbread pie crust (such as Keebler)
½   cup frozen fat-free whipped topping, thawed
Lime zest (optional)

1. Combine gelatin and 2 tablespoons mango nectar in a large microwave-safe bowl. Let stand 5 minutes. Microwave at HIGH 20 to 30 seconds or until gelatin dissolves, stirring once. Stir in remaining mango nectar and lime rind; chill 5 minutes. Add mango, stirring gently to separate slices and evenly coat with gelatin. Spoon mango mixture into pie crust. Cover and chill at least 4 hours or until gelatin is set. Top each serving with whipped topping. Garnish with lime zest, if desired. YIELD: 8 servings (serving size: 1 slice pie and 1 tablespoon whipped topping).

*POINTS value: 4; **Exchanges:** 1 Starch, 1 Fruit, 1 Fat*
Per serving: CAL 189 (25% from fat); PRO 1.7g; FAT 5.3g (sat 1.1g); CARB 34.3g; FIB 1.7g; CHOL 0mg; IRON 0.1mg; SOD 117mg; CALC 10mg

CLASSIC STRAWBERRY PIE

prep: 15 minutes • cook: 14 minutes
other: 3 hours

½   (15-ounce) package refrigerated pie dough (such as Pillsbury)
1   (1-pound) package fresh strawberries, sliced (about 3 cups)
½   cup sugar
1   cup water
2½   tablespoons cornstarch
2   teaspoons lemon juice
2   teaspoons sugar-free strawberry-flavored gelatin
½   cup frozen reduced-calorie whipped topping, thawed

1. Preheat oven to 450°.
2. Unroll dough into a 9-inch pie plate. Fold edges under and flute; pierce bottom and sides with a fork. Bake at 450° for 9 minutes or until lightly browned. Cool completely.
3. Meanwhile, combine strawberries and sugar in a medium bowl; toss well, and set aside.
4. Combine water, cornstarch, and lemon juice in a small saucepan, stirring until well blended. Bring to a boil, and cook 1 minute or until thick, stirring constantly. Add gelatin, stirring until gelatin dissolves. Pour over strawberries, stirring to coat. Pour into prepared crust. Cover and chill at least 3 hours. Top each serving with whipped topping. YIELD: 8 servings (serving size: 1 slice pie and 1 tablespoon whipped topping).

*POINTS value: 5; **Exchanges:** 1½ Starch, ½ Fruit, 1½ Fat*
Per serving: CAL 208 (33% from fat); PRO 1.7g; FAT 7.7g (sat 3.5g); CARB 34.2g; FIB 1.3g; CHOL 5mg; IRON 0.3mg; SOD 109mg; CALC 14mg

TOFFEE ANGEL FOOD CAKE

prep: 9 minutes • cook: 40 minutes
other: 40 minutes

*No topping is necessary for this
dressed-up angel food cake. Toffee bits
and toasted pecans add plenty
of flavor and crunch to this
cinnamon-spiced cake.*

1   cup all-purpose flour
1½   cups granulated sugar
1½   teaspoons ground cinnamon
12   large egg whites
1½   teaspoons cream of tartar
¼   teaspoon salt
½   cup chopped pecans, toasted
½   cup almond toffee bits (such as
        Heath)
¼   cup packed light brown sugar
2   teaspoons vanilla extract

1. Preheat oven to 375°.
2. Lightly spoon flour into a dry
measuring cup; level with a knife.
Combine granulated sugar and cinnamon; stir well.
3. Place egg whites, cream of tartar,
and salt in a large bowl; beat with a
mixer at high speed until foamy.
Gradually add cinnamon-sugar mixture, beating until stiff peaks form.
Sift ¼ cup flour over egg white
mixture; fold in. Repeat procedure
with remaining flour, ¼ cup at a
time. Combine pecans, toffee bits,
and brown sugar; stir well. Gently
fold pecan mixture and vanilla into
egg white mixture.
4. Spoon batter into an ungreased
10-inch tube pan, spreading evenly.
Break air pockets by cutting through
batter with a knife. Bake at 375° for
40 minutes or until cake springs back
when lightly touched. Invert tube pan

onto a heatproof glass bottle, and
cool completely upside down in pan.
Loosen cake from sides of pan using a
narrow metal spatula. Invert angel
food cake onto a serving platter. YIELD:
12 servings (serving size: 1 slice).
Note: This cake may brown nicely
and test done before 40 minutes, but
the sticky nature of the toffee bits
and sugar make it necessary to bake
the cake for the full amount of time.

POINTS value: 6; **Exchanges:** 3 Starch, ½ Fat
Per serving: CAL 261 (24% from fat); PRO 5.2g;
FAT 7.1g (sat 1.3g); CARB 44.9g; FIB 0.9g;
CHOL 3mg; IRON 0.8mg; SOD 160mg; CALC 14mg

CHOCOLATE MARMALADE
CAKE

prep: 21 minutes • cook: 29 minutes
other: 55 minutes

*To preserve the creamy frosting, store left-
over cake in a cake saver, or cover cake
loosely with nonstick foil. The cake keeps
well in the refrigerator up to 3 days.*

Cooking spray
1½   cups all-purpose flour
1½   teaspoons baking powder
¼   teaspoon salt
⅓   cup butter, softened
¾   cup granulated sugar
1   large egg
1   large egg white
¾   cup 1% low-fat milk
1½   teaspoons grated orange
        rind
1¼   teaspoons vanilla extract
1½   cups sifted powdered sugar
¼   cup unsweetened cocoa
3   tablespoons 1% low-fat
        milk
1½   tablespoons butter, softened
⅓   cup orange marmalade

1. Preheat oven to 350°.
2. Coat an 8-inch square baking pan
with cooking spray; line bottom of
pan with wax paper. Coat wax paper
with cooking spray; set aside.
3. Lightly spoon flour into dry
measuring cups; level with a knife.
Combine flour, baking powder,
and salt.
4. Beat butter with a mixer at medium
speed until creamy; gradually add
granulated sugar, beating until fluffy.
Add egg and egg white, and beat at
medium speed just until blended.
Add flour mixture to sugar mixture
alternately with ¾ cup milk, beginning and ending with flour mixture.
Stir in orange rind and vanilla.
5. Pour batter into prepared pan.
Sharply tap pan once on counter to
remove air bubbles. Bake at 350° for
29 minutes or until a wooden pick
inserted in center comes out clean;
cool in pan for 10 minutes on a
wire rack. Remove from pan, and
carefully peel off wax paper; cool
completely on wire rack.
6. Combine powdered sugar and
next 3 ingredients in a large bowl.
Beat with a mixer at low speed just
until blended, and stir in orange
marmalade.
7. Place cake on a plate; spread frosting over top and sides of cake. YIELD:
16 servings (serving size: 1 slice).

POINTS value: 4; **Exchanges:** 2 Starch, 1 Fat
Per serving: CAL 190 (26% from fat); PRO 2.6g;
FAT 5.6g (sat 2.7g); CARB 33.7g; FIB 0.8g;
CHOL 27mg; IRON 0.9mg; SOD 136mg;
CALC 53mg

FROZEN PUMPKIN LAYER CAKE

(pictured on page 46)
prep: 21 minutes • cook: 3 minutes
other: 10 hours and 10 minutes

We couldn't stop eating this dessert at taste testing. It earned our highest rating. The concentrated spicy flavor of pumpkin butter replaces the more traditional canned pumpkin. It's a great make-ahead recipe for the holidays.

½ cup chopped pecans
Butter-flavored cooking spray
1 tablespoon light brown sugar
12 cinnamon graham crackers (3 full cracker sheets), crushed (about ½ cup)
1 (8-inch) round angel food cake (about 15 ounces), cut into ½-inch-thick slices (about 25 slices)
1 (9-ounce) jar country pumpkin butter (such as Dickinson's)
1½ teaspoons ground cinnamon
¾ teaspoon pumpkin pie spice
1 (1.75-quart) carton vanilla light ice cream, softened and divided
1 (8-ounce) container frozen fat-free whipped topping, thawed
½ cup fat-free caramel topping

1. Place pecans in a nonstick skillet; coat pecans with cooking spray. Add brown sugar; cook over medium heat 3 minutes or until nuts are toasted and sugar melts, stirring occasionally. Remove from heat; cool. Combine sugared pecans and cracker crumbs in a small bowl; toss gently.
2. Arrange half of angel food cake slices in bottom of a 10-inch springform pan.

3. Combine pumpkin butter, cinnamon, and pumpkin pie spice in a small bowl. Place half of pumpkin butter mixture and half of ice cream in a food processor; pulse 12 times or just until blended. Spread pumpkin-ice cream mixture over cake layer in pan, and sprinkle with half of pecan mixture. Top with remaining cake slices; freeze 5 minutes.
4. Place remaining half of pumpkin butter mixture and remaining half of ice cream in food processor; pulse 12 times or just until blended. Spread pumpkin-ice cream mixture over cake layer in pan, and sprinkle with half of remaining pecan mixture. Cover and freeze 2 hours. Spread whipped topping evenly over cake, and sprinkle with remaining pecan mixture. Cover and freeze 8 hours or until firm. Let stand 5 minutes before serving. Run a knife around outside edge of dessert to loosen from pan; remove sides of pan. Drizzle with caramel topping. YIELD: 16 servings (serving size: 1 slice).

POINTS value: 7; **Exchanges:** 3½ Starch, 1½ Fat
Per serving: CAL 318 (21% from fat); PRO 4.7g; FAT 7.1g (sat 2.5g); CARB 56.6g; FIB 1.0g; CHOL 31mg; IRON 0.4mg; SOD 312mg; CALC 132mg

---

SPRINGFORM AND FUNCTION

A springform pan is a round, deep pan with tall, removable sides; it's most often used for baking cheesecakes. Look for a pan with extended edges around the base to keep batter from leaking.

BANANAS FOSTER SUNDAE

prep: 6 minutes • cook: 3 minutes

For a more sophisticated dessert, add a tablespoon of banana liqueur or rum to the sauce just before serving. The POINTS value will not change.

2 cups vanilla light ice cream, softened
1 (1.4-ounce) chocolate-covered English toffee bar (such as Skor), chopped
1 tablespoon butter
⅓ cup packed light brown sugar
2 tablespoons water
1 medium banana, sliced
¼ teaspoon vanilla extract

1. Combine ice cream and chopped toffee bar in a bowl; stir well, and freeze until firm.
2. Meanwhile, melt butter in a medium nonstick skillet over medium heat. Stir in brown sugar and water. Cook 1 minute or until sugar dissolves and mixture begins to thicken, stirring constantly. Add banana and vanilla; cook 1 minute, stirring to coat banana. Serve banana sauce over ice cream. YIELD: 4 servings (serving size: ½ cup ice cream and 3 tablespoons sauce).

POINTS value: 6; **Exchanges:** 2½ Starch, ½ Fruit, 1 Fat
Per serving: CAL 275 (25% from fat); PRO 3.6g; FAT 8.0g (sat 4.3g); CARB 49.1g; FIB 2.1g; CHOL 18mg; IRON 0.5mg; SOD 109mg; CALC 129mg

One Pound at a Time

TAJUANA GORDON • **HEIGHT** 5'4" • **BEFORE** 242 LBS. • **AFTER** 147 LBS.

Tip: "Whether you want to lose 100 pounds or 10, you have to lose it one pound at a time."

Three pregnancies left Tajuana Gordon with three beautiful children and 95 extra pounds. "I didn't even have the energy or motivation to take my young daughter outside to play," Tajuana recalls. "I used the excuse that I was tired. And I was tired. Carrying around the extra weight made me tired."

Occasionally, Tajuana got together with friends to exercise, but she never took losing weight too seriously. "We just worked out so that we could eat ice cream," she laughs. But Tajuana's attitude changed when her father suffered (yet survived) a heart attack. Realizing that she might be genetically prone to heart disease, Tajuana considered her own mortality.

"Weight Watchers *gave me consistency, not tricks.*"

Fear got her attention, but a friend's 50-pound weight loss brought inspiration. "When I learned about her *Weight Watchers* experience, I asked my 'ice cream friends' to join *Weight Watchers* with me," she recalls. "I felt that if I could lose just one pound a week, that would be fine." But when her friends each lost five to six pounds the first week and Tajuana lost none, she felt encouraged by their successes but discouraged with her own efforts.

So during the second week, Tajuana started an exercise routine. "I went to Curves® and used their hydraulic machines, but I only lost one-half of a pound," she says. Although she was

beginning to think, "What about me?," Tajuana never gave up. "When I didn't have time to go to Curves®, I did aerobics and a walking video at home, and soon I began losing one or two pounds each week."

Tajuana's balance of healthy eating and exercise slowly led to her weight loss, but it also became her lifestyle. "*Weight Watchers* gave me consistency, not tricks. Portion control, exercise, and making decisions about what I put into my body allowed me to meet my goal one week at a time," she explains. "Even though I only lost one or two pounds each week, I knew that didn't matter. Whether you want to lose 100 pounds or 10, you have to lose it one pound at a time."

The pound-after-pound weight loss eventually accumulated to 95 pounds and brought other changes. "Today, morning workouts get my day going and give me the energy to play all day with my three-year-old," she says. "And shopping for clothes is no longer a chore but a myriad of choices. I am not forced to shop in one store or one department anymore. Now I can shop wherever I want and find stylish clothes that fit." Yet Tajuana's greatest relief came from her recent physical exam. "Hearing my doctor say that I was in great health was the ultimate reward."

Peanut Butter-Chocolate Cookies,
page 33

Piña Colada Ice Cream,
page 50

43

Fudgy Chocolate
Chip Pancakes,
page 36

Fresh Mango Pie,
page 38

Caramelized Pears with
Spiced Ice Cream,
page 34

Frozen Pumpkin
Layer Cake,
page 40

Caramel-Apple Galette,
page 37

Chunky Brownie-Nut
Ice Cream,
opposite page

CHUNKY BROWNIE-NUT ICE CREAM

(pictured on opposite page)
**prep: 18 minutes • cook: 22 minutes
other: 2 hours**

If you love the specialty ice creams that are sold in the little-bitty cartons in the grocery store, then here's a recipe you've got to try! This creamy frozen treat has all of the same chunky, fun ingredients but with less saturated fat.

1	cup sugar
¼	cup butter, softened
1	large egg
1	large egg white
1	teaspoon vanilla extract
¾	cup all-purpose flour
½	cup unsweetened cocoa
½	teaspoon baking powder
⅛	teaspoon salt
2	tablespoons semisweet chocolate minichips
	Cooking spray
1	(1.75-quart) carton vanilla light ice cream, softened
½	cup chopped unsalted peanuts
¼	cup fat-free caramel topping (such as Smucker's)

1. Preheat oven to 350°.
2. Combine sugar and butter in a large bowl; beat with a mixer at medium speed until blended. Add egg and egg white, 1 at a time, beating just until blended. Stir in vanilla.
3. Lightly spoon flour into dry measuring cups; level with a knife. Combine flour and next 3 ingredients. Add flour mixture to butter mixture, stirring just until blended. Stir in chocolate minichips.
4. Spread batter into an 8-inch square baking pan coated with cooking spray. Bake at 350° for 22 minutes or just until a wooden pick inserted in center comes out clean (do not overcook). Cool completely on a wire rack.
5. Spoon ice cream into a large freezer-safe container. Crumble brownies over ice cream. Add peanuts and caramel topping; stir until well blended. Cover and freeze until firm. YIELD: 16 servings (serving size: ½ cup).

*POINTS value: 6; Exchanges: 2½ Starch, 2 Fat
Per serving: CAL 271 (33% from fat); PRO 5.5g; FAT 10.2g (sat 4.5g); CARB 40.0g; FIB 1.5g; CHOL 51mg; IRON 0.9mg; SOD 116mg; CALC 106mg*

COCONUT-ALMOND CHOCOLATE ICE CREAM

**prep: 34 minutes • cook: 13 minutes
other: 5 hours and 30 minutes**

Our taste-testing panel gave this rich ice cream our highest rating. To us, it tastes just like a well-known chocolate-covered coconut and almond candy bar.

1	cup sugar
⅛	teaspoon salt
2	large egg yolks
2	cups fat-free half-and-half
1	(13.5-ounce) can light coconut milk
1	(12-ounce) can evaporated fat-free milk
1½	teaspoons vanilla extract
½	teaspoon coconut extract
⅓	cup flaked sweetened coconut, toasted
⅓	cup sliced almonds, toasted
⅓	cup fat-free hot fudge topping (such as Smucker's)

1. Combine first 3 ingredients in a large saucepan; stir well with a whisk. Gradually add half-and-half and milks, stirring until well blended. Bring to a simmer over medium heat, and cook 10 minutes or until mixture reaches 160°, stirring constantly with a whisk. Remove from heat; stir in extracts. Cool to room temperature, and chill at least 2 hours. Stir in coconut, almonds, and hot fudge topping.
2. Pour mixture into the freezer can of a 4-quart ice cream freezer; freeze according to manufacturer's instructions. Spoon ice cream into a freezer-safe container; cover and freeze at least 2 hours or until firm. YIELD: 12 servings (serving size: ½ cup).

*POINTS value: 4; Exchanges: 2 Starch, ½ Fat
Per serving: CAL 188 (21% from fat); PRO 4.0g; FAT 4.3g (sat 2.4g); CARB 32.4g; FIB 0.6g; CHOL 35mg; IRON 0.5mg; SOD 127mg; CALC 129mg*

A PERFECT TOAST

For the best results when toasting nuts and coconut, use the oven instead of a skillet. To toast nuts, place any kind of whole or chopped nuts in a shallow pan or on a baking sheet, and bake at 350° for 6 to 8 minutes. Be sure to watch the nuts carefully, since they can go from toasted to burned quickly. To toast coconut, spread evenly on a baking sheet, and bake at 350° for 5 minutes or until lightly browned. Stir as necessary to prevent burning (the coconut close to the edges of the baking sheet will toast faster than what's in the middle).

PIÑA COLADA ICE CREAM

(pictured on page 43)
prep: 6 minutes • cook: 12 minutes
other: 4 hours and 30 minutes

*This ice cream combines all of the
traditional flavors of a piña colada
with caramel and toasted pecans for
added flavor and crunch.*

2   cups fat-free half-and-half
1   (13.5-ounce) can light coconut
     milk
1   (12-ounce) can evaporated
     fat-free milk
½   cup sugar
2   large egg yolks
½   cup flaked sweetened coconut,
     toasted
½   cup chopped pecans, toasted
½   cup fat-free caramel topping
1   teaspoon rum extract
½   teaspoon coconut extract
1   (8-ounce) can crushed pineapple
     in juice, undrained
8   teaspoons flaked sweetened
     coconut, toasted

1. Combine first 3 ingredients in a
large saucepan. Bring to a boil over
medium-high heat, stirring frequently.
Combine sugar and egg yolks in a
small bowl. Gradually add about
one-fourth hot milk mixture to
eggs, stirring constantly with a
whisk. Add to remaining hot milk
mixture, stirring constantly. Remove
from heat; stir in ½ cup coconut and
next 5 ingredients. Cool completely,
stirring occasionally. Cover and chill
at least 1 hour.
2. Pour mixture into the freezer can
of a 4-quart ice cream freezer, and
freeze according to manufacturer's

instructions. Spoon ice cream into a
freezer-safe container. Cover and
freeze at least 2 hours or until firm.
Sprinkle each serving with toasted
coconut. YIELD: 16 servings (serving
size: ½ cup ice cream and ½ teaspoon
coconut).

POINTS value: 4; **Exchanges:** 1½ Starch, 1 Fat
Per serving: CAL 162 (31% from fat); PRO 2.8g;
FAT 5.4g (sat 2.4g); CARB 24.5g; FIB 0.6g;
CHOL 26mg; IRON 0.4mg; SOD 98mg;
CALC 87mg

TRIPLE CHOCOLATE-
COCONUT MILK SHAKE

prep: 7 minutes • cook: 5 minutes

*We worked hard to get a milk shake
that is decadent enough for dessert,
yet healthier than its full-fat counterpart.
We're confident we succeeded. If
you're serving more than two people,
simply double the ingredients
for four servings.*

1¼ cups chocolate fudge fat-free,
     no sugar added ice cream
     (such as Edy's)
½   cup 1% low-fat chocolate
     milk
2   tablespoons cream of coconut
1   tablespoon fat-free chocolate
     syrup
2   tablespoons canned refrigerated
     light whipped cream (such as
     Reddi-wip)
2   teaspoons flaked sweetened
     coconut, toasted

1. Place first 4 ingredients in a
blender; process until smooth. Pour
milk shake into chilled glasses; top
with whipped cream and toasted

coconut. YIELD: 2 servings (serving
size: ¾ cup milk shake, 1 tablespoon
whipped cream, and 1 teaspoon
coconut).

POINTS value: 5; **Exchanges:** 3 Starch, ½ Fat
Per serving: CAL 242 (15% from fat); PRO 6.5g;
FAT 4.1g (sat 3.1g); CARB 45.9g; FIB 1.4g;
CHOL 4mg; IRON 0.4mg; SOD 134mg;
CALC 159mg

FROSTY CAPPUCCINO

prep: 7 minutes • other: 2 hours

2   cups vanilla fat-free ice cream,
     softened
3   cups chilled strong brewed
     coffee, divided
2   tablespoons sugar
1   teaspoon unsweetened cocoa
1   teaspoon ground cinnamon

1. Combine ice cream, 1 cup coffee,
and sugar in a blender. Process just
until smooth. Stir in remaining 2
cups coffee. Serve over crushed ice
in chilled glasses or mugs. Sprinkle
evenly with cocoa and cinnamon.
Serve immediately. YIELD: 4 (1¼-cup)
servings.

POINTS value: 3; **Exchanges:** 2 Starch
Per serving: CAL 130 (0% from fat); PRO 3.3g;
FAT 0.1g (sat 0.0g); CARB 30.6g; FIB 0.4g;
CHOL 0mg; IRON 0.2mg; SOD 47mg;
CALC 89mg

Fish & Shellfish

CHILI-GLAZED CATFISH WITH BOK CHOY

prep: 7 minutes • cook: 20 minutes

A spicy Vietnamese glaze adds loads of flavor to this simple dish of pan-seared catfish and steamed bok choy. Keep this glaze on hand to turn any white fish fillet or chicken breast into an interesting ethnic meal.

2   heads bok choy (about 1½ pounds), sliced
4   (6-ounce) catfish fillets
⅛   teaspoon salt
½   cup all-purpose flour
1   teaspoon five-spice powder
½   teaspoon black pepper
2   teaspoons canola oil, divided
Cooking spray
½   cup water
4   teaspoons cornstarch
⅓   cup fresh lime juice (about 2½ limes)
1   tablespoon sugar
2   tablespoons fish sauce
2   tablespoons seasoned rice vinegar
1   tablespoon hot chili sauce (such as Sriracha)
2   tablespoons diagonally sliced green onions (about 1 onion)

1. Place bok choy in a vegetable steamer. Steam, covered, 6 minutes or until tender. Set aside; keep warm.
2. Pat fillets dry with paper towels; sprinkle with salt. Combine flour, five-spice powder, and pepper in a shallow dish, and stir well. Dredge fillets in flour mixture, and shake off excess flour.
3. Heat 1 teaspoon oil in a large nonstick skillet coated with cooking spray over medium-high heat. Add

2 fillets to pan; cook 3 to 4 minutes on each side or until fish flakes easily when tested with a fork. Remove fillets from pan; keep warm. Wipe pan clean with paper towels. Repeat procedure with remaining 1 teaspoon oil and fillets.
4. While fish cooks, combine water and cornstarch in a small saucepan. Add lime juice and next 4 ingredients; bring to a boil, stirring constantly. Cook 1 minute or until thick, stirring constantly. Serve fillets over bok choy; drizzle with glaze, and sprinkle with green onions.
YIELD: 4 servings (serving size: 1 fillet, ¾ cup bok choy, 3 tablespoons glaze, and 1½ teaspoons green onions).

POINTS value: 8; **Exchanges:** ½ Starch, 3 Vegetable, 3 Lean Meat, 1 Fat
Per serving: CAL 339 (41% from fat); PRO 30.4g; FAT 15.7g (sat 3.2g); CARB 19.7g; FIB 0.5g; CHOL 80mg; IRON 3.4mg; SOD 1,124mg; CALC 183mg

---

FRESH FLAVORS

You'll notice lots of lime juice, cilantro, and jalapeño pepper in this chapter's recipes, so stock up your fridge. These ingredients add excitement to fish and shellfish in a variety of entrées with Asian, Mexican, and Southwestern flavors.

GRILLED GROUPER WITH CUCUMBER SALSA

prep: 25 minutes • cook: 14 minutes
other: 2 hours

2   cups diced seeded peeled cucumber (about 2 medium)
⅓   cup thinly sliced green onions
¼   cup chopped fresh cilantro
½   teaspoon grated lime rind
¼   cup fresh lime juice (about 2 limes)
2   tablespoons finely chopped seeded jalapeño pepper
1   tablespoon olive oil
⅛   teaspoon salt
1   garlic clove, minced
4   (6-ounce) grouper fillets (about 1½ inches thick)
2   teaspoons olive oil
⅛   teaspoon salt
⅛   teaspoon black pepper
Cooking spray

1. Combine first 9 ingredients in a bowl; stir well. Cover and chill at least 2 hours.
2. Prepare grill.
3. Brush fillets evenly with 2 teaspoons oil; sprinkle with ⅛ teaspoon salt and ⅛ teaspoon black pepper. Place fillets on grill rack coated with cooking spray; grill 7 minutes on each side or until fish flakes easily when tested with a fork. Serve fish with cucumber salsa. YIELD: 4 servings (serving size: 1 fillet and ½ cup salsa).

POINTS value: 5; **Exchanges:** 1 Vegetable, 5 Very Lean Meat
Per serving: CAL 227 (31% from fat); PRO 33.6g; FAT 7.7g (sat 1.2g); CARB 4.1g; FIB 0.9g; CHOL 63mg; IRON 1.7mg; SOD 241mg; CALC 60mg

SPICY GRILLED GROUPER COCKTAIL

prep: 26 minutes • cook: 12 minutes
other: 2 hours

Who says an entrée has to be on a plate? Break from tradition and serve this cool, summery meal in a stemmed glass with baked tortilla chips.
If you close your eyes, you'll think you're dining in a cantina in Mexico.

1 pound grouper or other firm white fish fillets (about ½ inch thick)
¼ teaspoon salt
⅛ teaspoon black pepper
Cooking spray
½ cup diced seeded plum tomato (about 2 tomatoes)
½ cup diced green bell pepper
½ cup diced red bell pepper
1 teaspoon grated lime rind
⅓ cup fresh lime juice (about 2½ limes)
¼ cup diced red onion
3 tablespoons chopped fresh cilantro
3 tablespoons diced seeded jalapeño pepper
1 tablespoon olive oil
¼ teaspoon salt
⅛ teaspoon black pepper

1. Prepare grill.
2. Sprinkle fillets evenly with ¼ teaspoon salt and ⅛ teaspoon black pepper. Place fillets on grill rack coated with cooking spray; grill 6 to 7 minutes on each side or until fish flakes easily when tested with a fork. Remove fish from grill, and flake fish into bite-sized pieces.
3. Combine fish and remaining ingredients in a medium bowl; toss gently. Cover and chill at least 2 hours. YIELD: 3 servings (serving size: about 1 cup).

POINTS value: 5; **Exchanges:** 2 Vegetable, 3 Lean Meat
Per serving: CAL 218 (27% from fat); PRO 30.5g; FAT 6.6g (sat 1.1g); CARB 9.2g; FIB 1.3g; CHOL 56mg; IRON 1.9mg; SOD 480mg; CALC 56mg

FISH TACOS

prep: 28 minutes • cook: 15 minutes

Cutting the fish into chunks before dredging and baking creates four sides of crispy breading and a tasty taco.

2 ounces baked tortilla chips (about 40 chips)
½ cup dry breadcrumbs
1 teaspoon black pepper
½ teaspoon salt
1 cup low-fat buttermilk
4 teaspoons 40%-less-salt taco seasoning, divided
1 pound grouper fillet, cut into 36 (1-inch) chunks
Cooking spray
⅓ cup reduced-fat sour cream
⅓ cup light mayonnaise
1 tablespoon fresh lime juice
12 (6-inch) corn tortillas
1 (10-ounce) package angel hair slaw
1¼ cups thinly sliced red bell pepper strips
½ cup thinly sliced green onions (about 3 onions)
¼ cup cilantro leaves
6 lime wedges

1. Preheat oven to 425°.
2. Place tortilla chips in a food processor; pulse 5 to 6 times to form coarse crumbs to measure ¾ cup. Place crumbs in a shallow dish, and stir in breadcrumbs, black pepper, and salt.
3. Combine buttermilk and 2 teaspoons taco seasoning in a shallow bowl. Dip fish chunks, 1 at a time, into buttermilk mixture; dredge in crumb mixture. Place fish chunks on a baking sheet coated with cooking spray. Lightly coat fish with cooking spray. Bake at 425° for 15 minutes or until fish flakes easily when tested with a fork.
4. While fish cooks, combine remaining 2 teaspoons taco seasoning, sour cream, mayonnaise, and lime juice in a bowl; stir well.
5. Heat tortillas according to package directions. Top each tortilla with 3 fish chunks and ¼ cup slaw. Divide bell pepper, green onions, and cilantro evenly among tacos, and drizzle evenly with sour cream mixture. Serve immediately with lime wedges. YIELD: 6 servings (serving size: 2 tacos).

POINTS value: 8; **Exchanges:** 2 Starch, 2 Vegetable, 2 Lean Meat, 1 Fat
Per serving: CAL 371 (25% from fat); PRO 28.6g; FAT 10.3g (sat 2.7g); CARB 42.9g; FIB 3.8g; CHOL 54mg; IRON 2.0mg; SOD 884mg; CALC 148mg

BUYING FRESH FISH

Look for fish that's blemish-free, neither slick nor soggy, and springs back when touched. If it smells "fishy," it's not fresh. Avoid fish displayed directly on ice—the contact can cause quality to deteriorate. Buying fish that's frozen at sea is your next-best alternative.

ROASTED HALIBUT WITH ORANGE-BRAISED FENNEL

prep: 20 minutes • cook: 33 minutes

Serve with orzo or crusty bread to enjoy every drop of the flavorful sauce.

4   (6-ounce) halibut or other firm white fish fillets (about 1 inch thick)
1   tablespoon olive oil, divided
¾   teaspoon salt, divided
½   teaspoon black pepper, divided
1   large fennel bulb
1   cup orange juice
¼   cup mirin (sweet rice wine)
1   tablespoon butter, softened
¼   teaspoon lime juice
½   small garlic clove, finely chopped

1. Preheat oven to 425°.
2. Rub fillets with 1½ teaspoons olive oil; sprinkle with ¼ teaspoon salt and ¼ teaspoon pepper.
3. Rinse fennel thoroughly. Trim stalks to within 1 inch of bulb. Discard hard outside stalks; chop 1 tablespoon fennel fronds, and set aside. Reserve remaining fennel fronds for garnish, if desired. Cut out tough core from bottom of bulb. Starting at 1 side, cut bulb horizontally into 4 (½-inch-thick) slices.
4. Heat remaining 1½ teaspoons oil in a large ovenproof skillet over medium-high heat. Add fennel slices, and cook 3 minutes on each side or until browned (slices may separate). Pour orange juice and mirin over fennel, and sprinkle with remaining ½ teaspoon salt and remaining ¼ teaspoon pepper. Bring to a boil; reduce heat, and simmer, uncovered, 10 minutes (if fennel slices separate,

arrange pieces in 4 circles). Place fillets on top of fennel slices; spoon orange juice mixture over fillets. Bake at 425° for 10 minutes or until fish flakes easily when tested with a fork.
5. While fish cooks, combine chopped fennel fronds, butter, lime juice, and chopped garlic in a bowl; stir well.
6. Using a spatula, gently lift fennel and fish out of pan, and place in wide, shallow bowls. Spoon pan juices over fish, and top with fennel butter. YIELD: 4 servings (serving size: 1 fillet, 1 fennel slice, ¼ cup orange sauce, and about 1½ teaspoons fennel butter).

POINTS value: 7; **Exchanges:** 1 Starch, 5 Very Lean Meat, 1 Fat
Per serving: CAL 323 (29% from fat); PRO 36.7g; FAT 10.4g (sat 2.5g); CARB 15.7g; FIB 2.0g; CHOL 62mg; IRON 2.1mg; SOD 586mg; CALC 119mg

BROILED SALMON WITH CURRIED HONEY GLAZE

prep: 3 minutes • cook: 10 minutes

A handful of ingredients and only 13 minutes are all you need to turn salmon into a sweet and tangy entrée with a beautiful amber-colored glaze. Serve with steamed sugar snap peas and rice to complete the meal.

¼   cup honey
2   teaspoons curry powder
4   teaspoons county-style Dijon mustard
½   teaspoon salt
4   (6-ounce) salmon fillets (about 1 inch thick)
Cooking spray

1. Preheat broiler.
2. Combine first 4 ingredients in a small bowl; stir until smooth. Place fillets on a broiler pan coated with cooking spray. Brush honey mixture over fillets. Broil 10 minutes or until fish flakes easily when tested with a fork. YIELD: 4 servings (serving size: 1 fillet).

POINTS value: 8; **Exchanges:** 1 Starch, 5 Lean Meat
Per serving: CAL 346 (35% from fat); PRO 36.7g; FAT 13.6g (sat 3.1g); CARB 18.6g; FIB 0.4g; CHOL 87mg; IRON 1.1mg; SOD 503mg; CALC 34mg

BAKED LEMON GRASS SNAPPER

prep: 15 minutes • cook: 19 minutes

Lemon grass is an herb used in Thai cooking. Look for long, thin stalks in the produce section of supermarkets. Dried lemon grass is also available in the Asian or spice section of supermarkets.

2   teaspoons olive oil
¼   cup chopped peeled fresh lemon grass (about 2 stalks)
¼   cup minced shallots (about 2 large)
2   garlic cloves, minced
1½ tablespoons low-sodium soy sauce
¼   teaspoon crushed red pepper
1   lemon, thinly sliced
Cooking spray
2   (6-ounce) snapper fillets
2   tablespoons chopped fresh cilantro
1   green onion, thinly sliced

1. Preheat oven to 425°.
2. Heat oil in a nonstick skillet over medium-high heat. Add lemon grass,

shallots, and garlic; sauté 3 minutes or until tender. Remove from heat; stir in soy sauce and red pepper.

3. Place lemon in an 11 x 7-inch baking dish coated with cooking spray; arrange fillets over lemon slices. Spoon lemon grass mixture evenly over fillets. Bake at 425° for 15 minutes or until fish flakes easily when tested with a fork. Sprinkle with cilantro and green onions. **YIELD:** 2 servings (serving size: 1 fillet).

POINTS value: 5; **Exchanges:** 1 Starch, 5 Very Lean Meat
Per serving: CAL 263 (25% from fat); PRO 37.4g; FAT 7.3g (sat 1.2g); CARB 14.1g; FIB 3.2g; CHOL 63mg; IRON 2.0mg; SOD 410mg; CALC 119mg

SALMON BURGERS WITH CUCUMBER-DILL TARTAR SAUCE

prep: 14 minutes • cook: 9 minutes other: 1 hour

¾   pound salmon fillet, skinned
⅓   cup tartar sauce (such as Hellmann's), divided
2   tablespoons chopped red onion
1   teaspoon lemon juice
½   teaspoon dried dill, divided
½   teaspoon salt
¼   teaspoon black pepper
½   cup panko (Japanese) breadcrumbs
¼   cup chopped seeded cucumber
Cooking spray
3   curly leaf lettuce leaves
3   (1½-ounce) reduced-calorie wheat sandwich buns

1. Cut fillet into large chunks. Place fillet, 1 tablespoon tartar sauce, onion, lemon juice, ¼ teaspoon dill,

salt, and pepper in a food processor; pulse 7 times or until blended. Spoon into a bowl; stir in breadcrumbs.

2. Shape fish mixture into 3 patties; cover and chill at least 1 hour.

3. Combine remaining tartar sauce, remaining ¼ teaspoon dill, and cucumber in a bowl; stir well. Cover and chill until ready to serve.

4. Coat salmon patties with cooking spray. Place a large nonstick skillet over medium-high heat until hot. Add salmon patties, and cook 4 minutes on each side or until lightly browned. Place 1 salmon patty and 1 lettuce leaf on bottom half of each bun; top each with 2 tablespoons tartar sauce mixture and remaining bun halves. **YIELD:** 3 servings (serving size: 1 burger).

POINTS value: 8; **Exchanges:** 2 Starch, 3 Lean Meat, 1 Fat
Per serving: CAL 367 (38% from fat); PRO 29.8g; FAT 16.3g (sat 2.9g); CARB 31.1g; FIB 4.7g; CHOL 67mg; IRON 2.0mg; SOD 910mg; CALC 63mg

HEART SMART

Fish such as tuna and salmon give you much more than just great taste. These fish are rich in omega-3 fatty acids (also known as fish oil), which have been linked to promoting heart health and helping reduce the risk of heart disease. The American Heart Association recommends that all adults, excluding pregnant women, eat two servings of fish per week. Try any of the flavorful dishes on these pages, and your heart will thank you.

GRILLED TUNA STEAK WITH FRESH SALSA

(pictured on page 67)
prep: 11 minutes • cook: 6 minutes other: 30 minutes

2   cups diced plum tomatoes (about 6 tomatoes)
¼   cup thinly sliced green onions
¼   cup fresh lime juice
2   tablespoons chopped fresh cilantro
2   tablespoons minced seeded jalapeño pepper
1   tablespoon olive oil
2   teaspoons balsamic vinegar
½   teaspoon salt, divided
½   teaspoon black pepper, divided
4   (6-ounce) tuna steaks (about 1 inch thick)
Cooking spray
Lime wedges (optional)

1. Combine first 7 ingredients in a bowl; stir in ¼ teaspoon salt and ¼ teaspoon black pepper. Let stand 30 minutes.

2. Prepare grill.

3. Lightly coat both sides of tuna steaks with cooking spray; sprinkle with remaining salt and pepper. Place steaks on grill rack; grill 3 minutes on each side or until fish is medium-rare or desired degree of doneness. Serve with salsa, and, if desired, lime wedges. **YIELD:** 4 servings (serving size: 1 steak and ½ cup salsa).

POINTS value: 7; **Exchanges:** 1 Vegetable, 5 Lean Meat
Per serving: CAL 307 (36% from fat); PRO 40.7g; FAT 12.2g (sat 2.7g); CARB 7.4g; FIB 1.5g; CHOL 65mg; IRON 2.3mg; SOD 373mg; CALC 23mg

SNAPPER WITH LIME-HERB SUCCOTASH

**prep: 12 minutes • cook: 10 minutes
other: 2 hours**

*Succotash, a blend of corn, lima
beans, and sometimes bell peppers,
is now available in the frozen food
section of the supermarket. When
mixed with cilantro, basil, tomato, and
lime, this colorful succotash is the
perfect complement to grilled fish.*

4   (6-ounce) red snapper, grouper,
     or orange roughy fillets
½   cup finely chopped green
     onions (about 4 onions)
¼   cup fresh lime juice
2   teaspoons extravirgin olive oil
½   teaspoon salt
½   teaspoon freshly ground black
     pepper
1   garlic clove, chopped
2   cups frozen succotash, thawed
¼   cup chopped fresh cilantro
¼   cup diced seeded plum
     tomato (1 tomato)
2   tablespoons chopped fresh
     basil
Cooking spray

1. Place fish in a shallow dish.
Combine green onions and next
5 ingredients; spoon half of green
onion mixture over fish. Cover and
chill at least 2 hours.
2. Combine remaining green onion
mixture, succotash, and next 3 ingredients in a bowl. Cover and chill.
3. Prepare grill.
4. Place fish on a grill rack coated
with cooking spray. Grill 5 minutes
on each side or until fish flakes easily
when tested with a fork. Serve with
succotash mixture. YIELD: 4 servings

(serving size: 1 fillet and ½ cup
succotash mixture).
Note: If frozen succotash is not
available in your area, substitute 1
cup each of frozen baby lima beans
and whole-kernel corn.

POINTS value: 5; **Exchanges:** 1 Starch, ½ Vegetable,
5 Very Lean Meat
Per serving: CAL 278 (17% from fat); PRO 38.6g;
FAT 5.4g (sat 1.0g); CARB 19.2g; FIB 4.0g;
CHOL 63mg; IRON 1.3mg; SOD 444mg;
CALC 75mg

SWORDFISH WITH LEMON-CAPER SAUCE

prep: 13 minutes • cook: 14 minutes

*After the swordfish is cooked, wine is
added to the hot pan to loosen the
browned bits from the bottom of the
pan. This procedure creates a highly
flavored sauce that perfectly
complements the fish.*

4   (6-ounce) swordfish steaks
     (about 1½ inches thick)
½   teaspoon salt, divided
¼   teaspoon freshly ground black
     pepper
2   tablespoons all-purpose flour
1½   teaspoons canola oil
Cooking spray
¼   cup dry white wine
1   teaspoon minced shallots or
     red onion
½   cup fat-free, less-sodium
     chicken broth
1½   tablespoons fresh lemon
     juice
1   teaspoon butter
1½   teaspoons chopped fresh
     parsley
2   teaspoons capers
Lemon slices (optional)

1. Sprinkle fish with ¼ teaspoon salt
and pepper. Dredge fish in flour.
2. Heat oil in a large nonstick skillet
coated with cooking spray over
medium-high heat. Add fish; cook
4 minutes on each side or until fish
flakes easily when tested with a fork.
Remove fish from pan; keep warm.
3. Add wine to pan, scraping pan to
loosen browned bits. Add shallots,
and cook until liquid nearly evaporates (shallots will be soft). Add
chicken broth and lemon juice, and
cook until liquid is reduced by about
one-third. Remove from heat. Add
butter, stirring until butter melts.
Stir in remaining ¼ teaspoon salt,
parsley, and capers. Serve sauce over
fish, and garnish with lemon slices, if
desired. YIELD: 4 servings (serving size:
1 steak and 1 tablespoon sauce).

POINTS value: 6; **Exchanges:** 4½ Very Lean Meat,
2 Fat
Per serving: CAL 249 (36% from fat); PRO 34.6g;
FAT 9.6g (sat 2.5g); CARB 3.8g; FIB 0.2g;
CHOL 69mg; IRON 1.7mg; SOD 576mg;
CALC 11mg

SNAPPER FACTS

As a result of red snapper's
increasing popularity and soar-
ing prices, there are several
"imposter" fish in local markets
that are labeled as red snapper
but are actually other kinds of
snapper. Pacific red snapper
and silk snapper are commonly
mislabeled as red snapper.

When purchasing this fish,
be sure to buy from a trusted,
knowledgeable vendor.
Yellowtail and Caribbean are
similar types of snapper that can
be substituted for red snapper.

PAN-FRIED TILAPIA WITH TANGY TARTAR SAUCE

(pictured on page 66)
prep: 11 minutes • cook: 18 minutes

A dusting of flour, a little oil, and a hot skillet create a golden crust on these fillets. A dollop of tartar sauce offers the finishing touch. Keep this tartar sauce in the fridge to add flavor to fish and sandwiches. One tablespoon has a POINTS value of 1.

¼   cup reduced-fat mayonnaise
     (such as Hellmann's)
¼   cup plain fat-free yogurt
1   tablespoon thinly sliced fresh
     chives
1   tablespoon chopped fresh
     parsley
1   tablespoon grated lemon rind
2   tablespoons fresh lemon juice
2   tablespoons chopped
     cornichons (about 4 pickles)
1   tablespoon capers, coarsely
     chopped
1   teaspoon Dijon mustard
¼   teaspoon freshly ground black
     pepper
⅛   teaspoon sugar
½   cup all-purpose flour
1   tablespoon freshly ground black
     pepper
1   teaspoon dried Italian
     seasoning
½   teaspoon salt
4   (6-ounce) tilapia fillets
1   tablespoon olive oil,
     divided
Fresh chives (optional)
Lemon slices (optional)

1. Combine first 11 ingredients in a small bowl; cover and chill until ready to serve.

2. Combine flour and next 3 ingredients in a shallow dish. Dredge fillets in flour mixture.

3. Heat 1½ teaspoons oil in a large nonstick skillet over medium-high heat. Add 2 fillets; cook 4 minutes on each side or until fish flakes easily when tested with a fork. Repeat procedure with remaining oil and fillets. Serve fish with tartar sauce. Garnish with fresh chives and lemon slices, if desired. YIELD: 4 servings (serving size: 1 fillet and 1 tablespoon tartar sauce).

Note: Substitute baby dill pickles for the cornichons, if desired.

POINTS value: 7; **Exchanges:** 1 Starch, 5 Very Lean Meat, 1 Fat
Per serving: CAL 319 (32% from fat); PRO 35.8g; FAT 10.9g (sat 2.0g); CARB 17.2g; FIB 1.4g; CHOL 152mg; IRON 3.4mg; SOD 841mg; CALC 242mg

---

GRILLING FISH & SEAFOOD

When you grill seafood, it's particularly important that the rack be very clean. Any residue on the rack could interfere with the seafood's delicate flavor; a clean rack also helps prevent sticking. You should always place seafood on a hot grill rack and leave it there for several minutes before you try to move it. This way, a sear will develop between the fish and the grill rack, which will further help prevent sticking.

Lightly spray the grill rack with cooking spray before placing it over the coals. This keeps the food from sticking and makes the grill rack easier to clean.

GRILLED TROUT WITH SHALLOT VINAIGRETTE

prep: 8 minutes • cook: 18 minutes

You can use your oven broiler instead of firing up the grill, if desired.

2   tablespoons finely chopped
     shallots (about 1 large)
1   tablespoon chopped fresh
     parsley
3   tablespoons sherry vinegar
2   teaspoons chopped fresh chives
2   teaspoons fresh lemon juice
½   teaspoon salt
⅛   teaspoon black pepper
1   tablespoon olive oil
Cooking spray
4   (6-ounce) trout fillets
2   apple-smoked bacon slices,
     cooked and crumbled

1. Prepare grill.

2. Combine first 7 ingredients in a small bowl. Gradually add oil, stirring until well blended.

3. Cut a 16 x 12-inch sheet of heavy-duty foil; lightly coat 1 side of foil with cooking spray. Place foil on grill rack. Place fillets, skin sides down, on prepared foil. Spoon 1 teaspoon vinaigrette over each fillet. Cover and grill 10 minutes or until fish flakes easily when tested with a fork. Drizzle remaining vinaigrette evenly over each serving; top with crumbled bacon. YIELD: 4 servings (serving size: 1 fillet, 1 tablespoon shallot vinaigrette, and 1½ teaspoons bacon).

POINTS value: 7; **Exchanges:** 2 Very Lean Meat, 2 Fat
Per serving: CAL 297 (44% from fat); PRO 37.6g; FAT 14.2g (sat 3.6g); CARB 2.9g; FIB 0.1g; CHOL 105mg; IRON 0.9mg; SOD 452mg; CALC 117mg

HERB-DUSTED SEARED SCALLOPS

prep: 5 minutes • cook: 15 minutes

For a golden crust, be sure your skillet is hot, don't crowd the scallops in the pan, and turn the scallops only once during cooking.

8   rectangular buttery crackers (such as Club)
½   teaspoon dried oregano
½   teaspoon dried basil
½   teaspoon dried marjoram
¼   teaspoon salt
¼   teaspoon dried thyme
¼   teaspoon white pepper
1   pound sea scallops (about 14)
1   tablespoon olive oil, divided
2   tablespoons lemon juice
1   tablespoon chopped fresh parsley

1. Place first 7 ingredients in a food processor; process until crackers are finely ground. Place crumb mixture in a shallow dish.
2. Pat scallops dry with paper towels. Dredge scallops in crumb mixture.
3. Heat 1½ teaspoons oil in a large nonstick skillet over medium-high heat. Add half of scallops; cook 3 minutes on each side or until golden. Remove scallops from pan. Repeat procedure with remaining oil and scallops. Sprinkle with lemon juice and parsley, and serve immediately. YIELD: 3 servings (serving size: about 4 ounces scallops).

*POINTS value: 5; **Exchanges:** 1 Starch, 3 Very Lean Meat, 1 Fat*
Per serving: CAL 224 (32% from fat); PRO 26.2g; FAT 7.8g (sat 1.1g); CARB 11.0g; FIB 0.5g; CHOL 50mg; IRON 1.0mg; SOD 554mg; CALC 55mg

STEAMED MUSSELS IN COCONUT-LIME BROTH

prep: 10 minutes • cook: 34 minutes

2   teaspoons vegetable or canola oil
¾   cup finely chopped shallots (about 2 large)
3   garlic cloves, finely chopped
1   (13.5-ounce) can light coconut milk
2   cups fat-free, less-sodium chicken broth
1   to 2 tablespoons grated lime rind
¼   cup fresh lime juice
1   tablespoon fish sauce
½   teaspoon crushed red pepper
1   basil sprig
4   pounds mussels, scrubbed and debearded
2   tablespoons chopped fresh basil

1. Heat oil in a large Dutch oven over medium heat. Add shallots and garlic; sauté 3 minutes. Add coconut milk and next 5 ingredients; bring to a boil. Add basil sprig. Reduce heat; simmer, uncovered, 15 minutes.
2. Add mussels; cover and simmer 10 minutes or until shells open. Remove from heat; discard any unopened shells. Place mussels in wide, shallow bowls; ladle broth over mussels. Sprinkle with chopped basil. YIELD: 4 servings (serving size: about 12 mussels, 1 cup broth, and 1½ teaspoons chopped basil).

*POINTS value: 6; **Exchanges:** 1 Starch, 3 Lean Meat, 1 Fat*
Per serving: CAL 277 (37% from fat); PRO 26.8g; FAT 11.3g (sat 5.2g); CARB 18.8g; FIB 0.7g; CHOL 54mg; IRON 8.5mg; SOD 1,234mg; CALC 73mg

SHRIMP FRIED RICE WITH EDAMAME

prep: 17 minutes • cook: 26 minutes

Traditional fried rice gets an update with Japanese green soybeans. Dark sesame oil adds a distinct "toasted" flavor when stirred in just before serving. Because of its high smoke point, peanut oil is ideal for stir-frying.

2   teaspoons peanut oil
2   tablespoons thinly sliced shallots (about 1 large)
1   large egg, lightly beaten
1   pound peeled and deveined medium shrimp, coarsely chopped
1   teaspoon minced peeled fresh ginger
4   cups cooked jasmine or other white rice, cooked according to package directions without salt or fat
1   cup fully-cooked refrigerated shelled edamame
½   cup shredded carrot (about 1 medium)
⅓   cup chopped green onions (about 3 onions)
¼   teaspoon freshly ground black pepper
3   tablespoons low-sodium soy sauce
2   tablespoons dark sesame oil

1. Heat peanut oil over medium-high heat in a wok or large nonstick skillet. Add shallots and egg; stir-fry 30 seconds or until egg is soft-scrambled. Add shrimp and ginger, and stir-fry 2 to 3 minutes or until shrimp turn pink. Add rice and next 4 ingredients, and stir-fry

1 minute. Stir in soy sauce and sesame oil. YIELD: 6 servings (serving size: 1⅓ cups).

Note: Chilled rice works best when preparing fried rice because the grains don't stick together. However, when you're in a rush, freshly cooked rice will work in this dish.

POINTS value: 7; **Exchanges:** 2 Starch, 2 Vegetable, 2 Very Lean Meat, 1 Fat
Per serving: CAL 330 (27% from fat); PRO 22.6g; FAT 9.6g (sat 1.5g); CARB 36.1g; FIB 2.4g; CHOL 150mg; IRON 3.9mg; SOD 339mg; CALC 77mg

SPICY BBQ SHRIMP AND CORN SALAD WITH RANCH DIPPING SAUCE

prep: 23 minutes • cook: 10 minutes

Chop the corn salad and make the sauce the day before to save time.

1½ pounds unpeeled large shrimp (about 32 shrimp)
¼ cup spicy barbecue sauce (such as KC Masterpiece Spicy Original)
1 teaspoon white vinegar
¼ teaspoon ground red pepper
Butter-flavored cooking spray
2 cups frozen whole-kernel corn, thawed
½ cup finely chopped onion
½ cup chopped red bell pepper
1 tablespoon minced seeded jalapeño pepper
2 large garlic cloves, minced
Ranch Dipping Sauce

1. Peel shrimp, leaving tails intact.
2. Combine barbecue sauce, vinegar, and ground red pepper in a bowl. Add shrimp, tossing gently to coat.

3. Heat a large nonstick skillet over medium-high heat. Add shrimp, and sauté 6 minutes or until shrimp are done. Remove from pan, and keep warm.
4. Coat pan with cooking spray. Add corn and next 4 ingredients; sauté 3 minutes or until vegetables are tender and corn is lightly browned. Spoon corn mixture onto plates; top with shrimp. Serve with Ranch Dipping Sauce. YIELD: 4 servings (serving size: about 8 shrimp, ½ cup corn salad, and about ⅓ cup Ranch Dipping Sauce).

POINTS value: 7; **Exchanges:** 3 Starch, 1 Vegetable, 3 Very Lean Meat
Per serving: CAL 348 (9% from fat); PRO 31.2g; FAT 3.4g (sat 0.7g); CARB 49.7g; FIB 3.5g; CHOL 253mg; IRON 5.0mg; SOD 1,156mg; CALC 90mg

RANCH DIPPING SAUCE

Try this sauce with boiled shrimp, too.

1 cup fat-free ranch dressing
2 tablespoons extrahot prepared horseradish
1 teaspoon white vinegar
1 large garlic clove, minced

1. Combine all ingredients in a small bowl; stir well. Cover and chill until ready to serve. YIELD: 1¼ cups (serving size: about ⅓ cup).

POINTS value: 2; **Exchanges:** 1½ Starch
Per serving: CAL 105 (7% from fat); PRO 0.6g; FAT 0.8g (sat 0.2g); CARB 23.5g; FIB 0.7g; CHOL 1mg; IRON 0.1mg; SOD 732mg; CALC 24mg

SAUTÉED SHRIMP WITH ARTICHOKES AND CILANTRO

prep: 5 minutes • cook: 7 minutes

This quick-and-easy dish is simple enough to prepare on a weeknight but special enough for guests. Serve over hot pasta.

1 tablespoon olive oil
Cooking spray
1 pound peeled and deveined large shrimp
1 (14-ounce) can quartered artichoke hearts, drained
2 tablespoons finely chopped fresh cilantro
1 tablespoon fresh lemon juice
¼ teaspoon black pepper
⅛ teaspoon salt

1. Heat oil in a large nonstick skillet coated with cooking spray over medium heat. Add shrimp and artichokes; cook 5 minutes or until shrimp are done, stirring occasionally. Add chopped cilantro and remaining ingredients. YIELD: 3 servings (serving size: 1 cup).

POINTS value: 5; **Exchanges:** 2 Vegetable, 4 Very Lean Meat, 1 Fat
Per serving: CAL 247 (27% from fat); PRO 33.7g; FAT 7.3g (sat 1.2g); CARB 10.6g; FIB 3.0g; CHOL 230mg; IRON 3.7mg; SOD 811mg; CALC 81mg

SHRIMP AND FENNEL RISOTTO

(pictured on page 67)
prep: 19 minutes • cook: 55 minutes

Risotto is traditionally made with Arborio rice because of its high starch content and firm texture.

1   (32-ounce) container fat-free, less-sodium chicken broth
1   tablespoon butter
1½ cups finely chopped fennel bulb (about 1 medium)
¼   cup minced shallots (about 2 large)
2   garlic cloves, minced
1   cup uncooked Arborio rice
⅔   cup dry white wine
1½ pounds peeled and deveined medium shrimp
1½ tablespoons minced fennel fronds
1   teaspoon grated lemon rind
½   teaspoon freshly ground black pepper
⅓   cup (1⅓ ounces) shredded fresh Parmesan cheese, divided

1. Bring broth to a simmer in a medium saucepan (do not boil). Keep warm over low heat.
2. Melt butter in a large saucepan over medium-high heat. Add fennel bulb, shallots, and garlic, and sauté 4 minutes or until tender. Add rice, and cook 2 minutes, stirring constantly. Add wine, and cook until liquid is nearly absorbed, stirring constantly. Add warm broth, ½ cup at a time, stirring constantly; cook until each portion of broth is absorbed before adding the next (about 30 minutes total).

3. Stir in shrimp, fennel fronds, lemon rind, and pepper; cook 8 minutes or until shrimp are done, stirring occasionally. Stir in ¼ cup Parmesan cheese. Spoon risotto into bowls; sprinkle with remaining Parmesan cheese. **YIELD: 5 servings** (serving size: 1¼ cups risotto and about ¾ teaspoon cheese).

POINTS value: 6; **Exchanges:** 2 Starch, 1 Vegetable, 3 Very Lean Meat
Per serving: CAL 313 (14% from fat); PRO 28.8g; FAT 4.8g (sat 2.2g); CARB 37.0g; FIB 2.2g; CHOL 211mg; IRON 5.4mg; SOD 813mg; CALC 115mg

SHRIMP AND SAUSAGE JAMBALAYA

prep: 9 minutes • cook: 28 minutes other: 5 minutes

We kept the hot sauce to a minimum in this recipe to make it family-friendly.

1½ teaspoons olive oil
½   cup vertically sliced onion
⅓   cup diced celery
2   large garlic cloves, minced
4   ounces light turkey, pork, and beef smoked sausage (such as Hillshire Farm), thinly sliced
⅛   teaspoon dried oregano
1   bay leaf
1   thyme sprig
1   cup uncooked long-grain rice
1   (14½-ounce) can diced tomatoes, undrained
1¼ cups fat-free, less-sodium chicken broth
1   cup frozen cut okra
¼   teaspoon hot sauce
¾   pound peeled and deveined medium shrimp
    Hot sauce (optional)

1. Heat oil in a large skillet over medium-high heat. Add onion, celery, and garlic; sauté 2 minutes. Add sausage and next 3 ingredients; sauté 2 minutes. Add rice; cook 1 minute, stirring constantly. Add tomatoes, chicken broth, okra, and ¼ teaspoon hot sauce; bring to a boil.
2. Cover, reduce heat, and simmer 15 minutes. Add shrimp; cover and cook 5 minutes or until shrimp are done. Remove from heat; let stand 5 minutes. Discard bay leaf and thyme sprig. Serve with additional hot sauce, if desired. **YIELD: 5 servings** (serving size: 1½ cups).

POINTS value: 6; **Exchanges:** 2 Starch, 2 Vegetable, 2 Lean Meat
Per serving: CAL 312 (20% from fat); PRO 23.1g; FAT 6.8g (sat 1.9g); CARB 38.9g; FIB 3.0g; CHOL 118mg; IRON 4.1mg; SOD 589mg; CALC 107mg

DEVEINING SHRIMP

Recipes often call for shrimp to be peeled and deveined, but there's neither danger nor any change in flavor when the thin black line (or vein) is left where it is. If you're butterflying shrimp, deveining occurs automatically.

Meatless Main Dishes

SALAD PIZZAS WITH FETA

prep: 11 minutes • cook: 20 minutes
other: 10 minutes

*We've challenged what traditionally
defines a pizza by skipping the
sauce and topping the crusts with
a lightly dressed salad of mixed
gourmet greens. These pizzas are
fresh and delicious and easy to
make at home.*

1   (11-ounce) can refrigerated
    French bread dough
Cooking spray
⅓   cup chopped green onions
    (about 2 onions)
1   teaspoon dried basil
1½ tablespoons extravirgin olive
    oil
1½ tablespoons cider vinegar
¼   teaspoon black pepper
Dash of salt
1   garlic clove, minced
3   cups gourmet salad greens
1   (3½-ounce) package crumbled
    reduced-fat feta cheese with
    basil and tomatoes

1. Preheat oven to 350°.
2. Unroll dough; cut into 4 equal
portions. Press each portion of
dough into a 6 x 8-inch rectangle
on a large baking sheet coated with
cooking spray. Sprinkle evenly with
green onions and basil, pressing gently into dough. Bake at 350° for 20
minutes or until crusts are crisp.
Remove crusts from pan; cool 10
minutes on a wire rack.
3. Combine oil and next 4 ingredients in a large bowl, stirring with a
whisk until well blended. Add
greens, tossing to coat. Place crusts
on individual serving plates; top

evenly with salad. Sprinkle evenly
with feta cheese. Serve immediately.
YIELD: 4 servings (serving size: 1 pizza).

POINTS value: 6; **Exchanges:** 2 Starch, 1 Vegetable,
1 Very Lean Meat, 2 Fat
Per serving: CAL 300 (34% from fat); PRO 12.2g;
FAT 11.3g (sat 4.2g); CARB 37.5g; FIB 3.1g;
CHOL 9mg; IRON 2.6mg; SOD 882mg;
CALC 99mg

MEXICAN PIZZA

prep: 10 minutes • cook: 8 minutes
other: 5 minutes

*To turn up the heat in this pizza,
use hot salsa.*

2   teaspoons fresh lime juice
1   (15-ounce) can black beans,
    rinsed and drained
1   (10-ounce) Italian cheese-
    flavored thin pizza crust (such
    as Boboli)
1   teaspoon 40%-less-sodium taco
    seasoning
1   (12-ounce) package frozen
    burger-style recipe crumbles,
    thawed
1½ cups (6 ounces) preshredded
    reduced-fat colby-Jack cheese
2   cups shredded iceberg lettuce
2   cups chopped tomato
1   cup salsa
½   cup reduced-fat sour cream

1. Preheat oven to 450°.
2. Combine lime juice and beans in
a bowl; mash with a potato masher.
3. Place pizza crust on a large chopping block, and spread black bean
mixture over crust, leaving a 1-inch
border. Combine taco seasoning and
crumbles; toss well, and spread over
beans. Top with cheese.

4. Slide pizza off chopping block
onto oven rack. Bake at 450° for
8 to 10 minutes or until cheese
melts. Remove pizza to cutting
board; let stand 5 minutes. Top pizza
with lettuce and tomato, and cut
into 8 slices. Serve immediately with
salsa and sour cream. YIELD: 8 servings
(serving size: 1 slice pizza, 2 tablespoons salsa, and 1 tablespoon sour
cream).

POINTS value: 6; **Exchanges:** 2 Starch, 2 Medium-
Fat Meat
Per serving: CAL 279 (33% from fat); PRO 20.0g;
FAT 10.2g (sat 5.1g); CARB 29.3g; FIB 4.8g;
CHOL 23mg; IRON 3.6mg; SOD 769mg;
CALC 301mg

DAILY DAIRY

One serving of dairy is 8 ounces
(1 cup) of milk, 1 to 1½ ounces
of cheese, or 8 ounces (1 cup)
of yogurt. Consuming at least
three servings of dairy daily may
play a vital role in weight loss
and management. Studies find
that the nutrient mix in dairy
foods, especially calcium and
protein, may improve the body's
ability to burn fat and speed up
metabolism. Plus, dairy foods
help build and strengthen bones
and reduce the risk of osteoporo-
sis, high blood pressure, and
certain cancers.

"BEEF" AND BEAN BURRITOS

prep: 8 minutes • cook: 15 minutes

1   teaspoon olive oil
Cooking spray
½   cup chopped onion
2   garlic cloves, minced
8   ounces (about 2½ cups) frozen
     burger-style recipe crumbles
2   tablespoons 40%-less-sodium
     taco seasoning
2   cups fresh baby spinach leaves
½   cup chopped tomato
½   cup frozen whole-kernel
     corn
1   tablespoon fresh lime juice
1   (15-ounce) can black beans,
     rinsed and drained
6   (10-inch) reduced-carb whole
     wheat flour tortillas
1   cup (4 ounces) shredded
     reduced-fat extrasharp Cheddar
     cheese
3   cups shredded iceberg lettuce
¾   cup salsa
6   tablespoons reduced-fat sour
     cream

1. Heat olive oil in a large nonstick skillet coated with cooking spray over medium heat. Add onion and garlic; cook 3 minutes or until tender. Add crumbles and taco seasoning; cook 4 minutes or until crumbles are thawed, stirring occasionally. Add spinach and tomato; cook 3 minutes or until spinach wilts, stirring frequently. Stir in corn, lime juice, and beans; cook 3 minutes or until thoroughly heated.
2. Heat tortillas according to package directions. Spoon ½ cup burrito filling and about 2½ tablespoons cheese down center of each tortilla; roll up. Serve immediately on a bed of lettuce with salsa and sour cream.

YIELD: 6 servings (serving size: 1 burrito, ½ cup lettuce, 2 tablespoons salsa, and 1 tablespoon sour cream).

POINTS value: 10; **Exchanges:** 3 Starch, 1 Vegetable, 2 Medium-Fat Meat, 1 Fat
Per serving: CAL 454 (33% from fat); PRO 25.2g; FAT 16.3g (sat 6.1g); CARB 50.8g; FIB 26.8g; CHOL 21mg; IRON 4.0mg; SOD 1,300mg; CALC 234mg

ROASTED VEGETABLE BURRITOS

prep: 15 minutes • cook: 31 minutes

2   poblano chiles, cut into
     ½-inch strips (about 1 cup)
1   red bell pepper, cut into
     ½-inch strips (about 1½ cups)
1   medium zucchini, diced (about
     1½ cups)
1   medium red onion, coarsely
     chopped (about 1 cup)
2   tablespoons extravirgin olive
     oil
½   teaspoon salt
½   teaspoon ground cumin
2   garlic cloves, minced
Cooking spray
2   large tomatoes, peeled, seeded,
     and chopped (about 1½ cups)
½   cup chopped fresh cilantro
1   tablespoon fresh lime juice
½   teaspoon salt
1   cup fresh corn kernels
6   (8-inch) 97%-fat-free flour
     tortillas
1½   cups (6 ounces) shredded
     reduced-fat sharp Cheddar
     cheese
6   tablespoons fat-free sour cream

1. Preheat oven to 475°.
2. Combine first 8 ingredients in a large bowl, tossing gently to coat vegetables. Spread vegetable mixture in a 15 x 10-inch jelly-roll pan coated with cooking spray. Bake at 475° for 30 minutes or until browned, stirring occasionally.
3. While vegetables roast, combine tomato, cilantro, lime juice, and salt in a small bowl; toss well, and set salsa aside.
4. Remove roasted vegetables from oven; stir in corn.
5. Heat tortillas according to package directions. Sprinkle ¼ cup cheese down the center of each tortilla; top each with ½ cup vegetable mixture, and roll up. Serve with salsa and sour cream. YIELD: 6 servings (serving size: 1 burrito, ¼ cup salsa, and 1 tablespoon sour cream).
Note: You may substitute frozen corn for fresh, if desired. Thaw and drain the corn before stirring it into the roasted vegetables. It is not necessary to cook the corn.

POINTS value: 7; **Exchanges:** 1½ Starch, 3 Vegetable, 1 Very Lean Meat, 2 Fat
Per serving: CAL 318 (35% from fat); PRO 13.3g; FAT 12.9g (sat 4.8g); CARB 39.6g; FIB 2.6g; CHOL 21mg; IRON 1.9mg; SOD 937mg; CALC 307mg

SODIUM SOLUTIONS

The current recommendation for daily sodium intake for healthy adults is 2,300 milligrams or less per day. When eating higher-sodium foods like sandwich meat, bread, or condiments, be sure to choose lower-sodium accompaniments like fruit or vegetables to balance out the meal.

REUBEN DOGS

(pictured on page 69)
prep: 6 minutes • cook: 2 minutes
other: 30 minutes

¼   cup cider vinegar
2   tablespoons sugar
1   tablespoon olive oil
½   teaspoon caraway seeds
1   (10-ounce) package angel hair
     slaw
8   (1¾-ounce) reduced-calorie
     whole wheat hot dog buns
8   meatless fat-free franks (such as
     Smart Dogs)
Cooking spray
1   cup (4 ounces) shredded
     reduced-fat Swiss cheese
¼   cup reduced-fat Thousand
     Island dressing

1. Prepare grill.
2. Combine first 4 ingredients in
a large bowl; stir well with a whisk.
Add slaw, tossing to coat. Cover and
chill 30 minutes.
3. Wrap buns in heavy-duty foil.
Place buns and franks on grill
rack coated with cooking spray, and
grill 2 to 3 minutes or until thoroughly heated.
4. Split buns, and sprinkle cheese
evenly on inside of buns. Add franks
to buns; top each with 1½ teaspoons
dressing and ⅓ cup slaw. **YIELD:** 8
servings (serving size: 1 hot dog).

POINTS value: 5; **Exchanges:** 2 Starch, 1 Vegetable,
1 Medium-Fat Meat
Per serving: CAL 271 (22% from fat); PRO 17.9g;
FAT 6.6g (sat 1.9g); CARB 34.4g; FIB 3.8g;
CHOL 3mg; IRON 4.2mg; SOD 564mg;
CALC 218mg

CHILI SLOPPY JOES

(pictured on page 69)
prep: 6 minutes • cook: 17 minutes

2   teaspoons olive oil
½   cup finely chopped onion
     (1 small)
½   cup finely chopped green bell
     pepper (1 small)
1   tablespoon bottled minced
     garlic
1   tablespoon prepared mustard
2   teaspoons chili powder
1   teaspoon ground cumin
1   (16-ounce) can chili beans in
     mild sauce (such as Bush's),
     undrained
1   (15.5-ounce) can sloppy joe
     sauce (such as Hunt's)
1   (12-ounce) package frozen
     burger-style recipe crumbles
10 (2-ounce) reduced-calorie
     wheat hamburger buns

1. Heat oil in a large nonstick skillet
over medium-high heat. Add onion,
bell pepper, and garlic, and sauté
3 minutes. Add mustard and next 5
ingredients; bring to a simmer.
Reduce heat to low, and simmer,
uncovered, 9 minutes or until thick,
stirring occasionally. Spoon onto
buns. **YIELD:** 10 servings (serving size:
1 bun and about ½ cup sauce).

POINTS value: 3; **Exchanges:** 2½ Starch, 1 Very
Lean Meat
Per serving: CAL 212 (14% from fat); PRO 12.8g;
FAT 3.7g (sat 0.5g); CARB 38.2g; FIB 7.3g;
CHOL 0mg; IRON 4.0mg; SOD 909mg;
CALC 56mg

SUMMER VEGGIE
QUESADILLAS

prep: 12 minutes • cook: 12 minutes
plus an additional 4 minutes per batch

2   teaspoons olive oil, divided
1   (8-ounce) package sliced
     mushrooms, chopped
½   cup finely chopped red onion
     (about 1 small)
1   cup diced zucchini (about
     1 medium)
1   cup diced yellow squash (about
     1 medium)
2   tablespoons 40%-less-sodium
     taco seasoning
2   garlic cloves, minced
8   (7-inch) flour tortillas
Cooking spray
1   (8-ounce) package preshredded
     reduced-fat colby-Jack cheese
1   cup green salsa
½   cup reduced-fat sour cream

1. Heat 1 teaspoon oil in a large
nonstick skillet over medium-high
heat. Add mushrooms and onion;
sauté 5 minutes or until tender.
Spoon into a large bowl; set aside.
Heat remaining 1 teaspoon oil in
pan. Add zucchini and squash; sauté 4
minutes or until tender. Add taco seasoning and garlic; cook 1 minute. Add
to mushroom mixture in bowl; toss
well. Wipe clean with a paper towel.
2. Coat 1 side of a tortilla with cooking spray. Place tortilla, coated side
down, in pan; top with 2 tablespoons
cheese, ¼ cup vegetable mixture, and
an additional 2 tablespoons cheese.
Fold tortilla in half; cook 3 minutes
or until lightly browned. Turn quesadilla over; cook 1 minute or until
lightly browned, pressing down on
(recipe continued on page 73)

Making a U-Turn

MARK BREAUX • **HEIGHT** 6'1" • **BEFORE** 455 LBS. • **AFTER** 205 LBS.

Reversal: "I no longer live life in the fast-food lane."

Mark Breaux battled obesity all of his life. And by the age of 40, he weighed 455 pounds. "I ate too much; made bad food choices, including a lot of fast food; and did nothing but watch television," he admits.

Mark's weight made it difficult for him to get in and out of vehicles. And flying on an airplane required a seat belt extension. "I dreaded the stares from other passengers as I searched for my seat. I knew they were thinking, 'Please don't let him sit next to me!'" And on his honeymoon trip to Nantucket, the pilot of the 15-passenger plane—seating passengers according to weight—separated Mark from the person wanting to sit beside him—his new bride, Bibiane.

For the first seven years of marriage, the couple attempted to conceive a child but were unsuccessful. "Extra weight disrupts the body's hormonal functions and is a common cause of infertility," Mark explains. Then, during a visit with Bibiane's

> *"My breakfasts changed from two fast-food bacon, egg, and cheese biscuits with an order of hash browns to a piece of toast with cheese or peanut butter."*

family in New Hampshire, Mark's father-in-law introduced him to *Weight Watchers*. "He had lost 50 pounds, and he turned the trip into a *Weight Watchers* boot camp. We helped prepare the Thanksgiving meal according to his **POINTS**, and it

tasted great. So Bibiane and I agreed that we would both join."

After their first *Weight Watchers* meeting, Mark and Bibiane stopped at the grocery to stock up on healthy foods. "I no longer live life in the fast-food lane. My breakfasts changed from two fast-food bacon, egg, and cheese biscuits with an order of hash browns to a piece of toast with cheese or peanut butter," he says. "For dinner, I started grilling fish and chicken, rather than eating the 16-ounce steaks that I used to cook or fast-food Mexican meals from the drive-through."

During his first week, Mark lost 22 pounds, and he continued to lose consistently for a total of 75 pounds in seven months. After losing weight, he was physically able to start walking on the treadmill and lifting weights. "Later, Bibiane and I participated in two Heart Association runs and one National Multiple Sclerosis Society run, running with the *Weight Watchers* team."

Over a three-year period, Mark lost over 200 pounds, meeting his goal. And through the weight-loss experience, he gained a fuller life.

"My confidence increased. I am respected by others, and this led to a promotion at work," he says. "And ultimately, my weight loss brought about the long-awaited birth of our baby daughter, Sarah."

Weight-loss results not typical.

Pan-Fried Tilapia
with Tangy Tartar Sauce,
page 57

Shrimp and Fennel
Risotto,
page 60

Grilled Tuna Steak with
Fresh Salsa,
page 55

Polenta Triangles with Goat
Cheese and Wild Mushrooms,
page 76

Chili Sloppy Joe,
page 64

Reuben Dog,
page 64

69

Coconut-Curry Tofu Stir-Fry, page 79

Black Beans and
Yellow Rice,
page 76

Through Thick and Thin

JANE COSCARELLI • **HEIGHT** 5'0" • **BEFORE** 185 LBS. • **AFTER** 130 LBS.
NICOLE DEWITT • **HEIGHT** 5'0" • **BEFORE** 137 LBS. • **AFTER** 107 LBS.

Advice: "Few people realize how large their portions are. Look at both what and how much you are eating."

After Nicole DeWitt's wedding day, she and her mother, Jane Coscarelli, anxiously awaited the arrival of the wedding pictures. But their excitement quickly diminished. "We had planned and planned for Nicole's big wedding. And then in pictures, there I was, larger than life," laughs Jane.

Nicole was also disappointed with her photos. "I thought the person in the pictures didn't look like me. It was shocking to see how heavy my face and body had become," she says.

Jane joined *Weight Watchers* and bought a treadmill for her office, making it her first "appointment" of each day.

Three months later and 15 pounds lighter, Jane's *Weight Watchers* success inspired Nicole. Given the distance (approximately 75 miles) between them, Jane and Nicole had to attend meetings in different cities. "So after each meeting, we held support sessions over the phone, comparing if we lost, gained, or stayed the same," Jane says.

Jane started the program by trying many recipes from *Weight Watchers* cookbooks. Even now, she continues to try two new recipes each week. "I like the variety and the fact that I do not have to restock the pantry. The recipes use everyday things that I have on hand."

And Nicole easily adapted the program and many of the recipes to fit her vegetarian lifestyle. Regardless of the recipe, Nicole now understands the importance of balance and portion control. "After measuring the amount of morning cereal I was eating, I saw that it was two and one-half cups! Few people realize how large their portions are. Look at both what and how much you are eating," she advises.

Jane lost 55 pounds, met her goal, and made Lifetime. Nicole also met her goal

"Even at a theme park, we were able to stay within our program, including our celebration cocktails."

and made Lifetime, losing 30 pounds. To celebrate their weight loss and Jane's 50th birthday, they took a girls-only trip to Disney World. "And even at a theme park, we were able to stay within our program, including our celebration cocktails."

Weight-loss results not typical.

(continued from page 64)
quesadilla with a spatula to flatten as it cooks. Remove from pan; keep warm. Repeat procedure with remaining tortillas, cheese, and vegetable mixture. Serve quesadillas immediately with salsa and sour cream. YIELD: 8 servings (serving size: 1 quesadilla, 2 tablespoons salsa, and 1 tablespoon sour cream).

POINTS value: 7; **Exchanges:** 2 Starch, 1 Vegetable, 1 High-Fat Meat, 1 Fat
Per serving: CAL 311 (35% from fat); PRO 14.4g; FAT 12.2g (sat 6.0g); CARB 35.5g; FIB 2.7g; CHOL 24mg; IRON 2.2mg; SOD 774mg; CALC 319mg

ARTICHOKE OMELETS

prep: 10 minutes • cook: 22 minutes

2 teaspoons butter
½ cup chopped onion (1 small)
2 garlic cloves, minced
1 cup chopped fresh mushrooms
1 (14-ounce) can artichoke hearts, rinsed, drained, and chopped
6 large egg whites
3 large eggs
1 tablespoon 2% reduced-fat milk
1 tablespoon Dijon mustard
1 teaspoon herbes de Provence
Cooking spray
¾ cup grated Parmesan cheese, divided

1. Melt butter in a medium nonstick skillet over medium heat. Add onion and garlic; sauté 3 minutes. Add mushrooms and artichoke hearts; sauté 2 minutes or until vegetables are tender. Remove from heat, and keep warm.

2. Combine egg whites and next 4 ingredients; stir well with a whisk. Heat a small nonstick skillet coated with cooking spray over medium heat. Pour one-third of egg mixture into pan. Cook 3 minutes; turn omelet over. Spread one-third of artichoke mixture onto half of omelet. Sprinkle ¼ cup cheese over omelet. Carefully loosen omelet with a spatula; fold in half. Cook 1 minute. Slide onto plate, and keep warm. Repeat procedure twice with cooking spray and remaining ingredients. YIELD: 3 servings (serving size: 1 omelet).

POINTS value: 6; **Exchanges:** 2 Vegetable, 1 Very Lean Meat, 2 Medium-Fat Meat, 1 Fat
Per serving: CAL 288 (43% from fat); PRO 25.8g; FAT 14.0g (sat 6.4g); CARB 15.2g; FIB 3.6g; CHOL 236mg; IRON 1.5mg; SOD 928mg; CALC 277mg

SPINACH, MUSHROOM, AND FETA FRITTATA

prep: 6 minutes • cook: 27 minutes

2 large eggs
1 (16-ounce) carton egg substitute
¼ teaspoon salt
¼ teaspoon black pepper
2 teaspoons olive oil
¾ cup chopped onion (1 small)
1 (8-ounce) package sliced mushrooms
1 (6-ounce) package fresh baby spinach
½ cup (2 ounces) crumbled feta cheese

1. Preheat broiler.
2. Combine first 4 ingredients in a large bowl; stir well with a whisk.

3. Heat oil in a large nonstick skillet over medium-high heat. Add onion and mushrooms; sauté 9 minutes or until liquid evaporates. Add spinach; cook 4 minutes or until liquid evaporates. Add egg mixture; stir well. Reduce heat to medium-low; cook 8 minutes or until edges are set. Sprinkle with cheese. Wrap handle of pan with foil, and broil 5 minutes or until egg is set and lightly browned. YIELD: 4 servings (serving size: 1 wedge).

Note: To speed up the cooking process of a frittata, loosen edges of frittata from pan with a spatula and allow raw egg mixture to run to the bottom of the pan.

POINTS value: 4; **Exchanges:** 2 Vegetable, 2 Medium-Fat Meat
Per serving: CAL 206 (39% from fat); PRO 20.0g; FAT 9.0g (sat 3.9g); CARB 12.3g; FIB 3.1g; CHOL 122mg; IRON 4.3mg; SOD 695mg; CALC 182mg

HERBES DE PROVENCE

Herbes de Provence is a mixture of dried herbs native to the Provence region of southern France. It traditionally contains rosemary, basil, bay leaves, and thyme. Other herbs, including savory, lavender, fennel seeds, and dried sage, are sometimes added. The proportion of the herbs in the mixture varies depending on the manufacturer. Herbes de Provence is used to flavor grilled meat or fish and side dishes, such as potatoes, rice, or pasta. Add herbes de Provence to the recipe for Artichoke Omelets on this page to give an old classic new flavor.

CARAMELIZED ONION, SAGA, AND SAGE BREAD PUDDING

prep: 22 minutes • cook: 1 hour and 8 minutes • other: 35 minutes

1½ cups fat-free milk
1 (4-ounce) package Saga blue cheese, crumbled
1 cup egg substitute
1 tablespoon chopped fresh sage
½ teaspoon salt
¼ teaspoon freshly ground black pepper
8 cups (¾-inch) cubed French bread (about 14 ounces)
1 teaspoon olive oil
4 cups thinly sliced onion (about 1¼ pounds)
Cooking spray

1. Preheat oven to 350°.
2. Combine milk and cheese in a blender or food processor; process until smooth. Pour into a large bowl. Stir in egg substitute and next 3 ingredients. Add bread cubes; toss gently to coat. Let stand 30 minutes.
3. While bread mixture stands, heat oil in a large nonstick skillet over medium heat. Add onion; sauté 25 minutes or until soft and lightly browned. Stir into bread mixture.
4. Spoon bread mixture into an 11 x 7-inch baking dish coated with cooking spray. Bake at 350° for 42 minutes or until set. Let stand for 5 minutes before serving. YIELD: 8 servings.

POINTS value: 4; Exchanges: 2 Starch, 1 Vegetable, 1 Medium-Fat Meat
Per serving: CAL 232 (24% from fat); PRO 12.3g; FAT 6.1g (sat 2.7g); CARB 34.3g; FIB 3.4g; CHOL 14mg; IRON 1.6mg; SOD 679mg; CALC 192mg

MOZZARELLA-ROTINI SKILLET SUPPER

prep: 8 minutes • cook: 19 minutes other: 5 minutes

2 cups uncooked rotini (about 6 ounces corkscrew pasta)
2 teaspoons olive oil
Cooking spray
2¾ cups diced peeled eggplant (about 1 medium)
2 cups diced zucchini (about 2 small)
2 garlic cloves, minced
1 tablespoon dried Italian seasoning
1 tablespoon balsamic vinegar
½ teaspoon salt
1 (26-ounce) jar tomato and basil pasta sauce (such as Classico)
1 (16-ounce) package frozen bell pepper stir-fry (such as Bird's Eye), thawed
1 cup (4 ounces) shredded part-skim mozzarella cheese

1. Cook pasta according to package directions, omitting salt and fat.
2. While pasta cooks, heat oil in a large nonstick skillet coated with cooking spray. Add eggplant, zucchini, and garlic; sauté 5 minutes or until tender. Drain pasta. Add pasta, Italian seasoning, and next 4 ingredients to eggplant mixture; cook 5 minutes or until thoroughly heated, stirring occasionally. Remove from heat; sprinkle with cheese. Cover; let stand 5 minutes or until cheese melts. YIELD: 6 servings (serving size: 1⅓ cups).

POINTS value: 5; Exchanges: 1 Starch, 3 Vegetable, 1 Fat
Per serving: CAL 250 (22% from fat); PRO 12.3g; FAT 6.2g (sat 2.3g); CARB 38.6g; FIB 4.9g; CHOL 11mg; IRON 2.8mg; SOD 682mg; CALC 236mg

ARTICHOKE AND TOMATO PASTA

prep: 5 minutes • cook: 19 minutes

Ideal for the times when you need a meal with a low POINTS value, this tossed pasta can be served warm, at room temperature, or chilled.

2¾ cups uncooked penne pasta (about 8 ounces tube-shaped pasta)
2 teaspoons olive oil
1½ cups vertically sliced onion
4 garlic cloves, minced
⅓ cup canned vegetable broth (such as Swanson)
1 (14-ounce) can quartered artichoke hearts, drained
2 cups grape tomatoes
1 cup (4 ounces) crumbled reduced-fat feta cheese
½ cup chopped fresh basil
½ teaspoon freshly ground black pepper
¼ teaspoon salt

1. Cook pasta according to package directions, omitting salt and fat.
2. Meanwhile, heat oil in a large nonstick skillet over medium heat. Add onion; sauté 10 minutes or until golden brown. Add garlic; sauté 1 minute. Add broth; sauté 1 minute.
3. Drain pasta. Combine pasta, onion mixture, artichokes, and remaining ingredients in a large bowl; toss well. YIELD: 6 servings (serving size: 1½ cups).

POINTS value: 4; Exchanges: 2 Starch, 1 Vegetable, 1 Fat
Per serving: CAL 228 (20% from fat); PRO 11.0g; FAT 5.0g (sat 2.0g); CARB 36.7g; FIB 3.0g; CHOL 7mg; IRON 2.2mg; SOD 539mg; CALC 74mg

SPAGHETTI WITH ROASTED EGGPLANT SAUCE

prep: 16 minutes • cook: 35 minutes

Roasting the vegetables adds depth of flavor. They roast while the pasta cooks and the sauce simmers—coming together for a fabulous dish.

5   teaspoons olive oil, divided
1   (8-ounce) package mushrooms, chopped
4   cups diced peeled eggplant (about 1 small)
1   cup chopped onion (1 medium)
1   teaspoon finely chopped fresh rosemary
½   teaspoon salt
⅛   teaspoon black pepper
6   ounces uncooked spaghetti
⅛   teaspoon crushed red pepper
2   garlic cloves, thinly sliced
1   tablespoon chopped fresh thyme
1   (28-ounce) can crushed tomatoes
¼   cup (1 ounce) shredded fresh Parmesan cheese

1. Preheat oven to 425°.
2. Brush jelly-roll pan with 2 teaspoons oil. Combine mushrooms and next 5 ingredients in a large bowl; toss well. Spread vegetables in a single layer on jelly-roll pan. Bake at 425° for 35 minutes or until tender, stirring once.
3. While vegetables roast, cook pasta according to package directions, omitting salt and fat. Drain well.
4. While pasta cooks, heat remaining 1 tablespoon oil in a large saucepan over medium heat. Add red pepper and garlic; sauté 2 minutes. Stir in thyme and tomatoes; reduce heat, and simmer, uncovered, 10 minutes, stirring occasionally.
5. Combine roasted vegetables, pasta, and tomato sauce; toss well. Sprinkle with Parmesan cheese. YIELD: 4 servings (serving size: 1½ cups).

POINTS value: 8; **Exchanges:** 3 Starch, 2 Vegetable, 2 Fat
Per serving: CAL 375 (30% from fat); PRO 13.5g; FAT 12.4g (sat 2.4g); CARB 57.2g; FIB 6.9g; CHOL 4mg; IRON 4.9mg; SOD 649mg; CALC 164mg

"MEATY" MEATLESS SPAGHETTI WITH FRESH SPINACH

(pictured on page 3)
prep: 6 minutes • cook: 18 minutes

Sautéing the soy crumbles in garlic and onion boosts the flavor of the crumbles and adds another dimension to the bottled pasta sauce. The addition of fresh spinach adds extra vitamins and a touch of color. Follow cooking times closely for optimum texture.

1   teaspoon olive oil
1   cup chopped onion (1 medium)
2   teaspoons minced garlic
1   (12-ounce) package frozen burger-style recipe crumbles
2   tablespoons dry red wine or water
1   (26-ounce) jar tomato and basil pasta sauce (such as Classico)
2   cups fresh baby spinach, coarsely chopped
10   ounces uncooked spaghetti
5   tablespoons (1½ ounces) grated fresh Parmesan cheese

1. Heat oil in a large saucepan over medium heat. Add onion and garlic; sauté 4 minutes. Add crumbles; sauté 5 minutes or until crumbles are completely thawed. Add wine and pasta sauce; reduce heat to medium-low, and simmer 3 minutes or until thoroughly heated. Stir in spinach, and simmer 4 minutes or until spinach wilts.
2. While sauce simmers, cook pasta according to package directions, omitting salt and fat.
3. Serve sauce over hot cooked pasta, and sprinkle each serving with cheese. YIELD: 5 servings (serving size: 1 cup pasta, about 1 cup sauce, and 1 tablespoon cheese).

POINTS value: 8; **Exchanges:** 3 Starch, 3 Vegetable, 1½ Lean Meat
Per serving: CAL 403 (16% from fat); PRO 24.6g; FAT 7.3g (sat 1.5g); CARB 60.4g; FIB 8.5g; CHOL 4mg; IRON 6.0mg; SOD 839mg; CALC 201mg

VEGGING OUT

If you make good food choices, a vegetarian diet can supply you with all of the nutrients your body needs. For vegetarians who eat dairy products and eggs, the nutrient issues are similar to those for nonvegetarians. For vegans, or those who don't eat dairy products or eggs, be sure to include foods high in protein (legumes, nuts, seeds), vitamins B12 and D (fortified breakfast cereals and soy products), iron (legumes and iron-fortified cereals and breads), calcium (legumes, broccoli, and fortified tofu), and zinc (whole wheat bread and legumes) in your daily diet.

POLENTA TRIANGLES WITH GOAT CHEESE AND WILD MUSHROOMS

(pictured on page 68)
prep: 13 minutes • cook: 39 minutes
other: 2 hours

3 cups fat-free, less-sodium chicken broth, divided
1 cup water
1 cup instant dry polenta
1 cup grated Parmesan cheese
Cooking spray
2½ teaspoons olive oil, divided
2 (4-ounce) packages gourmet blend mushrooms (baby bella, shiitake, and oyster mushrooms), sliced
¼ cup chopped shallots (2 large)
¼ to ½ teaspoon black pepper
⅛ teaspoon salt
½ cup dry white wine
2 teaspoons cornstarch
1 tablespoon chopped fresh thyme
1 tablespoon chopped fresh parsley
½ cup (2 ounces) crumbled goat cheese
Thyme sprigs (optional)

1. Combine 1½ cups broth and 1 cup water in a medium saucepan; bring to a boil over high heat. Gradually add polenta, stirring with a whisk. Reduce heat to low; cook 5 minutes or until very thick, stirring constantly. Stir in Parmesan cheese. Spoon polenta into an 8-inch square baking dish coated with cooking spray, spreading evenly. Press plastic wrap onto surface of polenta; chill 2 hours or until firm.
2. Cut polenta into 4 squares. Cut each square in half diagonally to form triangles.

3. Heat 1 teaspoon oil in a large nonstick skillet over medium-high heat. Add half of polenta triangles; cook 4 minutes on each side or until golden. Remove from pan; keep warm. Repeat procedure with 1 teaspoon oil and remaining polenta.
4. Heat remaining ½ teaspoon oil in pan over medium-high heat. Add mushrooms and next 3 ingredients; sauté 3 minutes or until golden brown. Combine remaining 1½ cups broth, wine, and cornstarch; stir until well blended. Add broth mixture, thyme, and parsley to mushroom mixture; bring to a boil, and cook 7 minutes or until slightly thick, stirring constantly. Spoon sauce over polenta; sprinkle with goat cheese. Garnish with thyme sprigs, if desired. YIELD: 4 servings (serving size: 2 polenta triangles, ½ cup mushroom sauce, and 2 tablespoons goat cheese).

POINTS value: 8; **Exchanges:** 3 Starch, 1½ High-Fat Meat
Per serving: CAL 374 (34% from fat); PRO 20.2g; FAT 13.9g (sat 7.4g); CARB 43.2g; FIB 4.9g; CHOL 32mg; IRON 1.9mg; SOD 900mg; CALC 361mg

---

BRAVO FOR BEANS

Incorporating beans into your diet may lower your body's levels of "bad" cholesterol, thanks to high amounts of soluble fiber. Studies have shown that a cup of beans per day—particularly kidney, navy, pinto, black, chickpea, or butter beans—can reduce your levels of cholesterol up to 10% in 6 weeks.

BLACK BEANS AND YELLOW RICE

(pictured on page 71)
prep: 11 minutes • cook: 39 minutes

1½ teaspoons olive oil
1 cup chopped green bell pepper
1 cup chopped onion (1 medium)
2 garlic cloves, minced
2 (15-ounce) cans black beans, rinsed and drained
1½ cups bottled chunky salsa
½ cup water
1 tablespoon fresh lime juice
½ teaspoon ground cumin
2 (3.5-ounce) bags boil-in-bag long-grain rice
½ teaspoon ground turmeric
¼ cup reduced-fat sour cream
Fresh cilantro sprigs (optional)

1. Heat oil in a large saucepan over medium-high heat until hot. Add bell pepper, onion, and garlic; sauté 5 minutes or until tender. Stir in beans and next 4 ingredients; bring to a boil. Cover, reduce heat, and simmer 30 minutes.
2. While black bean mixture cooks, cook rice according to package directions, adding turmeric to cooking water and omitting salt and fat. Drain rice.
3. Spoon rice evenly onto serving plates, and top with black bean mixture. Serve with sour cream, and, if desired, garnish with cilantro. YIELD: 4 servings (serving size: ¾ cup rice, 1¼ cups black beans, and 1 tablespoon sour cream).

POINTS value: 7; **Exchanges:** 4 Starch, 1 Vegetable
Per serving: CAL 350 (11% from fat); PRO 11.8g; FAT 4.1g (sat 1.5g); CARB 70.1g; FIB 7.6g; CHOL 8mg; IRON 3.7mg; SOD 646mg; CALC 92mg

SPANISH FRIED RICE

prep: 8 minutes • cook: 40 minutes
other: 30 minutes

1   (10-ounce) package saffron
    yellow rice mix (such as Vigo)
Cooking spray
1   tablespoon olive oil, divided
1   cup coarsely chopped onion
    (1 medium)
1   tablespoon minced garlic
½   cup frozen petite green peas
⅓   cup chopped fresh flat-leaf
    parsley
½   teaspoon black pepper
1   (19-ounce) can chickpeas
    (garbanzo beans), rinsed and
    drained
1   (12-ounce) jar roasted red bell
    peppers, drained and cut into
    1-inch pieces
1   (2¼-ounce) can sliced ripe
    olives, drained

1. Cook rice according to package
directions, omitting salt and fat. Spread
rice onto a baking sheet coated with
cooking spray. Let stand 30 minutes or
until completely cool.
2. Heat 1 teaspoon oil in a nonstick
skillet coated with cooking spray over
medium-high heat. Add onion and
garlic; sauté 5 minutes. Add remaining
2 teaspoons oil and rice. Cook 6 minutes or until lightly browned, stirring
occasionally. Stir in peas and remaining ingredients; cook 1 minute or
until thoroughly heated. YIELD: 5 servings (serving size: about 1¼ cups).

POINTS value: 6; **Exchanges:** 3½ Starch, 1 Vegetable,
1 Fat
Per serving: CAL 335 (15% from fat); PRO 9.6g;
FAT 5.7g (sat 0.6g); CARB 63.0g; FIB 5.2g;
CHOL 0mg; IRON 2.2mg; SOD 427mg;
CALC 56mg

POTATO AND MUSHROOM BAKE

prep: 30 minutes • cook: 1 hour and 29
minutes • other: 10 minutes

2   pounds Yukon gold potatoes
    (about 7 medium)
1   teaspoon olive oil
Cooking spray
1½ cups chopped onion
2   garlic cloves, minced
1   pound portobello mushroom
    caps, sliced
¾   teaspoon salt, divided
¾   teaspoon black pepper, divided
¼   cup fat-free, less-sodium
    chicken broth
1   (15-ounce) container fat-free
    ricotta cheese
1   (8-ounce) package shredded
    part-skim mozzarella cheese,
    divided
1   large egg white
1   (10-ounce) container
    refrigerated light Alfredo sauce
¼   cup chopped fresh basil
2   tablespoons chopped fresh
    oregano

1. Place potatoes in a Dutch oven,
and cover with water; bring to a
boil. Reduce heat, and simmer 30
minutes or until tender; drain.
2. Preheat oven to 400°.
3. Heat oil in a large nonstick skillet
coated with cooking spray over
medium-high heat. Add onion and
garlic; sauté 3 minutes. Add sliced
mushrooms, ½ teaspoon salt, and
½ teaspoon pepper; sauté 5 minutes
or until tender. Add broth; cook 5
minutes, stirring occasionally.
4. While mushroom mixture cooks,
combine ricotta, 1 cup mozzarella,
and egg white in a bowl; stir well.

Combine Alfredo sauce, basil, and
oregano in another bowl; stir well.
5. Peel potatoes, and cut into ¼-
inch slices. Arrange half of potato
slices in a 13 x 9-inch baking dish
coated with cooking spray; sprinkle
with ⅛ teaspoon salt and ⅛ teaspoon pepper. Top with half of
mushroom mixture. Spread half of
ricotta mixture evenly over mushroom layer. Spread half of Alfredo
sauce mixture over ricotta layer.
Repeat procedure once, ending with
Alfredo sauce mixture. Cover with
foil coated with cooking spray. Bake
at 400° for 30 minutes. Uncover and
sprinkle with remaining 1 cup
cheese. Bake 15 minutes or until
cheese melts and casserole is bubbly.
Let stand 10 minutes before serving.
YIELD: 10 servings.

POINTS value: 5; **Exchanges:** 1½ Starch,
1 Vegetable, 1 Medium-Fat Meat
Per serving: CAL 231 (26% from fat); PRO 14.1g;
FAT 6.6g (sat 3.8g); CARB 28.2g; FIB 2.2g;
CHOL 29mg; IRON 0.6mg; SOD 507mg;
CALC 288mg

YUKON GOLD POTATOES

Yukon gold potatoes are truly
versatile—they are good for
baking, broiling, frying, and
mashing. Their moist, creamy
texture and sweet, buttery flavor
make them the favorite of the
gold potatoes.

Yukon golds are slightly flat
and oval in shape with light gold,
thin skin and light yellow flesh.
Unlike traditional baking potatoes,
Yukon golds should be stored in
the refrigerator to prevent them
from turning green and bitter.

POTATO GRATIN WITH CHIPOTLE SAUCE

prep: 19 minutes • cook: 55 minutes
other: 10 minutes

Chipotle chiles are red jalapeños that have been dried and smoked. They are packed in a piquant red sauce.

3   pounds Yukon gold potatoes
      (about 10 medium)
Cooking spray
2   teaspoons olive oil
½   cup chopped onion
2   garlic cloves, minced
⅓   cup all-purpose flour
2½   cups 1% low-fat milk
2   cups (8 ounces) shredded
      Monterey Jack cheese
½   teaspoon salt
½   teaspoon ground cumin
¼   teaspoon black pepper
1   drained canned chipotle chile
      in adobo sauce, chopped

1. Preheat oven to 350°.
2. Pierce potatoes with a fork. Microwave at HIGH 12 to 15 minutes or until tender; cool slightly and cut into ½-inch slices. Layer potato slices in a 13 x 9-inch baking dish coated with cooking spray.
3. Heat oil in a large nonstick skillet over medium heat. Add onion and garlic; sauté 5 minutes or until soft. Spoon onion mixture over potatoes.
4. Place flour in a small bowl; gradually add milk, stirring with a whisk until blended. Pour mixture into pan, and cook over medium-high heat 2 minutes or until thick, stirring constantly. Add cheese and next 4 ingredients; stir until cheese melts. Pour cheese mixture over potato mixture.

5. Bake at 350° for 35 minutes or until bubbly. Let stand 10 minutes before serving. YIELD: 8 servings (serving size: about 1 cup).

POINTS value: 7; **Exchanges:** 2 Starch, ½ Low-Fat Milk, 1 Medium-Fat Meat
Per serving: CAL 310 (31% from fat); PRO 13.8g; FAT 10.9g (sat 6.1g); CARB 40.4g; FIB 2.6g; CHOL 28mg; IRON 2.1mg; SOD 377mg; CALC 335mg

STUFFED PORTOBELLO MUSHROOMS

prep: 14 minutes • cook: 29 minutes
other: 7 minutes

5   large portobello mushroom
      caps (about 1 pound)
Cooking spray
1¼   cups fat-free, less-sodium
      chicken broth
⅔   cup uncooked couscous
2   tablespoons extravirgin olive
      oil, divided
1   large garlic clove, finely
      chopped
1   (6-ounce) package fresh baby
      spinach
½   teaspoon dried oregano,
      divided
¼   teaspoon salt
⅛   teaspoon black pepper
¾   cup rinsed and drained canned
      chickpeas (garbanzo beans)
1   (3½-ounce) package crumbled
      reduced-fat feta cheese
1   large tomato, cut into 5 slices
½   cup dry breadcrumbs

1. Preheat oven to 500°.
2. Lightly coat both sides of mushroom caps with cooking spray; place mushrooms, gills down, on a foil-lined baking sheet. Bake at 500° for

6 minutes; turn caps over, and bake an additional 4 minutes.
3. Preheat broiler.
4. Bring broth to a boil in a small saucepan; stir in couscous. Remove from heat; cover and let stand 5 minutes. Fluff with a fork; set aside.
5. Heat 1 tablespoon oil in a large skillet over medium heat. Add garlic; sauté 1 minute. Increase heat to medium-high. Add spinach, ¼ teaspoon oregano, salt, and pepper; sauté 3 minutes or until spinach wilts. Remove from heat; cover and let stand 2 minutes. Stir in cooked couscous, chickpeas, and feta cheese. Spoon about ½ cup mixture into each mushroom cap, pressing gently; top each mushroom with a tomato slice. Broil 6 minutes or until thoroughly heated.
6. Combine remaining 1 tablespoon oil, remaining ¼ teaspoon oregano, and breadcrumbs, and toss well. Sprinkle breadcrumb mixture evenly over tomato slices. Broil 1 minute. YIELD: 5 servings (serving size: 1 mushroom cap).

POINTS value: 5; **Exchanges:** 2 Starch, 2 Vegetable, 2 Fat
Per serving: CAL 297 (29% from fat); PRO 14.1g; FAT 9.8g (sat 2.6g); CARB 40.3g; FIB 6.3g; CHOL 7mg; IRON 2.8mg; SOD 976mg; CALC 116mg

SPINACH PIE

prep: 25 minutes • cook: 42 minutes
other: 10 minutes

Butter-flavored cooking spray
1½ cups chopped onion (1 large)
3   garlic cloves, minced
1   (24-ounce) carton 2% low-fat
     cottage cheese
2   (10-ounce) packages frozen
     chopped spinach, thawed,
     drained, and squeezed dry
2   (3½-ounce) packages
     crumbled reduced-fat feta
     cheese
4   large eggs
1   tablespoon all-purpose flour
½   teaspoon freshly ground black
     pepper
¼   teaspoon salt
½   (16-ounce) package frozen
     phyllo dough (20 sheets)

1. Preheat oven to 375°.
2. Heat a large nonstick skillet
coated with cooking spray over
medium-high heat. Add onion; sauté
5 minutes. Add garlic; sauté 1
minute. Place in a large bowl; cool
5 minutes. Add cottage cheese and
next 6 ingredients; stir well.
3. Coat a 13 x 9-inch baking dish
with cooking spray. Place 1 sheet of
phyllo dough in bottom of dish, and
coat lightly with cooking spray.
Repeat procedure with 9 sheets of
phyllo dough and cooking spray.
Spread spinach mixture over phyllo,
leaving a ½-inch border. Place 1
sheet of phyllo dough on top of
spinach mixture; coat lightly with
cooking spray. Repeat procedure
with remaining 9 sheets of phyllo
dough and cooking spray. Coat top
of pie with cooking spray. Tuck

corners of phyllo dough down
around filling.
4. Bake at 375° for 35 minutes or
until filling is set and phyllo is golden
brown. Let stand 5 minutes. Cut into
8 squares. YIELD: 8 servings (serving
size: 1 square).

POINTS value: 6; **Exchanges:** 1 Starch, 2 Vegetable,
2 Medium-Fat Meat
Per serving: CAL 290 (30% from fat); PRO 25.2g;
FAT 9.9g (sat 4.6g); CARB 26.3g; FIB 3.7g;
CHOL 121mg; IRON 3.1mg; SOD 987mg;
CALC 263mg

COCONUT-CURRY TOFU
STIR-FRY

(pictured on page 70)
prep: 19 minutes • cook: 20 minutes
other: 30 minutes

1   (14-ounce) package extrafirm
     tofu
3   tablespoons low-sodium soy
     sauce
2   teaspoons grated lime rind
2   tablespoons fresh lime juice
2   teaspoons green curry paste
½   teaspoon salt
1   (13.5-ounce) can light coconut
     milk
⅔   cup uncooked basmati rice
2   teaspoons dark sesame oil,
     divided
Cooking spray
3   tablespoons minced peeled
     fresh ginger
2   garlic cloves, minced
4   medium zucchini, cut in half
     lengthwise and sliced (about
     4 cups)
2   red bell peppers, cut into thin
     strips (about 3½ cups)
6   green onions, cut into 1-inch
     pieces

1. Wrap tofu in several layers of
heavy-duty paper towels. Press with
a heavy object for about 30 minutes
to remove excess water. Remove
paper towels; pat tofu dry, and cut
into ¾-inch cubes.
2. While tofu drains, combine soy
sauce and next 5 ingredients in a
small bowl; set aside.
3. Cook rice according to package
directions, omitting salt and fat.
4. While rice cooks, heat 1 teaspoon
sesame oil in a large nonstick skillet
coated with cooking spray over
medium-high heat. Add tofu; cook
10 minutes or until lightly browned
on all sides. Remove tofu from pan;
keep warm.
5. Heat remaining 1 teaspoon
sesame oil in pan. Add ginger and
garlic, and sauté 30 seconds. Add
zucchini and bell pepper; sauté 2
minutes. Add green onions; sauté 4
minutes or until vegetables are crisp-
tender. Add soy sauce mixture and
tofu. Bring to a boil; reduce heat,
and simmer 2 minutes. Serve immediately over hot cooked basmati rice.
YIELD: 4 servings (serving size: 1½
cups stir-fry and ½ cup rice).

POINTS value: 8; **Exchanges:** 2 Starch, 3 Vegetable,
2 Very Lean Meat, 2 Fat
Per serving: CAL 358 (32% from fat); PRO 16.4g;
FAT 13.6g (sat 6.0g); CARB 47.3g; FIB 2.3g;
CHOL 0mg; IRON 3.1mg; SOD 779mg;
CALC 116mg

PEANUT TOFU STIR-FRY

prep: 14 minutes • cook: 27 minutes
other: 30 minutes

1   (16-ounce) package firm tofu,
     drained
1½   cups uncooked instant rice
½   teaspoon salt, divided
1   teaspoon grated lime rind
½   cup fat-free, less-sodium
     chicken broth
1   tablespoon low-sodium soy sauce
2   teaspoons cornstarch
½   teaspoon chili garlic sauce
4   teaspoons roasted peanut oil,
     divided
2   cups preshredded carrot
2   cups thinly sliced red onion
4   cups very thinly sliced bok choy
2   garlic cloves, minced
2   tablespoons chopped unsalted,
     dry-roasted peanuts

1. Wrap tofu in several layers of
heavy-duty paper towels. Press with
a heavy object for about 30 minutes
to remove excess water. Remove
paper towels; pat tofu dry, and cut
into 1-inch cubes. Set aside.
2. Cook rice according to package
directions, using ¼ teaspoon salt and
omitting fat. Stir in lime rind.
Remove from heat; keep warm.
3. Combine broth and next 3 ingredients in a small bowl; stir with a
whisk until well blended. Set aside.
4. Heat 1 tablespoon oil in a large
nonstick skillet over medium-high
heat. Add tofu and remaining ¼ teaspoon salt; stir-fry 7 minutes or until
golden brown. Place in a large bowl;
keep warm.
5. Heat ½ teaspoon oil in pan over
medium-high heat. Add carrot and
onion; stir-fry 4 minutes or until

crisp-tender. Add to tofu; keep
warm. Heat remaining ½ teaspoon
oil in pan. Add bok choy and garlic;
stir-fry 2 minutes or until crisp-
tender. Add broth mixture; cook 30
seconds or until thick, stirring constantly. Stir in tofu mixture. Sprinkle
with peanuts. Serve over lime rice.
YIELD: 6 servings (serving size:
1⅓ cups stir-fry and ½ cup rice).

POINTS value: 5; **Exchanges:** *1 ½ Starch,
1 Vegetable, 1 Very Lean Meat, 1 Fat*
Per serving: CAL 229 (31% from fat); PRO 10.4g;
FAT 8.2g (sat 1.3g); CARB 30.5g; FIB 3.3g;
CHOL 0mg; IRON 2.3mg; SOD 421mg;
CALC 203mg

STIR-FRIED VEGETABLES
AND TOFU

prep: 20 minutes • cook: 29 minutes

1   cup uncooked jasmine or other
     long-grain rice
2   tablespoons olive oil, divided
⅔   cup julienne-cut carrot
¼   cup dry white wine, divided
2   garlic cloves, minced
2   cups julienne-cut zucchini
1½   cups julienne-cut yellow squash
1   (8-ounce) package button
     mushrooms, quartered
1   (8-ounce) package cremini
     mushrooms, quartered
1   (12.3-ounce) package reduced-
     fat extrafirm tofu, drained and
     cut into cubes
3   tablespoons low-sodium soy
     sauce
2   cups fresh bean sprouts
¼   teaspoon salt
¼   teaspoon black pepper

1. Cook rice according to package
directions, omitting salt and fat.

2. While rice cooks, heat 1 tablespoon oil in a large nonstick skillet
over medium-high heat. Add carrot;
stir-fry 4 minutes. Add 2 tablespoons
wine and garlic; stir-fry 3 minutes.
Add zucchini and squash; stir-fry 5
minutes. Add remaining 2 tablespoons wine and mushrooms, and
stir-fry 5 minutes. Remove from pan.
3. Heat 1 tablespoon oil in pan over
medium-high heat. Add tofu; sauté
7 minutes. Add soy sauce; cook 1
minute. Stir in sprouts, salt, and pepper. Return vegetable mixture to
pan; stir-fry 2 minutes. Serve over
rice. YIELD: 6 servings (serving size:
1 cup stir-fry and ½ cup rice).

POINTS value: 4; **Exchanges:** *2 Starch, 1 Vegetable,
1 Lean Meat, 1 Fat*
Per serving: CAL 225 (22% from fat); PRO 10.1g;
FAT 5.5g (sat 0.8g); CARB 36.0g; FIB 2.6g;
CHOL 0mg; IRON 3.4mg; SOD 418mg; CALC 58mg

CHOOSING TOFU

Tofu (soybean curd) is low in
both saturated fat and calories:
3 ounces of tofu have only 35 to
55 calories. Generally you'll find
two types of tofu in the produce
section of the supermarket.
• Silken tofu is custardlike and
ideal to puree for dressings,
dips, soups, milk shakes, cheesecakes, and smoothies.
• Regular (Momen, or Chinese-
style) is packed in water in plastic tubs and pouches. Its dense,
firm texture makes it ideal to
sauté, grill, broil, or stir-fry, so
choose this style for the recipes
on this page.
   For a lighter recipe, substitute
reduced-fat tofu for regular tofu.

Meats

LOADED NACHOS

(pictured on page 2)
prep: 17 minutes • cook: 10 minutes

¼   cup reduced-fat sour cream
     (such as Breakstone's)
2   tablespoons bottled salsa
1   pound lean ground sirloin
1   cup chopped onion (about
     1 medium)
½   cup chopped green bell
     pepper
1   cup bottled salsa
1   tablespoon chili powder
2   teaspoons ground cumin
¼   teaspoon salt
4   cups bite-sized baked tortilla
     chips
1   cup shredded iceberg lettuce
1   cup chopped tomato (about
     1 medium)
½   cup (2 ounces) shredded
     reduced-fat sharp Cheddar
     cheese
¼   cup pickled jalapeño pepper
     slices

1. Combine sour cream and 2 tablespoons salsa in a small bowl; stir well.
Cover and chill until ready to serve.
2. Cook beef, onion, and bell pepper in a large nonstick skillet over
medium-high heat until browned,
stirring to crumble beef. Drain well;
return meat mixture to pan. Stir in
1 cup salsa, chili powder, cumin, and
salt; bring to a simmer over medium
heat, and cook 3 minutes.
3. Place 1 cup chips on each of 4
serving plates; top each with ¾ cup
meat mixture, ¼ cup lettuce, ¼ cup
tomato, 2 tablespoons cheese, and 1
tablespoon jalapeño slices. Drizzle
2 tablespoons sour cream mixture
over each serving. **YIELD:** 4 servings.

POINTS value: 7; **Exchanges:** 1½ Starch, 3 Vegetable,
3 Lean Meat
Per serving: CAL 358 (30% from fat); PRO 31.4g;
FAT 11.8g (sat 5.3g); CARB 36.9g; FIB 5.6g;
CHOL 78mg; IRON 3.6mg; SOD 892mg;
CALC 180mg

BEEF STROGANOFF

prep: 11 minutes • cook: 25 minutes

*Thin ribbons of steak smothered in a
creamy mushroom sauce—all served
over hot egg noodles—will leave your
family begging for more.*

1   pound boneless sirloin steak,
     trimmed
1   tablespoon vegetable oil,
     divided
Cooking spray
2   cups uncooked medium egg
     noodles (about 4 ounces
     uncooked noodles)
1   cup chopped onion
2   garlic cloves, minced
¼   cup dry red wine
2   (8-ounce) packages sliced
     mushrooms
½   cup less-sodium beef broth
2   teaspoons Dijon mustard
½   teaspoon salt
½   teaspoon black pepper
⅛   teaspoon ground nutmeg
1   tablespoon all-purpose flour
3   tablespoons water
1   (8-ounce) container low-fat
     sour cream
¼   cup chopped fresh parsley

1. Cut steak diagonally across grain
into thin slices. Heat 1 teaspoon oil
in a Dutch oven coated with cooking
spray over medium-high heat. Add
half of steak, and sauté 3 minutes.
Remove from pan, and set aside.

Repeat procedure with 1 teaspoon
oil and remaining steak.
2. Prepare noodles according to
package directions, omitting salt
and fat.
3. While noodles cook, heat remaining 1 teaspoon oil in pan over
medium-high heat. Add onion and
garlic; sauté 3 minutes. Add red wine
and mushrooms; cook, uncovered,
5 minutes or until liquid evaporates,
scraping pan to loosen browned bits.
4. Return steak to pan. Add broth
and next 4 ingredients. Reduce heat
to medium-low; cook, uncovered,
5 minutes. Combine flour and water,
stirring with a whisk until well
blended. Stir flour mixture into steak
mixture; cook 3 minutes. Remove
from heat. Stir in sour cream and
parsley. Serve immediately over noodles. **YIELD:** 4 servings (serving size:
½ cup noodles and 1¼ cups
stroganoff).

POINTS value: 9; **Exchanges:** 2 Starch, 1½ Vegetable,
4 Lean Meat
Per serving: CAL 403 (32% from fat); PRO 32.4g;
FAT 14.5g (sat 5.8g); CARB 38.3g; FIB 3.0g;
CHOL 108mg; IRON 4.8mg; SOD 523mg;
CALC 113mg

FAT FACTS

The maximum fat content in any
ground beef is 30 percent (70
percent lean). Look for labels
that tell the amount of percent
fat to percent lean—then there
will be no guessing.
   Here's how they stack up:
Ground round: 11 percent fat
Ground sirloin: 15 percent fat
Ground chuck: 20 percent fat
Ground beef: 30 percent fat

CURRIED BEEF WITH PEANUTTY COCONUT SAUCE

prep: 22 minutes • cook: 25 minutes
other: 30 minutes

2   tablespoons water
1   tablespoon red curry paste
1½ pounds boneless top sirloin
    steak, trimmed
1   cup uncooked jasmine rice
2   teaspoons sesame oil, divided
½   pound asparagus spears,
    diagonally cut into
    1-inch pieces (about 2 cups)
1   cup snow peas, cut in
    half diagonally
½   cup shredded carrot (about
    1 medium)
¾   cup fat-free, less-sodium
    chicken broth
¾   cup chopped green onions
⅓   cup reduced-fat peanut butter
⅓   cup light coconut milk
2   tablespoons fresh lime juice
1   tablespoon low-sodium soy
    sauce

1. Combine water and curry paste
in a large bowl; stir with a whisk
until smooth. Cut steak diagonally
across grain into ¼-inch-thick slices;
cut slices into thin strips. Add steak
to curry paste, tossing to coat. Cover
and chill at least 30 minutes.
2. Cook rice according to package
directions, omitting salt and fat.
3. While rice cooks, heat ½ teaspoon oil in a large nonstick skillet
over medium-high heat. Add half of
steak; sauté 3 minutes or until steak
is done. Remove steak from skillet;
keep warm. Repeat procedure with
½ teaspoon oil and remaining steak.
4. Heat remaining 1 teaspoon oil in
pan over medium-high heat. Add

asparagus, snow peas, and carrot;
sauté 5 minutes or until vegetables
are crisp-tender. Stir in broth and
next 5 ingredients; cook 3 minutes,
stirring constantly. Return steak to
pan; cook 2 minutes or until thoroughly heated. Serve over hot
cooked rice. YIELD: 6 servings (serving
size: about ½ cup rice and ¾ cup
curried beef).

POINTS value: 7; **Exchanges:** 1 Starch, 2 Vegetable,
3 Lean Meat, 1 Fat
Per serving: CAL 332 (36% from fat); PRO 27.9g;
FAT 13.2g (sat 4.2g); CARB 24.7g; FIB 3.0g;
CHOL 63mg; IRON 3.3mg; SOD 383mg;
CALC 25mg

TEXAS FLANK STEAK WITH PICO DE GALLO

prep: 20 minutes • cook: 12 minutes
other: 6 hours and 5 minutes

¼   cup olive oil
2   tablespoons low-sodium soy
    sauce
1   tablespoon fresh lime juice
1   teaspoon salt
½   teaspoon black pepper
1   garlic clove, minced
1½ pounds flank steak,
    trimmed
1½ cups diced tomato (about
    2 medium)
1½ cups diced red onion (about
    1 medium)
⅓   cup chopped fresh cilantro
1½ tablespoons minced seeded
    jalapeño pepper
1   tablespoon fresh lime juice
¼   teaspoon salt
¼   teaspoon black pepper
1   garlic clove, minced
Cooking spray

1. Combine first 6 ingredients in a
large zip-top plastic bag. Add steak;
seal bag, and marinate steak in
refrigerator at least 6 hours, turning
bag occasionally.
2. Prepare grill.
3. Combine tomato and next 7
ingredients in a bowl; toss gently,
and set aside.
4. Remove steak from bag; discard
marinade. Place steak on grill rack
coated with cooking spray; grill 6
minutes on each side or until desired
degree of doneness. Let stand 5 minutes. Cut steak diagonally across
grain into thin slices. Serve with
pico de gallo. YIELD: 6 servings (serving size: 3 ounces steak and about
½ cup pico de gallo).

POINTS value: 5; **Exchanges:** 1½ Vegetable,
3 Lean Meat
Per serving: CAL 227 (45% from fat); PRO 23.6g;
FAT 11.4g (sat 3.4g); CARB 7.0g; FIB 1.2g;
CHOL 45mg; IRON 1.9mg; SOD 433mg;
CALC 30mg

DINNER TIPS

For a great south-of-the-border
meal, serve this flank steak
recipe with black beans and
warm flour tortillas. Create your
own flavor variation by adding
chopped jícama, oranges,
avocado, and cucumbers to the
pico de gallo.

Flank steak tends to toughen
as it stands, so you'll want to
slice the entire steak immediately
after cooking. Use a sharp
knife, and cut diagonally (at an
angle) across the grain.

BRACIOLA

prep: 28 minutes • cook: 2 hours and 17 minutes

1   (1-pound) lean flank steak
½   cup chopped onion
¼   cup fresh French breadcrumbs
3   tablespoons raisins
3   tablespoons shredded fresh Parmesan cheese
1   tablespoon pine nuts, toasted
1   teaspoon dried parsley
½   teaspoon dried oregano
½   teaspoon dried rosemary
½   teaspoon dried thyme
¼   teaspoon salt
¼   teaspoon black pepper
1   garlic clove, minced
1   (14-ounce) can fat-free, less-sodium chicken broth, divided
1   tablespoon olive oil
2   (8-ounce) cans no-salt-added tomato sauce
1   (8-ounce) can roasted garlic tomato sauce

1. Place flank steak on a large chopping block; pound steak to ¼-inch thickness using a meat mallet or rolling pin.
2. Combine onion and next 11 ingredients in a bowl; stir in ⅓ cup chicken broth. Spread stuffing over flank steak to within ½ inch of edges. Roll up steak, jelly-roll fashion, starting with 1 long side. Secure steak at 2-inch intervals with twine.
3. Heat oil in a large nonstick skillet over medium-high heat. Add steak roll; cook 8 minutes, browning on all sides. Add remaining chicken broth and 3 cans tomato sauce.
4. Bring to a boil; cover, reduce heat, and simmer 2 hours, turning

steak over once. Cut braciola into 4 slices. YIELD: 4 servings (serving size: 1 slice braciola and ¾ cup sauce).

POINTS value: 7; **Exchanges:** 1 Starch, 2 Vegetable, 3 Lean Meat, 1 Fat
Per serving: CAL 329 (42% from fat); PRO 25.4g; FAT 15.4g (sat 5.1g); CARB 22.5g; FIB 4.0g; CHOL 52mg; IRON 4.4mg; SOD 927mg; CALC 98mg

FILET MIGNON WITH THREE-HERB GREMOLATA

prep: 8 minutes • cook: 5 minutes

1   tablespoon chopped fresh parsley
2   teaspoons fresh thyme leaves
1   teaspoon chopped fresh rosemary
1   teaspoon grated lemon rind
1   garlic clove, minced
4   (4-ounce) beef tenderloin steaks (½ inch thick), trimmed
1   teaspoon kosher salt or ½ teaspoon table salt
¼   teaspoon freshly ground black pepper

1. Combine first 5 ingredients in a small bowl; stir well, and set aside.
2. Sprinkle steaks evenly with salt and pepper. Heat a large nonstick skillet over medium-high heat. Add steaks; cook 2 minutes on each side or until desired degree of doneness. Top steaks with gremolata. Serve immediately. YIELD: 4 servings (serving size: 1 steak and about 1½ teaspoons gremolata).

POINTS value: 3; **Exchanges:** 3 Lean Meat, 1 Fat
Per serving: CAL 147 (42% from fat); PRO 19.3g; FAT 6.9g (sat 2.6g); CARB 0.6g; FIB 0.5g; CHOL 57mg; IRON 2.9mg; SOD 514mg; CALC 14mg

GRILLED TENDERLOIN STEAKS WITH CHIMICHURRI SAUCE

prep: 8 minutes • cook: 10 minutes

Grilled steaks, chicken, and fish require nothing more than a little salt and pepper when served with this flavorful sauce from Argentina.

1   cup fresh flat-leaf parsley leaves
⅓   cup white wine vinegar
¼   cup fresh cilantro leaves
½   teaspoon salt
½   teaspoon black pepper
½   teaspoon crushed red pepper
¼   teaspoon ground cumin
2   garlic cloves, peeled and halved
2   tablespoons olive oil
4   (4-ounce) beef tenderloin steaks (1 inch thick), trimmed
¼   teaspoon salt
¼   teaspoon black pepper
Cooking spray

1. Place first 8 ingredients in a food processor; process until smooth. With processor on, slowly pour olive oil through food chute; process until well blended. Pour chimichurri sauce into a small bowl; set aside.
2. Prepare grill.
3. Sprinkle steaks with ¼ teaspoon salt and ¼ teaspoon black pepper. Place steaks on grill rack coated with cooking spray; grill 5 minutes on each side or until desired degree of doneness. Serve steaks with chimichurri sauce. YIELD: 4 servings (serving size: 1 steak and 2 tablespoons sauce).

POINTS value: 5; **Exchanges:** 3 Lean Meat, ½ Fat
Per serving: CAL 190 (52% from fat); PRO 22.7g; FAT 11.0g (sat 2.4g); CARB 1.9g; FIB 0.7g; CHOL 60mg; IRON 4.0mg; SOD 503mg; CALC 29mg

COFFEE-CRUSTED BEEF TENDERLOIN

(pictured on page 90)
prep: 15 minutes • cook: 40 minutes

1   tablespoon freshly ground dark roast coffee
1   teaspoon kosher salt or ½ teaspoon table salt
1½   teaspoons freshly ground black pepper, divided
1   (2-pound) beef tenderloin, trimmed
Cooking spray
1   tablespoon all-purpose flour
1   (14-ounce) can less-sodium beef broth
2   cups brewed dark roast coffee
1   tablespoon olive oil
¾   cup chopped shallots
3   garlic cloves, minced
2   teaspoons brown sugar
¼   teaspoon kosher salt or ⅛ teaspoon table salt
Thyme sprigs (optional)

1. Preheat oven to 500°.
2. Combine ground coffee, 1 teaspoon salt, and 1¼ teaspoons pepper; gently press onto beef. Place tenderloin on a rack coated with cooking spray in a shallow roasting pan. Bake at 500° for 20 minutes. Reduce oven temperature to 300°; bake tenderloin for 20 minutes or until a thermometer registers 145° (medium-rare) or desired degree of doneness. Remove from oven; let stand 10 minutes before slicing.
3. While beef cooks, place flour in a small bowl; gradually add broth and brewed coffee, stirring with a whisk until well blended.
4. Heat oil in a large nonstick skillet over medium heat. Add shallots; sauté 5 minutes or until tender. Stir in garlic; sauté 1 minute. Add broth mixture, and bring to a boil over medium-high heat, stirring frequently. Cook until sauce is reduced to 1 cup (about 20 to 25 minutes). Stir in remaining ¼ teaspoon pepper, brown sugar, and ¼ teaspoon salt. Serve sauce with sliced beef. Garnish with thyme sprigs, if desired. YIELD: 8 servings (serving size: about 3 ounces beef and ¼ cup sauce).

POINTS value: 4; **Exchanges:** 1 Vegetable, 3 Lean Meat
Per serving: CAL 183 (42% from fat); PRO 20.3g; FAT 8.5g (sat 2.8g); CARB 5.0g; FIB 0.3g; CHOL 57mg; IRON 2.9mg; SOD 431mg; CALC 17mg

VEAL FETTUCCINE WITH LEMON AND OLIVES

prep: 8 minutes • cook: 19 minutes

1   (9-ounce) package fresh fettuccine
1½   cups fat-free, less-sodium chicken broth
2   teaspoons cornstarch
1   pound veal cutlets
¼   teaspoon salt
¼   teaspoon black pepper
Cooking spray
½   cup sliced green olives
2   tablespoons fresh lemon juice (about 1 lemon)

1. Cook pasta according to package directions, omitting salt and fat.
2. While pasta cooks, combine chicken broth and cornstarch in a small bowl; stir well with a whisk. Set aside.
3. Place veal between 2 sheets of heavy-duty plastic wrap; flatten each piece to ¼-inch thickness using a meat mallet or rolling pin. Sprinkle both sides of veal with salt and pepper. Coat veal with cooking spray.
4. Place a large nonstick skillet over medium-high heat until hot. Add one-third of veal; cook 30 seconds on each side or just until browned. Remove veal from pan, and keep warm. Repeat procedure with remaining veal.
5. Add olives to pan; sauté 30 seconds. Stir in chicken broth mixture and lemon juice; cook 3 minutes or until sauce is slightly thick, stirring constantly. Drain pasta. Serve veal and olive sauce over fettuccine. YIELD: 4 servings (serving size: ¾ cup pasta, 3 ounces veal, and ½ cup sauce).

POINTS value: 7; **Exchanges:** 2 Starch, 3 Lean Meat
Per serving: CAL 346 (18% from fat); PRO 31.5g; FAT 7.0g (sat 1.4g); CARB 36.2g; FIB 2.4g; CHOL 91mg; IRON 1.5mg; SOD 757mg; CALC 35mg

HOW TO COOK VEAL

Veal has very little fat and can become tough and dry if not cooked properly. Veal roasts and shanks are best cooked by moist-heat methods, such as braising and stewing. Cutlets and scallops are best when quickly pan-fried or sautéed; chops are good when pan-fried, broiled, or grilled.

GRILLED VEAL CHOPS WITH PROSCIUTTO TOMATO SAUCE

(pictured on page 91)
prep: 8 minutes • cook: 19 minutes

*The sauce that's served with these chops is as versatile as it is quick to make. Try it over pasta or any grilled meat. It has a **POINTS** value of 1 per ¾-cup serving.*

1   teaspoon olive oil
½   cup finely chopped onion
2   garlic cloves, minced
¼   cup dry white wine or fat-free, less-sodium chicken broth
2   cups chopped tomato (about 2 medium)
1   tablespoon capers
¾   teaspoon salt, divided
¾   teaspoon black pepper, divided
1   ounce very thinly sliced prosciutto, cut into thin strips
4   (6-ounce) bone-in veal chops
Cooking spray
2   teaspoons chopped fresh flat-leaf parsley

1. Prepare grill.
2. Heat oil in a nonstick skillet over medium-high heat. Add onion; sauté 3 minutes or until tender. Add garlic; sauté 1 minute. Add wine; bring to a boil, and cook 2 minutes or until most of liquid evaporates. Stir in tomato, capers, ¼ teaspoon salt, ¼ teaspoon pepper, and prosciutto; bring to a boil. Remove from heat; keep warm.
3. Sprinkle veal chops with remaining ½ teaspoon salt and remaining ½ teaspoon pepper. Place chops on grill rack coated with cooking spray; cover and grill 6 minutes on each side or until desired degree of doneness. Spoon sauce over chops; sprinkle with parsley. YIELD: 4 servings (serving size: 1 chop, ¾ cup sauce, and ½ teaspoon parsley).

POINTS value: 4; **Exchanges:** 1 Vegetable, 3 Very Lean Meat, 1 Fat
Per serving: CAL 181 (29% from fat); PRO 25.2g; FAT 5.8g (sat 1.6g); CARB 6.9g; FIB 1.6g; CHOL 91mg; IRON 1.5mg; SOD 739mg; CALC 40mg

LAMB AND PORTOBELLO BOURGUIGNONNE

prep: 10 minutes • cook: 1 hour and 7 minutes

Bourguignonne is the French term for "as prepared in Burgundy." It refers to meat that is braised in red wine and garnished with mushrooms and onion.

¼   cup all-purpose flour
½   teaspoon garlic salt
¼   teaspoon black pepper
1   pound boneless leg of lamb, trimmed and cubed
1   tablespoon olive oil, divided
¼   cup minced shallots
1   (8-ounce) package baby portobello mushrooms
1   (10½-ounce) can condensed beef consommé, undiluted
½   cup dry red wine
1   tablespoon chopped fresh parsley
1   tablespoon yogurt-based butter-type spread
2⅔ cups frozen mashed potatoes
2½ cups fat-free milk

1. Combine first 3 ingredients in a large zip-top plastic bag; add lamb. Seal bag, and shake to coat lamb.
2. Heat 2 teaspoons oil in a large nonstick skillet over medium-high heat. Add lamb, and cook 4 minutes or until browned, stirring occasionally. Remove lamb from pan.
3. Heat remaining 1 teaspoon oil in pan. Add shallots and mushrooms; sauté 3 minutes. Add lamb, consommé, wine, and parsley; bring to a boil. Cover, reduce heat, and simmer 45 minutes or until lamb is tender. Stir in yogurt-based spread. Simmer, uncovered, 10 minutes or until sauce is thick.
4. Prepare mashed potatoes according to package directions using 2½ cups milk. Serve lamb mixture over mashed potatoes. YIELD: 4 servings (serving size: about ⅔ cup mashed potatoes and ¾ cup lamb mixture).

POINTS value: 8; **Exchanges:** 2½ Starch, 3 Lean Meat, ½ Fat
Per serving: CAL 377 (32% from fat); PRO 28.9g; FAT 13.2g (sat 3.9g); CARB 37.1g; FIB 3.2g; CHOL 60mg; IRON 3.5mg; SOD 489mg; CALC 166mg

LEMON-MINT LAMB CHOPS

prep: 8 minutes • cook: 8 minutes
other: 3 minutes

French-cut lamb chops have the meat and fat trimmed away from the end of the bone.

¼   cup chopped fresh mint
1   tablespoon grated lemon rind
2   teaspoons minced garlic
2   teaspoons olive oil
½   teaspoon salt
¼   teaspoon freshly ground black pepper
8   (3-ounce) French-cut lean lamb rib chops, trimmed

1. Prepare grill.
2. Combine first 6 ingredients; divide mixture in half. Pat half of mixture evenly on both sides of lamb. Set aside remaining mixture.
3. Place lamb on grill rack. Cover and grill 4 minutes on each side or until desired degree of doneness. Sprinkle reserved mint mixture evenly over lamb; let stand 3 minutes. YIELD: 4 servings (serving size: 2 chops).

POINTS value: 7; Exchanges: 5 Lean Meat, ½ Fat
Per serving: CAL 296 (49% from fat); PRO 34.4g; FAT 16.2g (sat 6.3g); CARB 1.0g; FIB 0.4g; CHOL 112mg; IRON 2.8mg; SOD 432mg; CALC 26mg

PORK CHOPS WITH FRUIT RELISH

prep: 5 minutes • cook: 10 minutes
other: 15 minutes

½   cup orange juice
1   tablespoon apricot preserves
½   cup sweetened dried cranberries
½   cup chopped dried apricots
4   (6-ounce) bone-in center-cut loin pork chops (about ½ inch thick), trimmed
2   teaspoons chopped fresh thyme, divided
½   teaspoon salt
¼   teaspoon black pepper
1   teaspoon olive oil
1   small Granny Smith apple, peeled and diced

1. Combine orange juice and preserves in a small saucepan; bring to a boil. Remove from heat; stir in cranberries and apricots. Cover and let stand 15 minutes or until liquid is nearly absorbed.

2. While relish stands, sprinkle chops with 1 teaspoon thyme, salt, and pepper. Heat oil in a large nonstick skillet over medium-high heat. Add chops; cook 4 minutes on each side or until well browned.
3. Stir remaining 1 teaspoon thyme and apple into fruit relish. Serve chops with relish. YIELD: 4 servings (serving size: 1 chop and about ⅓ cup relish).

POINTS value: 7; Exchanges: 2 Fruit, 4 Lean Meat
Per serving: CAL 328 (24% from fat); PRO 27.0g; FAT 8.7g (sat 2.8g); CARB 35.9g; FIB 2.7g; CHOL 74mg; IRON 2.1mg; SOD 348mg; CALC 40mg

CURRIED PORK CHOPS WITH MANGO SAUCE

prep: 11 minutes • cook: 7 minutes

With a spicy-sweet combination of curry and fresh mango, this sauce is a simple way to dress up pork chops.

½   cup diced peeled mango (about ½ mango)
⅓   cup fat-free, less-sodium chicken broth
2   tablespoons fresh lime juice
2   teaspoons olive oil
1   teaspoon honey
½   teaspoon curry powder
⅛   teaspoon salt
4   (4-ounce) boneless loin pork chops (about ½ inch thick)
½   teaspoon salt
½   teaspoon curry powder
Cooking spray

1. Combine first 7 ingredients in a food processor; process until smooth. Strain mixture through a sieve into a small bowl; discard solids. Set mango sauce aside.

2. Sprinkle chops with ½ teaspoon salt and ½ teaspoon curry powder. Heat a large nonstick skillet coated with cooking spray over medium-high heat. Add chops to pan; cook 3 minutes on each side or until done. Serve chops with mango sauce. YIELD: 4 servings (serving size: 1 chop and about 2 tablespoons sauce).
Note: To speed up the straining process, use a rubber spatula to press the mango mixture through the sieve.

POINTS value: 4; Exchanges: ½ Starch, 3 Very Lean Meat, 1 Fat
Per serving: CAL 189 (34% from fat); PRO 24.3g; FAT 7.2g (sat 2.0g); CARB 6.0g; FIB 0.6g; CHOL 71mg; IRON 1.2mg; SOD 479mg; CALC 20mg

SAFE COOKING TEMPERATURES

One of the major causes of foodborne illness is eating undercooked meat and poultry. Heating food to the correct temperature destroys harmful microorganisms. The most reliable way to test the doneness of meat is to use a meat thermometer. According to the United States Department of Agriculture (USDA), meat should be cooked until a thermometer inserted into the thickest part of the meat reads as follows:
Beef, Veal, Lamb, Pork:
    Internal Temperature: 160°
Ground Meat: 160°-165°
Chicken and Turkey:
    Ground: 165°
    Breasts: 170°
    Legs, Thighs, Wings: 180°
    Whole Bird: 180°

MERLOT-BRAISED PORK CHOPS

prep: 7 minutes • cook: 27 minutes

These chops are simmered uncovered to reduce and thicken the rich red wine sauce. Serve with hot cooked egg noodles or mashed potatoes.

¼ cup all-purpose flour
1 teaspoon salt
½ teaspoon dried rosemary, crushed
½ teaspoon black pepper
4 (6-ounce) bone-in center-cut loin pork chops, trimmed
2 teaspoons olive oil, divided
½ cup vertically sliced onion
1 (14-ounce) can fat-free, less-sodium chicken broth
1 cup Merlot or other dry red wine

1. Combine first 4 ingredients in a shallow dish. Dredge chops in flour mixture, shaking off and reserving excess flour. Heat 1 teaspoon oil in a large nonstick skillet over medium heat. Add chops; cook 3 minutes on each side or until browned. Remove chops from pan; keep warm. Add remaining 1 teaspoon oil to pan. Add onion, and sauté 4 minutes or until lightly browned.
2. Combine reserved flour mixture and chicken broth in a small bowl, stirring with a whisk until smooth. Add broth mixture to pan; bring to a boil, and cook 2 minutes or until slightly thick, scraping bottom of pan to loosen browned bits. Stir in wine. Add pork chops, and bring to a boil. Cook, uncovered, over medium heat 15 minutes or until sauce is thick and pork is tender.

YIELD: 4 servings (serving size: 1 chop and about ⅓ cup sauce).

POINTS value: 5; **Exchanges:** ½ Starch, 3½ Lean Meat
Per serving: CAL 236 (35% from fat); PRO 27.9g; FAT 9.1g (sat 2.7g); CARB 9.0g; FIB 0.6g; CHOL 70mg; IRON 1.8mg; SOD 919mg; CALC 32mg

GREEK PORK KEBABS WITH BLACK OLIVE SAUCE

prep: 19 minutes • cook: 13 minutes
other: 2 hours

Soak the wooden skewers at least 30 minutes before threading ingredients.

1½ teaspoons grated lemon rind, divided
3 tablespoons fresh lemon juice, divided
1 tablespoon olive oil, divided
½ teaspoon black pepper, divided
3 garlic cloves, minced and divided
1 pound pork tenderloin, trimmed and cut into 1-inch pieces
1 large red bell pepper, cut into 1½-inch pieces
1 large red onion, cut into 1½-inch pieces
¼ teaspoon salt
Cooking spray
¼ cup fat-free, less-sodium chicken broth
1 tablespoon chopped fresh flat-leaf parsley
4 pitted kalamata olives, diced (about 1½ tablespoons)

1. Combine 1 teaspoon lemon rind, 2 tablespoons lemon juice, 1 teaspoon olive oil, ¼ teaspoon black pepper, and 2 garlic cloves in a large zip-top plastic bag. Add pork; seal bag, and marinate in refrigerator 2 hours, turning bag occasionally.
2. Prepare grill.
3. Remove pork from bag; discard marinade. Thread pork, bell pepper, and onion alternately onto each of 4 (12-inch) skewers. Sprinkle with salt.
4. Place skewers on grill rack coated with cooking spray. Cover and grill 13 minutes or until pork is slightly pink, turning occasionally. Remove from grill; keep warm.
5. Combine remaining ½ teaspoon lemon rind, remaining 1 tablespoon lemon juice, remaining 2 teaspoons olive oil, remaining ¼ teaspoon pepper, remaining 1 garlic clove, chicken broth, parsley, and olives; stir well with a whisk. Serve sauce over kebabs. YIELD: 4 servings (serving size: 1 kebab and 1½ tablespoons sauce).

POINTS value: 5; **Exchanges:** 1 Vegetable, 3 Lean Meat
Per serving: CAL 204 (35% from fat); PRO 25.0g; FAT 7.8g (sat 1.9g); CARB 8.1g; FIB 0.8g; CHOL 74mg; IRON 1.8mg; SOD 305mg; CALC 24mg

---

PORK CHOPS

Pork chops, bone-in and boneless, are named for the section of the loin from which they're cut. **Rib chops** are from the section closest to the shoulder. **Center cut chops** are from the middle section of the loin; they include a lot of loin meat and a bit of tenderloin meat. Bone-in chops have a characteristic T-shaped bone. **Sirloin chops** are from the area around the hip and often include a big chunk of hip bone.

The Girlfriend Is Back

NIKKI BERRY • **HEIGHT** 5'6" • **BEFORE** 195 LBS. • **AFTER** 156 LBS.

Tip: "Get that number you weighed in high school out of your head and focus on being healthy instead."

Back in high school and college, Nikki Berry took pride in her shapely, athletic physique. Yet by the age of 29, she had gained 60 pounds and was embarrassed by her figure. "I never wanted to go anywhere, not even to take my kids to the park or go out with my husband," Nikki recalls.

So Nikki joined *Weight Watchers* online. "Although I enjoyed the support from women across the country and journaling online, I also ate my way through the maximum points." After six months, Nikki decided she needed the accountability of weekly meetings. "I know people who lost all of their weight online. But eventually, I needed the accountability of someone

"I always thought that I needed to weigh 135 because that is what I weighed in high school."

watching me step onto the scales," she explains.

Weight Watchers also gave Nikki tools for success, such as storyboarding, drinking six to eight glasses of water a day, eating fruits and vegetables, and exercising. "I eased into working out. But now I work out five days a week for one hour each day." Her routine includes aerobics at work, exercise videos at home, and six-mile walks on Sundays.

Combining the balanced diet and exercise, Nikki lost 45 pounds over the next year. "At times, I would stay at a plateau for three to six months, so I had to be mentally strong to keep going to the meetings. But rather than beat myself up when I couldn't lose two pounds each week, I celebrated each victory," she says.

Nikki also learned to concentrate on being healthy rather than obsessing about her fantasy weight. "I always thought that I needed to weigh 135 because that is what I weighed in high school. But I now wear a size eight and sometimes a size six at 156 pounds." She advises others to rethink their ideal weight. "Get that number you weighed in high school out of your head and focus on being healthy instead."

Enriched by the experience rather than feeling imprisoned by her weight, Nikki now enjoys social gatherings and taking her children to the park—and the beach. "Best of all, my husband and I are sweethearts again," she says. "One day, I asked him if he felt like he had his wife back. And he said, 'No, I feel like I have my high school girlfriend back!'"

Weight-loss results not typical.

89

Coffee-Crusted Beef Tenderloin,
page 85

Grilled Veal Chops with
Prosciutto Tomato Sauce,
page 86

Pork Loin with Apple, Pear, and Onion,
opposite page

PORK LOIN WITH APPLE, PEAR, AND ONION

(pictured on opposite page)
**prep: 15 minutes • cook: 1 hour
other: 2 hours and 10 minutes**

Hard apple cider adds depth of flavor to the sweet maple gravy, but nonalcoholic cider works fine, too.

2 teaspoons dried rosemary
1 teaspoon dried thyme
1 teaspoon dried marjoram
¾ teaspoon salt
¼ teaspoon freshly ground black pepper
1 (12-ounce) bottle hard apple cider (such as Woodpecker or Woodchuck)
1 (3-pound) boneless pork loin, trimmed
2 large tart cooking apples (such as Granny Smith, McIntosh, or Baldwin), cut into chunks
2 medium Bosc pears, each cut into 8 wedges
1 medium red onion, cut into 8 wedges
3 tablespoons brown sugar
2 tablespoons all-purpose flour
⅓ cup pure maple syrup
Rosemary sprigs (optional)

1. Combine first 6 ingredients in a large shallow dish or large zip-top plastic bag. Pierce pork several times with a fork, and add to marinade. Cover dish or seal bag; marinate in refrigerator at least 2 hours.
2. Preheat oven to 350°.
3. Remove pork from marinade, reserving marinade. Place pork in a shallow roasting pan; add apple, pear, and onion. Pour reserved marinade over pork, apple, pear, and onion;

sprinkle evenly with brown sugar. Bake at 350° for 1 hour or until thermometer registers 155° (slightly pink). Place pork on a serving platter, and let stand 10 minutes.
4. While pork stands, place flour in a medium saucepan. Carefully pour pan drippings into pan, stirring with a whisk until well blended. Stir in syrup. Bring to a boil; reduce heat, and simmer 1 minute or until gravy begins to thicken.
5. Slice roast; serve with fruit, onion, and gravy. Garnish with rosemary sprigs, if desired. YIELD: 12 servings (serving size: 3 ounces pork, about ⅓ cup fruit, and 1 tablespoon gravy).

POINTS value: 5; **Exchanges:** 1 Fruit, 1 Vegetable, 3 Lean Meat
Per serving: CAL 244 (23% from fat); PRO 25.1g; FAT 6.1g (sat 2.1g); CARB 19.1g; FIB 1.5g; CHOL 62mg; IRON 1.4mg; SOD 199mg; CALC 43mg

GRILLED TWO-MUSTARD PORK TENDERLOIN

**prep: 6 minutes • cook: 20 minutes
other: 8 hours and 10 minutes**

Our Test Kitchens staff voted this recipe perfect for entertaining, but it can easily be halved when preparing a smaller portion.

3 tablespoons olive oil
2 tablespoons stone-ground mustard
2 tablespoons Dijon mustard
¾ teaspoon salt
½ teaspoon black pepper
2 garlic cloves, minced
2 (1-pound) pork tenderloins, trimmed
Cooking spray

1. Combine first 6 ingredients in a large zip-top plastic bag. Add pork; seal bag, and marinate pork in refrigerator at least 8 hours, turning bag occasionally.
2. Prepare grill.
3. Remove pork from bag. Discard marinade. Place pork on grill rack coated with cooking spray; cover and grill 20 minutes or until a thermometer registers 155° (slightly pink). Let stand 10 minutes. YIELD: 8 servings (serving size: 3 ounces).

POINTS value: 4; **Exchanges:** 3 Lean Meat
Per serving: CAL 165 (36% from fat); PRO 24.1g; FAT 6.6g (sat 1.7g); CARB 0.8g; FIB 0.3g; CHOL 74mg; IRON 1.5mg; SOD 231mg; CALC 12mg

PERFECT PORK

Perfect pork will have a faint pink color and should be cooked to 155°. For bone-in and boneless chops, the chops need to be the thickness called for in the recipe. If they're thicker, they won't get done in the time specified in the recipe; if they're thinner, they'll be overcooked. Let larger cuts of pork, such as roasts and tenderloins, stand for 10 to 15 minutes after cooking to reabsorb juices and to allow the meat to finish cooking (standing raises the internal temperature by 5° to 10°). The United States Department of Agriculture (USDA) recommends cooking pork to 160°.

HAM STEAKS WITH CHUTNEY

prep: 10 minutes • cook: 17 minutes

Fresh pear and mixed dried fruit meld in this sweet, spiced chutney that's great with ham, pork chops, or chicken.

1   teaspoon olive oil
½   cup finely chopped onion
1   cup pear nectar or apple juice
¾   cup chopped peeled pear
     (about 1)
2   tablespoons light brown
     sugar
2   tablespoons cider vinegar
½   teaspoon ground ginger
1   (7-ounce) package dried mixed
     fruit, coarsely chopped
1   pound lean ham steak (about
     ½ inch thick), trimmed

1. Heat oil in a medium nonstick skillet over medium-high heat. Add onion; sauté 3 minutes or until soft. Add pear nectar and next 5 ingredients; bring to a boil. Reduce heat, and simmer, uncovered, 10 minutes or until most of liquid evaporates.
2. While chutney cooks, heat a large nonstick skillet over medium-high heat. Add ham; cook 4 minutes on each side or until ham is thoroughly heated and well browned. Divide ham into 4 equal portions; serve with fruit chutney. YIELD: 4 servings (serving size: 3 ounces ham and ½ cup chutney).

POINTS value: 7; Exchanges: ½ Starch, 3 Fruit, 3 Very Lean Meat
Per serving: CAL 340 (20% from fat); PRO 21.8g; FAT 7.6g (sat 0.2g); CARB 50.9g; FIB 5.2g; CHOL 60mg; IRON 2.8mg; SOD 1,188mg; CALC 35mg

SAUSAGE AND RICE-STUFFED PEPPERS

prep: 14 minutes • cook: 25 minutes

We used brown rice because it has a higher fiber content, but you can substitute long-grain rice.

½   cup uncooked instant brown
     rice
4   small green bell peppers
Cooking spray
6   ounces 50%-less-fat bulk pork
     breakfast sausage
½   cup chopped onion
¼   cup chopped fresh parsley
¼   cup ketchup
1   teaspoon Worcestershire sauce
½   teaspoon ground cumin
½   teaspoon hot sauce
¼   teaspoon salt
¼   teaspoon crushed red pepper
½   cup (2 ounces) finely shredded
     reduced-fat sharp Cheddar
     cheese

1. Cook rice according to package directions, omitting salt and fat.
2. Cut tops off bell peppers; discard tops, seeds, and membranes. Place peppers, cut sides down, in an 11 x 7-inch baking dish coated with cooking spray; cover with plastic wrap. Microwave at HIGH 3 minutes or until peppers are crisp-tender.
3. Cook sausage and onion in a large nonstick skillet coated with cooking spray over medium-high heat until browned, stirring to crumble sausage. Add cooked rice, parsley, and next 6 ingredients.
4. Preheat oven to 350°.
5. Turn peppers over, and spoon about ½ cup sausage mixture into each pepper; sprinkle with cheese.

6. Bake at 350° for 15 minutes or until cheese melts and rice mixture is thoroughly heated. YIELD: 4 servings (serving size: 1 stuffed pepper).

POINTS value: 6; Exchanges: 1½ Starch, 1 Vegetable, 1½ Medium-Fat Meat
Per serving: CAL 274 (39% from fat); PRO 13.8g; FAT 11.8g (sat 4.9g); CARB 28.2g; FIB 2.8g; CHOL 40mg; IRON 1.8mg; SOD 725mg; CALC 129mg

FRIED RICE WITH HAM AND PEAS

prep: 5 minutes • cook: 31 minutes

2   teaspoons dark sesame oil
½   cup frozen green peas
½   cup sliced green onions (about
     2 onions)
1¼   cups cooked long-grain rice
½   cup diced low-sodium ham
1   large egg, lightly beaten
2   tablespoons low-sodium soy
     sauce
1   tablespoon water

1. Heat oil in a large nonstick skillet over medium-high heat. Add peas and onions; sauté 3 minutes or until tender. Add rice and ham; cook until thoroughly heated. Push rice mixture to the sides of the pan, forming a well in the center.
2. Add egg to well, and cook until set, stirring occasionally. Stir rice mixture into egg mixture. Stir in soy sauce and water. YIELD: 2 servings (serving size: 1 cup).

POINTS value: 6; Exchanges: 2 Starch, 1 Vegetable, 1 Medium-Fat Meat, 1 Fat
Per Serving: CAL 310 (28% from fat); PRO 15.9g; FAT 9.5g (sat 2.2g); CARB 38.1g; FIB 2.9g; CHOL 131mg; IRON 2.8mg; SOD 802mg; CALC 37mg

Poultry

LINGUINE WITH CREAMY CHICKEN AND WALNUTS

prep: 8 minutes • cook: 13 minutes

6 ounces uncooked dried
   linguine
1 tablespoon water
2 teaspoons all-purpose flour
2 teaspoons olive oil
2 garlic cloves, minced
1 (8-ounce) package sliced
   mushrooms
1 cup fat-free milk
1 cup fat-free, less-sodium
   chicken broth
¾ cup (6 ounces) ⅓-less-fat
   cream cheese, cubed and
   softened
½ teaspoon black pepper
¼ teaspoon salt
¼ teaspoon ground nutmeg
2 (6-ounce) packages refrigerated
   diced roasted chicken breast
2 teaspoons butter
3 tablespoons coarsely chopped
   walnuts, toasted

1. Cook pasta according to package directions, omitting salt and fat.
2. While pasta cooks, combine water and flour in a small bowl; stir well with a whisk. Heat oil in a large nonstick skillet over medium-high heat. Add garlic and mushrooms; sauté 2 minutes or until mushrooms are tender. Add milk and next 4 ingredients. Bring to a simmer, and cook 3 minutes or until cream cheese melts and sauce is smooth, stirring constantly with a whisk. Stir in flour mixture. Add nutmeg and chicken. Bring to a boil; reduce heat, and simmer 4 minutes or until sauce begins to thicken, stirring occasionally. Add butter, stirring until butter melts. Serve sauce over hot cooked pasta; sprinkle with walnuts before serving. YIELD: 6 servings (serving size: ½ cup pasta, ½ cup sauce, and 1½ teaspoons walnuts).

POINTS value: 7; **Exchanges:** 1½ Starch, 1 Vegetable, 2 Medium-Fat Meat, 1 Fat
Per serving: CAL 328 (38% from fat); PRO 23.7g; FAT 13.8g (sat 6.1g); CARB 28.0g; FIB 1.7g; CHOL 62mg; IRON 2.0mg; SOD 866mg; CALC 69mg

THAI CHICKEN AND NOODLES

(pictured on page 114)
prep: 12 minutes • cook: 5 minutes
other: 13 minutes

Rice sticks can be found in Asian specialty markets or in the Asian section of large supermarkets. If you have leftovers, this dish packs and travels well for lunch at your desk the next day.

¼ pound uncooked rice sticks
   (rice-flour noodles)
½ cup fat-free, less-sodium
   chicken broth
¼ cup chili garlic sauce
3 tablespoons low-sodium soy
   sauce
2 teaspoons sugar
2 teaspoons anchovy paste
1 tablespoon roasted peanut oil
1½ cups snow peas, trimmed and
   diagonally cut into thirds
1 cup (2-inch) sliced green
   onions (about 4 onions)
2 garlic cloves, minced
2 cups shredded cooked chicken
   breast
2 cups fresh bean sprouts
2 tablespoons chopped unsalted
   dry-roasted peanuts

1. Place noodles in a large bowl; add warm water to cover. Let stand for 20 minutes.
2. Meanwhile, combine broth and next 4 ingredients, stirring until smooth.
3. Heat oil in a large nonstick skillet over medium-high heat. Add snow peas, green onions, and garlic; sauté 2 minutes or until crisp-tender. Add chicken and bean sprouts; sauté 1 minute or until thoroughly heated. Add broth mixture; cook 1 minute or until thoroughly heated.
4. Drain noodles. Add noodles to pan; toss until well blended. Sprinkle each serving with peanuts. YIELD: 4 servings (serving size: 1½ cups noodle mixture and 1½ teaspoons peanuts).

POINTS value: 7; **Exchanges:** 2 Starch, 1½ Vegetable, 3 Lean Meat
Per serving: CAL 343 (23% from fat); PRO 29.0g; FAT 8.6g (sat 1.7g); CARB 38.1g; FIB 3.6g; CHOL 61mg; IRON 7.8mg; SOD 1,727mg; CALC 61mg

HEALTHY OILS

Vegetable, seed, and nut oils are a major source of both vitamin E and unsaturated fats, which are essential to the American diet. The daily allowance in the United States Department of Agriculture (USDA) Food Guide Pyramid ranges from 3 to 7 teaspoons per day, depending on a person's age, sex, and level of physical activity. Look for oils labeled polyunsaturated (corn oil, sesame oil) or monounsaturated (canola or olive oil). Canola oil and extravirgin olive oil are two of the healthiest and most available cooking oils.

CHICKEN AND SWISS CHARD MANICOTTI CRÊPES

prep: 48 minutes • cook: 54 minutes other: 23 minutes

Crêpes are light, very thin pancakes that can be prepared in advance and frozen up to 2 months. Be sure to store them between single layers of wax paper so that they won't stick together. This recipe makes 4 extra crêpes, so you can freeze them for future use.

1¼ cups all-purpose flour
¼ teaspoon salt
1¼ cups water
5 large eggs
1 teaspoon olive oil
⅛ teaspoon crushed red pepper
2 garlic cloves, minced
1 tablespoon chopped fresh thyme
2 (14.5-ounce) cans garlic and olive oil petite diced tomatoes, undrained
4 Swiss chard leaves, stems removed
⅓ cup (1⅓ ounces) grated fresh Parmesan cheese, divided
¾ cup (3 ounces) shredded part-skim mozzarella cheese
¼ teaspoon ground nutmeg
⅛ teaspoon freshly ground black pepper
1 (15-ounce) container part-skim ricotta cheese
1 (6-ounce) package refrigerated grilled-flavored chicken breast strips, finely chopped
Cooking spray
2 ounces very thinly sliced prosciutto or ham (4 slices), each cut in half crosswise

1. Lightly spoon flour into dry measuring cups; level with a knife. Combine flour and salt in a medium bowl. Combine water and eggs in a bowl; stir well with a whisk. Add to flour mixture, stirring with a whisk until almost smooth. Let stand at room temperature 30 minutes.

2. While crêpe batter stands, heat oil in a large saucepan over medium-high heat. Add crushed red pepper and garlic; sauté 1 minute. Add thyme and tomatoes; reduce heat, and simmer, uncovered, 5 minutes or until sauce is thick and reduced to 2 cups. Remove sauce from heat, and set aside.

3. Steam Swiss chard leaves, covered, about 30 seconds or until leaves wilt. Drain and pat leaves dry with paper towels. Cut each leaf in half lengthwise; set aside.

4. Combine 3 tablespoons Parmesan cheese, mozzarella cheese, and next 4 ingredients in a bowl; stir well, and set aside.

5. Place a 10-inch crêpe pan or nonstick skillet coated with cooking spray over medium-high heat until hot. Remove pan from heat. Pour ⅓ cup batter into pan; quickly tilt pan in all directions so batter covers pan with a thin film. Cook about 1 minute. Carefully lift edge of crêpe with a spatula to test for doneness. The crêpe is ready to turn when it can be shaken loose from the pan and the underside is lightly browned. Turn crêpe over, and cook 15 to 30 seconds. Place crêpe on a wire rack; cool. Repeat procedure until all of the batter is used, stirring the batter before making each crêpe. Stack crêpes between single layers of wax paper or paper towels to prevent sticking.

6. Preheat oven to 350°.

7. Spoon 1½ cups tomato sauce in bottom of a 13 x 9-inch baking dish. Place half of a Swiss chard leaf on each of 8 crêpes; top each with a half slice of prosciutto. Spoon about ⅓ cup ricotta mixture down center of each crêpe. Fold over edges, and place, seam sides down, over tomato sauce in dish. Spoon remaining ½ cup tomato sauce evenly over crêpes, and sprinkle with remaining Parmesan cheese. Bake at 350°, uncovered, for 30 minutes or until sauce is bubbly. YIELD: 8 servings (serving size: 1 filled crêpe).

POINTS value: 6; **Exchanges:** 1 Starch, 2 Vegetable, 2 Medium-Fat Meat
Per serving: CAL 285 (36% from fat); PRO 21.8g; FAT 11.3g (sat 5.6g); CARB 23.3g; FIB 1.8g; CHOL 131mg; IRON 2.6mg; SOD 1,089mg; CALC 342mg

CRÊPE CREATIONS

Crêpes have long been the staple of simple French cuisine. Initially, crêpes were simply flavored with salty butter. Today, crêpes can be wrapped around just about anything to turn them into an elegant meal. Or they can just be folded and topped with something yummy. In Chicken and Swiss Chard Manicotti Crêpes, the flat crêpes are wrapped around the chicken filling. The end product resembles traditional manicotti.

CHICKEN TACOS VERDE

prep: 25 minutes • cook: 29 minutes

Tomatillos have a citrus, herbal flavor, and Anaheim chiles are mild, making both good partners for these special chicken soft tacos that earned our highest rating.

1	pound tomatillos
1¼	cups sliced onion (1 medium)
2	tablespoons chopped seeded jalapeño pepper (about 2 peppers)
2	tablespoons vegetable oil
2	Anaheim chiles, seeded and quartered
2	garlic cloves, peeled

Cooking spray

¾	cup fat-free, less-sodium chicken broth
3	cups shredded cooked chicken
1	tablespoon fresh lime juice
½	teaspoon salt
8	(7-inch) 97%-fat-free flour tortillas
½	cup fat-free sour cream

1. Preheat oven to 425°.
2. Discard husks and stems from tomatillos. Cut each tomatillo in half. Combine tomatillos and next 5 ingredients in a bowl; toss well. Arrange tomatillo mixture in a single layer on a jelly-roll pan coated with cooking spray. Bake at 425° for 15 minutes or until tomatillos are tender.
3. Place tomatillo mixture in a food processor; pulse 13 times or until chopped. Pour mixture into a large nonstick skillet. Add broth; bring to a boil over medium-high heat. Stir in chicken; reduce heat, and simmer, uncovered, 10 minutes or until liquid is absorbed. Remove from heat; stir in lime juice and salt.
4. Warm tortillas according to package directions. Spoon about ½ cup chicken mixture on one-half of each tortilla, and fold in half. Top each taco with 1 tablespoon sour cream. YIELD: 8 servings (serving size: 1 taco and 1 tablespoon sour cream).

POINTS value: 5; **Exchanges:** 1 Starch, 2 Vegetable, 2 Lean Meat
Per serving: CAL 248 (24% from fat); PRO 21.4g; FAT 6.6g (sat 1.2g); CARB 25.9g; FIB 2.6g; CHOL 46mg; IRON 2.2mg; SOD 478mg; CALC 64mg

PECAN-ENCRUSTED CHICKEN FINGERS WITH HONEY-MUSTARD DIPPING SAUCE

prep: 17 minutes • cook: 25 minutes
other: 10 minutes

You will never miss deep-fried chicken fingers after tasting these crunchy tenders coated with pecans.

1	teaspoon cornstarch
1	teaspoon lemon juice
1	large egg white
1	cup fresh breadcrumbs
½	cup very finely chopped pecans
¾	teaspoon salt
½	teaspoon dried oregano
½	teaspoon dried thyme
½	teaspoon paprika
¼	teaspoon ground red pepper
¼	teaspoon ground black pepper
1	pound chicken breast tenders

Cooking spray

2	tablespoons stone-ground mustard
2	tablespoons honey

1. Preheat oven to 450°.
2. Combine first 3 ingredients in a shallow dish; stir well. Combine breadcrumbs and next 7 ingredients in another shallow dish.
3. Dip chicken tenders in egg white mixture. Dredge chicken in breadcrumb mixture, pressing firmly to coat. Place chicken on a wire rack, and let stand 10 minutes. Place a jelly-roll pan in oven to heat while chicken stands.
4. Coat chicken tenders well with cooking spray. Remove hot pan from oven; coat with cooking spray. Place chicken on pan in a single layer. Bake at 450° for 20 to 25 minutes or until chicken is done.
5. While chicken bakes, combine mustard and honey in a small bowl; stir well. Serve chicken tenders with honey-mustard. YIELD: 4 servings (serving size: about 2 chicken tenders and 1 tablespoon honey mustard).

POINTS value: 7; **Exchanges:** 1 Starch, 4 Lean Meat
Per serving: CAL 300 (38% from fat); PRO 29.5g; FAT 12.6g (sat 1.4g); CARB 17.8g; FIB 2.1g; CHOL 66mg; IRON 1.9mg; SOD 601mg; CALC 48mg

TOMATILLOS

Tomatillos are used in a variety of Mexican green sauces and have a very tart flavor—not at all like a tomato.

The fruits are about 1 to 2 inches wide and have a papery outer husk. The tomatillo is used when it is still green. If a tomatillo is turning light yellow, it is ripe and past its prime for most uses.

CHICKEN DIJON

prep: 7 minutes • cook: 14 minutes

2   teaspoons olive oil
Cooking spray
1½ pounds skinless, boneless
     chicken breasts, cut into 1-inch
     pieces
¼   teaspoon salt
¼   teaspoon ground black pepper
¾   cup dry white wine or fat-free,
     less-sodium chicken broth
1   tablespoon chopped fresh
     thyme
1   bay leaf
½   cup reduced-fat sour cream
     (such as Breakstone's)
3   tablespoons Dijon mustard
1   (2.75-ounce) package
     uncooked quick-cooking
     wild rice

1. Heat oil in a large nonstick skillet coated with cooking spray over medium-high heat. Add chicken, salt, and pepper; sauté 6 minutes or until chicken is browned. Add wine, thyme, and bay leaf; bring to a boil, and cook 3 minutes, stirring occasionally. Reduce heat to low. Stir in sour cream and mustard; cook 2 minutes or until sauce begins to thicken, stirring constantly. Discard bay leaf.
2. Meanwhile, cook rice according to package directions, omitting salt and fat. Serve chicken mixture over rice. YIELD: 4 servings (serving size: ½ cup chicken mixture and ⅔ cup rice).

POINTS value: 7; **Exchanges:** 1 Starch, 6 Very Lean Meat, 1 Fat
Per serving: CAL 335 (25% from fat); PRO 42.9g; FAT 9.2g (sat 3.2g); CARB 18.7g; FIB 0.6g; CHOL 110mg; IRON 2.4mg; SOD 845mg; CALC 78mg

SWEET-SPICED CHICKEN AND VEGETABLES

prep: 15 minutes • cook: 1 hour and 3 minutes

You'll enjoy the aroma and flavor of this ginger and cinnamon–spiced feast. The texture of the chicken is best when the breast halves are seared whole and then cut into cubes before the dish is baked.

1   pound skinless, boneless
     chicken breast halves
¼   teaspoon salt
¼   teaspoon black pepper
Cooking spray
1¼ cups vertically sliced onion
     (about 1 medium)
2   carrots, peeled and cut into
     ½-inch pieces (about 2 cups)
1   parsnip, peeled and cut into
     ½-inch pieces (about 1 cup)
1   teaspoon ground ginger
½   teaspoon ground cinnamon
2   (14-ounce) cans fat-free,
     less-sodium chicken broth
1   (16-ounce) can chickpeas
     (garbanzo beans), rinsed and
     drained
1   (14.5-ounce) can diced
     tomatoes, undrained
¾   cup pitted prunes
1⅓ cups water
⅔   cup uncooked long-grain rice

1. Preheat oven to 350°.
2. Sprinkle chicken evenly with salt and pepper. Place a large ovenproof Dutch oven coated with cooking spray over medium-high heat until hot. Add chicken; cook 4 minutes on each side or until done. Remove chicken from pan. Add onion, carrot, and parsnip; sauté 5 minutes or until vegetables are crisp-tender. Stir in

ginger and cinnamon; cook 1 minute. Add broth, chickpeas, and tomatoes; bring to a boil.
3. Cut chicken into ½-inch pieces. Stir chicken and prunes into pan. Cover and bake at 350° for 45 minutes or until vegetables are tender.
4. Meanwhile, bring 1⅓ cups water to a boil. Add rice; cover, reduce heat, and simmer 15 minutes or until rice is tender and liquid is absorbed. Remove from heat, and let stand 5 minutes. Serve chicken mixture over rice. YIELD: 6 servings (serving size: 1⅓ cups chicken mixture and ½ cup rice).

POINTS value: 6; **Exchanges:** 2 Starch, 1 Fruit, 2 Vegetable, 2 Very Lean Meat
Per serving: CAL 338 (7% from fat); PRO 25.4g; FAT 2.5g (sat 0.5g); CARB 55.4g; FIB 7.5g; CHOL 44mg; IRON 2.5mg; SOD 808mg; CALC 106mg

FOOD SAFETY

Food safety is important when handling any type of raw meat—and most especially chicken and other poultry. Always rinse thoroughly with cold running water before cooking, and pat dry with paper towels. Always use a clean knife and cutting board, and make sure to sanitize those items before using them to cut any other raw food products like fruits and vegetables. Most importantly, wash your hands immediately after working with raw chicken to prevent cross-contamination with other foods. Cook chicken until done or to the temperature that is stated in the recipe.

CHICKEN PICCATA

prep: 13 minutes • cook: 15 minutes

4 (6-ounce) skinless, boneless
   chicken breast halves
½ teaspoon black pepper
¼ teaspoon salt
¼ cup all-purpose flour
1 tablespoon olive oil, divided
1 tablespoon minced shallots
¼ cup fat-free, less-sodium
   chicken broth
2 tablespoons fresh lemon juice
1 tablespoon capers
2 teaspoons chopped fresh
   parsley, divided

1. Place each chicken breast half
between 2 sheets of heavy-duty plastic wrap; pound to ½-inch thickness
using a meat mallet or rolling pin.
Sprinkle chicken evenly with pepper
and salt; dredge in flour.
2. Heat 1½ teaspoons oil in a large
nonstick skillet over medium-high
heat. Add half of chicken; cook 3
minutes on each side or until done.
Remove chicken from pan; keep
warm. Repeat procedure with
remaining 1½ teaspoons oil and
chicken. Add shallots to pan; sauté
1 minute or until tender. Add broth,
lemon juice, and capers. Increase
heat to high, and cook 1 minute. Stir
in 1 teaspoon parsley. Spoon sauce
evenly over chicken. Sprinkle with
remaining 1 teaspoon parsley. YIELD:
4 servings (serving size: 1 chicken
breast half and 1 teaspoon sauce).

POINTS value: 5; **Exchanges:** 1½ Vegetable, 5 Very
Lean Meat, 1 Fat
Per serving: CAL 252 (20% from fat); PRO 40.5g;
FAT 5.6g (sat 1.0g); CARB 7.4g; FIB 0.4g;
CHOL 99mg; IRON 1.7mg; SOD 359mg;
CALC 24mg

PARMESAN-BREADED CHICKEN WITH CREAMY SAGE SAUCE

prep: 27 minutes • cook: 20 minutes
other: 10 minutes

*Preheating the baking sheet gives this
"oven-fried" chicken a crispy coating.*

4 (6-ounce) skinless, boneless
   chicken breast halves
1 cup fresh French breadcrumbs
3 tablespoons (¾ ounce)
   shredded fresh Parmesan cheese
1 teaspoon dried oregano
½ teaspoon garlic salt
¼ teaspoon black pepper
1 tablespoon fresh lemon
   juice
1 teaspoon cornstarch
1 large egg white
Cooking spray
1 teaspoon olive oil
3 tablespoons minced shallots
   (about 2 large)
1 tablespoon all-purpose flour
⅔ cup fat-free, less-sodium
   chicken broth
⅓ cup dry white wine or fat-free,
   less-sodium chicken broth
1 teaspoon fresh lemon juice
2 teaspoons light stick butter
2 teaspoons chopped fresh sage
¼ teaspoon salt

1. Preheat oven to 450°.
2. Place each chicken breast half
between 2 sheets of heavy-duty plastic wrap; pound to ¼-inch thickness
using a meat mallet or rolling pin.
3. Combine breadcrumbs and next
4 ingredients in a shallow dish.
Combine 1 tablespoon lemon juice,
cornstarch, and egg white in another
shallow dish. Stir well with a whisk.

4. Dip each chicken breast half in
egg white mixture; dredge in breadcrumb mixture. Place chicken breast
halves on a wire rack; let stand 10
minutes. Place a baking sheet in
oven to heat while chicken stands.
5. Coat each chicken breast half well
with cooking spray. Remove hot
baking sheet from oven; coat with
cooking spray. Place chicken breast
halves on baking sheet, and bake at
450° for 20 to 25 minutes or until
chicken is done.
6. While chicken bakes, heat oil in a
small saucepan over medium-high
heat. Add shallots; sauté 2 minutes or
until tender. Sprinkle shallots with
flour; stir well, and cook 1 minute.
Add broth, wine, and 1 teaspoon
lemon juice; bring to a boil. Reduce
heat, and simmer 2 minutes or until
thick, stirring occasionally. Add butter, stirring with a whisk until butter
melts. Stir in chopped sage and salt.
Serve immediately with chicken
breast halves. YIELD: 4 servings (serving size: 1 chicken breast half and
3½ tablespoons sauce).

POINTS value: 7; **Exchanges:** 1 Starch, 1 Vegetable,
5 Very Lean Meat, 1 Fat
Per serving: CAL 338 (23% from fat); PRO 43.6g;
FAT 8.5g (sat 2.2g); CARB 19.4g; FIB 1.1g;
CHOL 105mg; IRON 2.0mg; SOD 573mg;
CALC 92mg

CHICKEN SALTIMBOCCA

prep: 12 minutes • cook: 24 minutes

*Traditionally made with veal in Italy,
saltimbocca means "jump into mouth"
because of its robust taste.*

4   (6-ounce) skinless, boneless
     chicken breast halves
¼   teaspoon salt
¼   teaspoon black pepper
⅓   cup all-purpose flour
1   tablespoon olive oil, divided
Cooking spray
⅔   cup dry white wine or fat-free,
     less-sodium chicken broth
2   teaspoons butter
2   teaspoons chopped fresh sage
1   ounce very thinly sliced
     prosciutto (2 slices), each cut
     in half crosswise
½   cup (2 ounces) shredded part-
     skim mozzarella cheese

1. Place each chicken breast half
between 2 sheets of heavy-duty plastic wrap; pound to ¼-inch thickness
using a meat mallet or rolling pin.
Sprinkle chicken evenly with salt and
pepper; dredge in flour.
2. Preheat broiler.
3. Heat 1½ teaspoons oil in a large
nonstick skillet coated with cooking
spray over medium–high heat. Add
2 chicken breast halves; cook 4 minutes on each side or until lightly
browned and done. Place chicken on
a jelly-roll pan coated with cooking
spray. Repeat procedure with
remaining oil and chicken. Add wine
to pan, scraping pan to loosen
browned bits. Bring to a boil; reduce
heat, and simmer 6 minutes or until
wine is reduced to ¼ cup. Add butter, stirring until butter melts.

4. While sauce simmers, sprinkle
sage evenly over chicken; top each
piece of chicken with half a slice of
prosciutto and 2 tablespoons cheese.
Broil 2 minutes or until cheese melts
and is lightly browned. Place chicken
on serving plates; spoon sauce evenly
over chicken. YIELD: 4 servings (serving size: 1 chicken breast half and
about 1 tablespoon sauce).

POINTS value: 7; **Exchanges:** ½ Starch, 6 Very Lean
Meat, 1½ Fat
Per serving: CAL 316 (30% from fat); PRO 45.7g;
FAT 10.5g (sat 3.7g); CARB 7.3g; FIB 0.3g;
CHOL 116mg; IRON 1.9mg; SOD 467mg;
CALC 117mg

ROSEMARY-FETA CHICKEN WITH CHERRY TOMATO-OLIVE SAUCE

(pictured on page 112)
prep: 7 minutes • cook: 34 minutes

1   (1.5-ounce) slice hearty white
     bread
¼   cup (2 ounces) crumbled feta
     cheese
1   tablespoon chopped fresh
     rosemary
½   teaspoon freshly ground black
     pepper, divided
¼   teaspoon salt
4   (6-ounce) skinless, boneless
     chicken breast halves
1   teaspoon olive oil
Cooking spray
½   cup halved pitted kalamata
     olives
⅓   cup minced shallots (about
     3 large)
⅓   cup fat-free, less-sodium
     chicken broth
1   pint grape tomatoes
Rosemary sprigs (optional)

1. Preheat oven to 375°.
2. Place bread in a food processor;
pulse 10 times or until coarse
crumbs measure ½ cup. Combine
breadcrumbs, cheese, and rosemary
in a small bowl. Toss well; set aside.
3. Sprinkle ¼ teaspoon pepper and
salt evenly over chicken. Heat oil in
a large nonstick skillet coated with
cooking spray over medium-high
heat. Add chicken; cook 3 to 4 minutes on each side or until browned.
4. Place chicken in an 11 x 7-inch
baking dish; top evenly with breadcrumb mixture, pressing down
slightly. Add olives and next 3 ingredients to dish, and sprinkle with
remaining ¼ teaspoon pepper. Bake
at 375° for 27 minutes or until
chicken is done. Garnish with
rosemary, if desired. YIELD: 4 servings
(serving size: 1 chicken breast half and
about ½ cup sauce).

POINTS value: 6; **Exchanges:** ½ Starch, 1 Vegetable,
5 Very Lean Meat, 1 Fat
Per serving: CAL 296 (23% from fat); PRO 43.2g;
FAT 7.7g (sat 2.4g); CARB 12.4g; FIB 1.6g;
CHOL 107mg; IRON 2.6mg; SOD 633mg;
CALC 101mg

SHALLOTS

Because of their low water
content, shallots have a more
concentrated flavor than onions.
They can also burn and toughen
easily, so use caution when
sautéing. When peeling a shallot,
remove a few of the outer layers
along with the peel. You might
need an extra shallot to make up
for the discarded layers, but this
method is faster than removing
only the thin peel.

APRICOT-THYME CRUSTED CHICKEN BREAST

prep: 15 minutes • cook: 20 minutes

Dried apricots add chewy texture and tart flavor to the breadcrumb coating on this chicken. Honey adds sweetness and helps the coating stick to the chicken.

4   (6-ounce) skinless, boneless chicken breast halves
3   tablespoons honey
½   teaspoon salt
¼   teaspoon black pepper
½   cup dry breadcrumbs
1   tablespoon olive oil
¼   cup diced dried apricots (about 6)
2   tablespoons minced green onions (about 1)
2   teaspoons grated orange rind
½   teaspoon dried thyme
Cooking spray

1. Preheat oven to 350°.
2. Brush chicken evenly with honey, and sprinkle with salt and pepper.
3. Combine breadcrumbs and oil in a shallow dish; toss well. Add apricots and next 3 ingredients; stir well. Dredge chicken in breadcrumb mixture, pressing to coat chicken well with mixture. Place chicken on a baking sheet coated with cooking spray, and coat chicken with cooking spray. Bake at 350° for 20 minutes or until done. YIELD: 4 servings (serving size: 1 chicken breast half).

POINTS value: 7; **Exchanges:** 1 Starch, 1 Fruit, 5 Very Lean Meat, 1 Fat
Per serving: CAL 348 (16% from fat); PRO 41.6g; FAT 6.3g (sat 1.2g); CARB 30.0g; FIB 1.5g; CHOL 99mg; IRON 2.6mg; SOD 506mg; CALC 56mg

OSSO BUCO-STYLE CHICKEN

prep: 9 minutes • cook: 1 hour and 49 minutes

4   (8-ounce) skinless chicken breast halves (bone-in)
¼   teaspoon salt
½   teaspoon black pepper
2   teaspoons olive oil
Cooking spray
2   cups diced onion (1 large)
¾   cup diced carrot (1 medium)
½   cup diced celery (1 stalk)
2   tablespoons minced garlic (about 7 cloves), divided
¾   cup dry white wine or fat-free, less-sodium chicken broth
1   (14-ounce) can fat-free, less-sodium chicken broth
1   (14-ounce) can diced tomatoes, drained
1   bay leaf
¼   cup chopped fresh flat-leaf parsley
1   tablespoon grated lemon rind

1. Preheat oven to 350°.
2. Sprinkle chicken evenly with salt and pepper.

3. Heat oil in an ovenproof Dutch oven coated with cooking spray over medium-high heat. Add chicken; cook 6 minutes on each side or until browned. Remove chicken from pan; set aside. Add onion, carrot, and celery to pan; sauté 5 minutes or until tender. Add 4 teaspoons garlic; sauté 1 minute. Add wine, scraping pan to loosen browned bits. Add broth, tomatoes, and bay leaf. Return chicken to pan; bring to a boil. Cover pan, and immediately place in oven. Bake at 350° for 1 hour and 30 minutes or until chicken is very tender. Discard bay leaf.
4. Meanwhile, combine remaining 2 teaspoons garlic, parsley, and lemon rind in a small bowl; stir well. Cover; chill until ready to serve.
5. Place 1 chicken breast half in each of 4 shallow bowls; spoon 1 cup vegetable-broth mixture over each breast half, and sprinkle each with about 1 tablespoon parsley mixture. YIELD: 4 servings.

POINTS value: 6; **Exchanges:** 4 Vegetable, 5 Very Lean Meat, ½ Fat
Per serving: CAL 303 (14% from fat); PRO 45.5g; FAT 4.7g (sat 0.9g); CARB 18.7g; FIB 3.9g; CHOL 105mg; IRON 2.4mg; SOD 602mg; CALC 87mg

---

SIMPLE CITRUS TIPS

Always grate citrus rind before sectioning or juicing the fruit. Hold the fruit firmly. Push down on a handheld grater, but don't push too hard. Just take off the color, not the white pith. Once you've removed the zest or peel, you can refrigerate the fruit up to 1 week.

1 medium orange = 1 to 2 tablespoons grated orange rind
1 medium lemon = 1¼ teaspoons grated lemon rind
1 medium lime = 1½ teaspoons grated lime rind

MOROCCAN CHICKEN TAGINE WITH COUSCOUS

prep: 8 minutes • cook: 1 hour and 22 minutes

Tagine is both the name of a traditional Moroccan dish and the cooking vessel used to prepare the recipe. The ceramic tagine has a base like a serving dish and a conical lid that keeps the moisture from evaporating. Use a Dutch oven with a tight-fitting lid to create this aromatic meal of stewed chicken and vegetables.

1   teaspoon salt
½   teaspoon ground ginger
½   teaspoon ground cinnamon
½   teaspoon ground coriander
½   teaspoon ground turmeric
¼   teaspoon ground nutmeg
¼   teaspoon ground cumin
¼   teaspoon black pepper
¼   teaspoon crushed red pepper
2   chicken breast halves (about 1 pound), skinned
2   chicken drumsticks (about ½ pound), skinned
2   chicken thighs (about ½ pound), skinned
2   teaspoons olive oil, divided
Cooking spray
2   medium onions, cut into wedges
4   garlic cloves, halved lengthwise
1   (14-ounce) can fat-free, less-sodium chicken broth, divided
½   cup golden raisins
2   medium carrots, cut into thirds
¾   cup water
1   cup uncooked whole wheat couscous
¼   cup chopped fresh parsley
2   tablespoons honey
2   tablespoons slivered almonds, toasted

1. Combine first 9 ingredients in a small bowl. Rub chicken with the spice mixture.
2. Heat 1 teaspoon oil in a Dutch oven coated with cooking spray over medium heat. Add chicken; cook 6 minutes, turning to brown on all sides. Remove chicken from pan; keep warm.
3. Heat remaining 1 teaspoon oil in pan. Add onions and garlic; sauté 2 minutes or just until lightly browned. Add 1⅓ cups broth, scraping bottom of pan to loosen browned bits. Return chicken to pan; bring to a boil. Cover, reduce heat, and simmer 50 minutes. Stir in raisins and carrots; cook, uncovered, 20 minutes or until carrots are tender.
4. Meanwhile, bring remaining broth and ¾ cup water to a boil in a medium saucepan; gradually stir in couscous. Remove from heat; cover and let stand 5 minutes. Add parsley; fluff with a fork. Serve chicken mixture over couscous. Drizzle honey evenly over chicken mixture, and sprinkle with almonds. YIELD: 4 servings (serving size: ¾ cup couscous, 1 breast half or 1 thigh and 1 drumstick, about ⅔ cup sauce, 1½ teaspoons honey, and 1½ teaspoons almonds).

POINTS value: 9; **Exchanges:** 2 Starch, 1 Fruit, 2½ Vegetable, 4 Very Lean Meat, ½ Fat
Per serving: CAL 434 (18% from fat); PRO 34.8g; FAT 8.5g (sat 1.4g); CARB 57.6g; FIB 7.0g; CHOL 87mg; IRON 3.3mg; SOD 976mg; CALC 84mg

ORANGE-DIJON CHICKEN

prep: 10 minutes • cook: 23 minutes

4   (3-ounce) skinless, boneless chicken thighs
¼   teaspoon salt, divided
¼   teaspoon freshly ground black pepper
Cooking spray
¼   cup orange juice
¼   cup fat-free, less-sodium chicken broth
¼   cup orange marmalade
1   tablespoon whole-grain Dijon mustard
2   garlic cloves, minced
1   tablespoon thinly sliced green onions

1. Sprinkle chicken with ⅛ teaspoon salt and pepper. Heat a large nonstick skillet coated with cooking spray over medium heat. Add chicken; cook 13 minutes or until done, turning occasionally. Remove from pan; keep warm.
2. Combine remaining ⅛ teaspoon salt, orange juice, broth, marmalade, and mustard in a bowl; stir well.
3. Recoat pan with cooking spray, and place over medium-high heat. Add garlic; sauté 1 minute. Add orange juice mixture; bring to a boil over high heat. Cook 6 minutes or until slightly thick, stirring constantly. Spoon sauce over chicken, and sprinkle with green onions. YIELD: 2 servings (serving size: 2 chicken thighs and ¼ cup sauce).

POINTS value: 7; **Exchanges:** 2 Fruit, 5 Very Lean Meat, 1 Fat
Per serving: CAL 334 (20% from fat); PRO 34.6g; FAT 7.4g (sat 1.7g); CARB 32.5g; FIB 0.6g; CHOL 141mg; IRON 2.2mg; SOD 732mg; CALC 49mg

CHICKEN BRAISED WITH TOMATOES AND OLIVES

prep: 7 minutes • cook: 50 minutes

Allow about 10 minutes to prepare the couscous while the chicken cooks, and dinner will come together easily.

½   teaspoon freshly ground black pepper, divided
¼   teaspoon salt
8   (3-ounce) skinless, boneless chicken thighs
1   teaspoon olive oil
Cooking spray
2½   cups thinly sliced onion (about 1 large)
2   garlic cloves, minced
2   cups fat-free, less-sodium chicken broth, divided
¼   cup halved pitted kalamata olives
2   teaspoons balsamic vinegar
1   (14.5-ounce) can diced tomatoes, undrained
¼   cup chopped fresh flat-leaf parsley
⅔   cup uncooked couscous

1. Sprinkle ¼ teaspoon pepper and salt evenly over chicken.
2. Heat oil in a large nonstick skillet coated with cooking spray over medium heat. Add chicken; cook 5 minutes on each side or until browned. Remove chicken from pan; keep warm. Add onion to pan; sauté 5 minutes or until tender. Add garlic; sauté 1 minute. Add ½ cup broth and next 3 ingredients. Return chicken to pan; bring to a boil. Cover, reduce heat, and simmer 30 minutes or until chicken is done. Stir in remaining ¼ teaspoon pepper and parsley.

3. Meanwhile, bring remaining 1½ cups chicken broth to a boil in a medium saucepan; gradually stir in couscous. Remove from heat; cover and let stand 5 minutes. Fluff with a fork. Serve chicken and sauce over couscous. YIELD: 4 servings (serving size: 2 chicken thighs, about ¾ cup sauce, and ¾ cup couscous).

POINTS value: 8; Exchanges: 1½ Starch, 3 Vegetable, 4 Very Lean Meat, 1 Fat
Per serving: CAL 393 (21% from fat); PRO 40.4g; FAT 9.0g (sat 2.0g); CARB 36.6g; FIB 4.6g; CHOL 141mg; IRON 3.2mg; SOD 816mg; CALC 73mg

CHICKEN WITH MUSHROOMS AND ROSEMARY

prep: 8 minutes • cook: 54 minutes

Serve over polenta or rice. Trim the woody stems from the shiitake mushrooms before slicing the caps.

1   teaspoon olive oil
¼   teaspoon salt, divided
½   teaspoon black pepper, divided
6   chicken thighs (about 2 pounds), skinned
1½   cups vertically sliced onion (1 medium)
1   (6-ounce) package baby portobello mushrooms, sliced (about 3¼ cups)
1   (3.2-ounce) package fresh shiitake mushrooms, sliced (about 2¾ cups)
2   tablespoons all-purpose flour
2   cups fat-free, less-sodium chicken broth
¼   cup dry white wine or fat-free, less-sodium chicken broth
1   tablespoon chopped fresh rosemary

1. Preheat oven to 350°.
2. Heat oil in a large ovenproof Dutch oven over medium-high heat. Sprinkle ⅛ teaspoon salt and ¼ teaspoon pepper evenly over chicken. Add chicken to pan; cook 5 minutes on each side or until browned. Remove from pan; set aside. Add onion and mushrooms to pan, and sauté 5 minutes or until liquid evaporates. Add flour, and cook 1 minute, stirring constantly. Gradually stir in remaining ⅛ teaspoon salt, remaining ¼ teaspoon pepper, broth, wine, and rosemary. Bring to a boil, scraping pan to loosen browned bits. Return chicken to pan.
3. Cover and bake at 350° for 30 minutes or until chicken is done. Remove chicken from pan; keep warm. Place pan over medium-high heat; cook 7 minutes or until mushroom sauce is slightly thick, stirring occasionally. YIELD: 3 servings (serving size: 2 chicken thighs and about 1 cup sauce).

POINTS value: 5; Exchanges: 3 Vegetable, 4 Very Lean Meat, 1 Fat
Per serving: CAL 258 (25% from fat); PRO 32.4g; FAT 7.1g (sat 1.6g); CARB 15.1g; FIB 1.8g; CHOL 115mg; IRON 2.7mg; SOD 739mg; CALC 43mg

---

MUSHROOM KNOW-HOW

Store fresh mushrooms in a wicker basket lined with a paper towel. Then cover with a slightly dampened paper towel, and store in the fridge. Avoid the vegetable bin as well as plastic—high humidity is death for mushrooms. Most will hold well for 3 to 7 days.

GARLIC-HERB ROASTED CHICKEN WITH POTATOES, CARROTS, AND ONIONS

(pictured on page 110)
prep: 15 minutes • cook: 1 hour and 10 minutes • other: 10 minutes

1   (3½-pound) roasting chicken
1½ teaspoons chopped fresh rosemary, divided
1½ teaspoons chopped fresh sage, divided
1½ teaspoons chopped fresh thyme, divided
½   teaspoon salt, divided
½   teaspoon black pepper, divided
5   teaspoons extravirgin olive oil, divided
2   large garlic cloves, minced
Cooking spray
5   small red potatoes (about 12 ounces), cut into 1-inch cubes
3   large carrots, halved lengthwise and cut into 2-inch pieces (about 10 ounces)
1   large red onion, cut into 8 wedges
8   large garlic cloves, halved

1. Preheat oven to 450°.
2. Remove and discard giblets and neck from chicken. Rinse chicken under cold water; pat dry. Trim excess fat. Lift wings up and over back; tuck under chicken. Combine 1 teaspoon each of rosemary, sage, and thyme, ¼ teaspoon each of salt and pepper, 1 teaspoon oil, and minced garlic. Starting at neck cavity, loosen skin from breast and thighs by inserting fingers and gently pushing between skin and meat. Rub 1½ teaspoons herb mixture in body cavity. Rub half of remaining herb mixture under skin. Rub remaining herb mixture and 2 teaspoons oil evenly over skin. Tie ends of legs together with twine. Place chicken, breast side up, on a rack coated with cooking spray in a shallow roasting pan.
3. Bake at 450° for 15 minutes.
4. Meanwhile, combine potatoes, carrots, onion, and halved garlic cloves in a large bowl. Add remaining rosemary, sage, thyme, salt, pepper, and remaining oil; toss gently to coat. Add vegetables to roasting pan. Bake an additional 15 minutes. Stir vegetables. Reduce oven temperature to 375°. Bake 40 minutes or until a thermometer inserted in chicken thigh registers 180°. Let stand 10 minutes. Discard skin. Serve chicken with vegetables. YIELD: 4 servings (servings size: about 1 chicken quarter and 1 cup vegetables).

POINTS value: 10; **Exchanges:** 2 Starch, 3 Vegetable, 5 Very Lean Meat, 1½ Fat
Per serving: CAL 482 (22% from fat); PRO 46.5g; FAT 11.8g (sat 2.3g); CARB 45.6g; FIB 5.6g; CHOL 132mg; IRON 3.7mg; SOD 496mg; CALC 80mg

CURRIED CHUTNEY-GLAZED CORNISH HENS

prep: 5 minutes • cook: 30 minutes

Serve these Indian-inspired hens with basmati rice and wilted fresh spinach seasoned with garlic and crushed red pepper flakes.

2   (1¼-pound) Cornish hens
Cooking spray
⅓   cup mango chutney
2½ tablespoons lemon juice
1   teaspoon curry powder

1. Preheat oven to 475°.
2. Remove and discard giblets and necks from hens. Rinse hens with cold water; pat dry. Remove skin; trim excess fat. Split hens in half lengthwise. Place hen halves, meaty sides up, on a foil-lined jelly-roll pan coated with cooking spray.
3. Combine chutney, lemon juice, and curry powder in a small saucepan; bring to a boil over medium-low heat. Remove from heat. Brush half of glaze evenly over hen halves.
4. Bake at 475° for 27 to 30 minutes or until done, basting with remaining glaze after 15 minutes. YIELD: 4 servings (serving size: 1 hen half).
Note: Get the butcher to halve the Cornish hens while they're frozen, or once they're thawed, use kitchen shears to cut the hens in half.

POINTS value: 4; **Exchanges:** 1 Fruit, 3½ Very Lean Meat, ½ Fat
Per serving: CAL 205 (18% from fat); PRO 24.5g; FAT 4.1g (sat 1.1g); CARB 15.6g; FIB 0.2g; CHOL 111mg; IRON 1.3mg; SOD 417mg; CALC 18mg

CORNISH GAME HENS

Cornish game hens are one of the smallest members of the poultry family, and they weigh from 1 to 2 pounds. Cornish hens usually are sold frozen, and they must be thawed before cooking. Look for the smallest Cornish hens you can find; they'll be the most tender and have the best flavor.

HORSERADISH-TURKEY MEAT LOAF

prep: 15 minutes • cook: 55 minutes
other: 10 minutes

1   cup chopped onion
¼   cup quick-cooking oats
1   tablespoon prepared horseradish
1   tablespoon ketchup
2   teaspoons Worcestershire sauce
½   teaspoon salt
½   teaspoon dried oregano
½   teaspoon dried basil
¼   teaspoon black pepper
1   large egg
1   garlic clove, minced
1¼   pounds ground turkey (light
     and dark meat)
Cooking spray
⅓   cup ketchup
1   tablespoon brown sugar
1   teaspoon prepared horseradish

1. Preheat oven to 350°.
2. Combine first 11 ingredients in a large bowl. Crumble turkey over oats mixture, mixing with hands just until blended. Pack turkey mixture into an 8 x 4-inch loaf pan coated with cooking spray. Combine ⅓ cup ketchup, brown sugar, and 1 teaspoon horseradish in a bowl; stir well. Spread half of ketchup mixture over meat loaf. Bake at 350° for 45 minutes.
3. Spread remaining ketchup mixture over meat loaf, and bake an additional 10 minutes or until done. Let stand for 10 minutes. Remove meat loaf from pan; cut loaf into 5 slices. YIELD: 5 servings (serving size: 1 slice).

POINTS value: 5; **Exchanges:** 3 Vegetable, 3 Lean Meat
Per serving: CAL 239 (36% from fat); PRO 25.9g;
FAT 9.6g (sat 2.9g); CARB 14.5g; FIB 1.3g;
CHOL 113mg; IRON 2.0mg; SOD 578mg;
CALC 71mg

TURKEY MEATBALLS WITH PENNE

(pictured on back cover)
prep: 23 minutes • cook: 25 minutes

Pair these flavorful meatballs with any shape of pasta, or use them to make a meatball hoagie. Four meatballs and ⅓ cup sauce in a hoagie roll topped with 1 tablespoon shredded fresh Parmesan cheese has a **POINTS** *value of 10.*

½   cup dry breadcrumbs
¼   cup (1 ounce) grated fresh
     Parmesan cheese
¼   cup 1% low-fat milk
2   tablespoons chopped fresh
     parsley
1   teaspoon dried oregano
1   teaspoon dried basil
1   teaspoon black pepper
½   teaspoon salt
1   large egg, lightly beaten
1   garlic clove, minced
1   (14-ounce) can fat-free,
     less-sodium beef broth, divided
1⅓   pounds ground turkey
     (light and dark meat)
Cooking spray
3   cups uncooked penne pasta
     (about 10 ounces uncooked)
1   (26-ounce) jar tomato and basil
     pasta sauce
6   tablespoons (1½ ounces)
     shredded fresh Parmesan cheese

1. Preheat oven to 450°.
2. Combine first 10 ingredients in a large bowl. Add ¼ cup broth to mixture; stir well. Crumble turkey over breadcrumb mixture, mixing with hands just until blended. Shape mixture into 24 (1-inch) meatballs. Arrange meatballs in a single layer on a jelly-roll pan coated with cooking spray. Pour remaining beef broth into pan. Bake at 450° for 25 minutes or until done. Discard broth.
3. Meanwhile, cook pasta according to package directions, omitting salt and fat. Heat pasta sauce in a saucepan over medium-high heat until thoroughly heated. Serve meatballs and sauce over pasta. Sprinkle each serving with shredded Parmesan cheese. YIELD: 6 servings (serving size: about ¾ cup pasta, 4 meatballs, ⅓ cup sauce, and 1 tablespoon cheese).

POINTS value: 10; **Exchanges:** 3 Starch, 1½ Vegetable, 3 Lean Meat
Per serving: CAL 461 (25% from fat); PRO 33.8g; FAT 13.0g (sat 4.0g); CARB 52.2g; FIB 4.3g; CHOL 129mg; IRON 4.5mg; SOD 987mg; CALC 281mg

---

MEAT LOAF

When making meat loaf, place all of the ingredients except the ground turkey or beef in a large bowl, and then crumble the meat over the mixture. Use your hands to mix the seasoning into the meat. After baking, use an instant-read thermometer to register the temperature of the center of the meat loaf to check for doneness (160° for beef, 165° for turkey). Allow the meat loaf to stand at room temperature for 10 minutes before cutting to prevent the slices from falling apart.

ALMOND-CRUSTED TURKEY CUTLETS WITH PAPAYA-ORANGE SALSA

prep: 35 minutes • cook: 12 minutes

Bits of lightly toasted almonds form a crunchy coating on these tender cutlets. Insure a perfect coating every time by using medium-low heat to keep the delicate nuts from burning. Topped with a colorful fruit salsa, this entrée needs nothing more than a side of rice to complete the meal.

2   large navel oranges
1   cup diced papaya (about 1)
2   tablespoons chopped fresh cilantro
1   tablespoon minced seeded jalapeño pepper (about 1)
1   tablespoon diced red onion
1   teaspoon ground cumin, divided
¾   teaspoon salt, divided
½   cup sliced almonds, coarsely chopped
1½ pounds turkey breast cutlets
¼   teaspoon freshly ground black pepper
2   teaspoons olive oil
Cooking spray

1. Peel and section oranges over a bowl; squeeze membranes to extract juice. Place orange sections and ¼ cup juice in a medium bowl; reserve remaining juice for another use. Discard membranes. Break orange sections into small pieces with 2 forks. Add papaya, cilantro, jalapeño, onion, ¼ teaspoon cumin, and ¼ teaspoon salt; toss gently, and set aside.
2. Place almonds in a shallow dish. Sprinkle turkey cutlets with remaining ¾ teaspoon cumin, remaining

½ teaspoon salt, and black pepper. Press both sides of each cutlet into the almonds to coat.
3. Heat oil in a large nonstick skillet coated with cooking spray over medium-low heat. Add cutlets, and cook 6 minutes on each side or until turkey is done. Serve with salsa. YIELD: 4 servings (serving size: 5 ounces turkey and ½ cup salsa).

POINTS value: 7; **Exchanges:** ½ Fruit, 1½ Vegetable, 6 Very Lean Meat, 1 Fat
Per serving: CAL 324 (26% from fat); PRO 45.5g; FAT 9.3g (sat 0.8g); CARB 15.2g; FIB 3.6g; CHOL 68mg; IRON 2.6mg; SOD 596mg; CALC 77mg

TURKEY CUTLETS WITH CILANTRO-ROASTED RED PEPPER SAUCE

prep: 29 minutes • cook: 32 minutes

4   teaspoons olive oil, divided
½   cup chopped onion
1¼ teaspoons chili powder, divided
2   garlic cloves, chopped
¼   cup fat-free, less-sodium chicken broth
½   cup chopped bottled roasted red bell pepper
½   cup chopped tomato
¾   teaspoon salt, divided
¼   cup chopped fresh cilantro, divided
2   teaspoons fresh lime juice
1½ pounds turkey breast cutlets
½   cup dry breadcrumbs
Cooking spray
½   cup (2 ounces) shredded reduced-fat Monterey Jack cheese

1. Heat 1 teaspoon oil in a large saucepan over medium heat. Add

onion; sauté 5 minutes or until tender. Add ½ teaspoon chili powder and garlic; sauté 1 minute. Add chicken broth, bell pepper, tomato, and ¼ teaspoon salt; bring to a boil. Cover, reduce heat, and simmer 5 minutes or until vegetables are tender. Place vegetable mixture in a food processor; process until smooth. Add 2 tablespoons cilantro and lime juice; pulse until well blended.
2. Preheat broiler.
3. Sprinkle remaining ½ teaspoon salt and remaining ¾ teaspoon chili powder evenly over both sides of cutlets. Place remaining 2 tablespoons cilantro and breadcrumbs in a shallow dish; dredge turkey in breadcrumb mixture, pressing to coat.
4. Heat remaining 1 tablespoon oil in a large nonstick skillet coated with cooking spray over medium heat. Add turkey; cook 5 minutes on each side. Cover and cook 6 minutes or until done. Sprinkle cheese evenly over turkey cutlets; cover and cook 1 minute or until cheese melts. Place turkey on serving plates; spoon sauce evenly over turkey. YIELD: 4 servings (serving size: 5 ounces turkey and ¼ cup sauce).

POINTS value: 7; **Exchanges:** 2 Vegetable, 6 Very Lean Meat, 1 Fat
Per serving: CAL 313 (26% from fat); PRO 47.3g; FAT 8.9g (sat 2.7g); CARB 10.9g; FIB 1.2g; CHOL 78mg; IRON 2.8mg; SOD 876mg; CALC 127mg

POLENTA WITH SAUSAGE AND MUSHROOM SAUCE

prep: 12 minutes • cook: 31 minutes

You get double duty out of this recipe—enough sauce for now and later. Use 3 cups of sauce for this recipe; then serve the remaining 3 cups over pasta another night, or freeze it to serve over polenta later in the month. A ¾-cup serving of sauce has a POINTS value of 3.

1   pound Italian turkey sausage
1½   cups chopped red bell pepper
1   cup chopped onion (about 1 medium)
1   (8-ounce) package sliced mushrooms
2   garlic cloves, minced
½   cup water
⅓   cup sliced sun-dried tomatoes, packed without oil
1   (28-ounce) can crushed tomatoes, undrained
1   teaspoon dried Italian seasoning
½   teaspoon freshly ground black pepper
1   (17-ounce) tube refrigerated prepared polenta, cut into 8 slices
     Cooking spray
1   tablespoon grated fresh Parmesan cheese

1. Remove casings from sausage. Cook sausage in a Dutch oven over medium-high heat until browned, stirring to crumble. Add bell pepper and onion; cook 3 minutes or until tender, stirring occasionally. Add mushrooms and garlic; cook 5 minutes or until vegetables are tender, stirring occasionally. Stir in water, sun-dried tomatoes, and crushed tomatoes; bring to a boil. Cover, reduce heat, and simmer 10 minutes. Add Italian seasoning and black pepper; simmer 5 minutes.

2. Meanwhile, heat a large nonstick skillet over medium-high heat. Coat polenta slices with cooking spray; add to pan. Cook 4 to 5 minutes on each side or until browned.

3. Place 2 polenta slices on each of 4 plates; top each with ¾ cup sauce and ¾ teaspoon cheese. YIELD: 4 servings.

POINTS value: 5; Exchanges: 1 Starch, 3 Vegetable, 1 Medium-Fat Meat
Per serving: CAL 240 (24% from fat); PRO 16.0g; FAT 6.3g (sat 1.9g); CARB 29.8g; FIB 5.2g; CHOL 49mg; IRON 3.1mg; SOD 828mg; CALC 65mg

PENNE WITH SAUSAGE, PEPPERS, AND TOMATOES

prep 5 minutes • cook 13 minutes

6   ounces penne (tubular pasta), uncooked
     Cooking spray
8   ounces sweet Italian turkey sausage, cut into ½-inch slices (about 2 sausages)
3   garlic cloves, minced
1   (14½-ounce) can no-salt-added whole tomatoes, undrained and chopped
1   (7-ounce) bottle roasted red bell peppers, drained and diced
½   teaspoon ground black pepper
¼   cup grated Parmesan cheese

1. Cook pasta according to package directions, omitting salt and fat; drain and keep warm.

2. Heat a large nonstick skillet coated with cooking spray over medium heat until hot. Add sausage, and cook 8 to 10 minutes or until browned, stirring often; drain well. Set sausage aside. Wipe drippings from pan with a paper towel.

3. Coat pan with cooking spray; add garlic, and sauté 1 minute. Add sausage and tomato. Bring to a boil; reduce heat, and simmer until most of liquid is evaporated. Stir in roasted bell peppers and ground black pepper. Remove from heat.

4. Place pasta in a large bowl; add sausage mixture, and toss. Spoon evenly onto serving plates, and sprinkle with cheese. YIELD: 4 servings (serving size: 1½ cups pasta and 1 tablespoon cheese).

POINTS value: 6; Exchanges: 2 Starch, 2 Vegetable, 1 Medium-Fat Meat
Per serving: CAL 298 (23% from fat); PRO 18.9g; FAT 7.5g (sat 2.7g); CARB 38.9g; FIB 2.5g; CHOL 52mg; IRON 2.6mg; SOD 627mg; CALC 99mg

Reducing the Rebel

JEAN BERRIDGE • **HEIGHT** 5'6" • **BEFORE** 256 LBS. • **AFTER** 150 LBS.

Tip: "Starting with one small change was a big step in the right direction."

Jean Berridge doesn't look much like a rebel. But when it came to losing weight, she was quite defiant. "Change is hard for me, so taking the first step was difficult. Although I usually embraced structure and organization, I didn't want to journal, read pamphlets, plan meals, re-create recipes, or weigh and measure food," she admits. "I guess I wanted it handed to me on a silver platter."

But Jean's health and her new doctor demanded change. "My previous doctor told me that I had borderline diabetes. My new doctor disagreed. He said that there was no such thing as borderline diabetes and that I had to take this seriously because it would damage my heart." He then prescribed diabetes medication and diabetic classes.

"After losing 106 pounds, I am almost half the person I was when I started Weight Watchers."

Jean attended the classes and had a consultation with a nutritionist and diabetic educator. Yet discussions about finger sticks and the dangers of diabetes overwhelmed her. "I told my educator how I felt, and she recommended *Weight Watchers*."

Unlike many women, Jean had never tried to lose weight. "I never tried to diet because I was afraid that I would fail. So I just kept gaining," she says. At her first *Weight Watchers* weigh-in, she was 100 pounds too heavy. "But I decided not to make all the changes at once and just do what I could handle, one step at time," she says. "I began by using Splenda®, and then I added other changes. Although I lost weight slowly, *Weight Watchers* teaches that slow loss is better because it stays off. Starting with one small change was a big step in the right direction."

Fortunately, Jean already had an exercise program, which also helped her to lose and maintain her weight. And slimming down helped her to pick up the pace. "I walk and jog three miles, six days a week, so I am now usually the fastest person on the track instead of the slowest," she says.

Although it took Jean one and one-half years to reach her goal, she looks and feels like a different person. "And in some ways, I am. After losing 106 pounds, I am almost half the person I was when I started *Weight Watchers*."

Achieving Lifetime, Jean is no longer rebellious. She still journals and attends weekly meetings. "I embraced the changes and made them a permanent part of my life. I am still learning about myself and will have to be constantly vigilant to maintain what I have achieved."

Garlic-Herb Roasted Chicken
with Potatoes, Carrots,
and Onions,
page 105

Tabbouleh,
page 121

Rosemary-Feta Chicken with
Cherry Tomato-Olive Sauce,
page 101

Caribbean Grilled Chicken Salad
with Honey-Lime Dressing,
page 124

Thai Chicken and Noodles,
page 96

Spicy Corn Salad,
page 121

115

Craving Apples

ROBERT SHUELL • **HEIGHT** 5'9" • **BEFORE** 278 LBS. • **AFTER** 174 LBS.

Tip: "Eating real, whole foods makes the junk-food cravings disappear."

At 278 pounds, officer Robert Shuell struggled to perform his duties with the New York Police Department (NYPD). "I always had a tendency to gain weight, but after TWA Flight 800 and September 11, 2001, my weight soared. Some people reach for a cigarette to deal with stress. I reached for food and ate for comfort."

Robert's comfort eating eventually left him 100 pounds overweight and with high blood pressure. That's when his doctor recommended *Weight Watchers*. "She was a doctor with a tiny waist, so I took her recommendation seriously and decided to give *Weight Watchers* an honest 100 percent try."

Yet Robert's "100 percent try" included an out. "Maybe I would just go to weigh and not stay for the meetings," he thought. "When I arrived and didn't see many guys in the group, it was intimidating. But once I saw the quality of the meetings, I stayed." And he advises others to do the same.

Robert also found the importance of having an inspirational *Weight Watchers* leader. Jenn McTigue coached Robert down 60 pounds by changing his food philosophy from quantity to quality. On top of that, Robert's blood pressure dropped to normal.

"Now I crave healthy foods rather than chemicals. The more processed a food gets, the progressively worse it is." Robert tries to grocery shop daily for the freshest ingredients, and he cooks most of his meals. "I buy around the perimeter of the grocery store. There is nothing in the middle aisles for me."

"Eating real, whole foods makes the junk-food cravings disappear. I now crave apples! If you start binging on ice cream, you can quickly take in 2,000 calories. Try to do that with apples," he laughs.

After Jenn relocated to another city, Robert found a new leader who stressed physical activity. "I purchased a treadmill, started walking, and logged the mileage. And after losing 70 pounds, I realized that I had walked 1,100 miles—enough to go from New York to Florida," he says.

Now down 104 pounds, this "Big Apple" officer is entertained by people's reactions to the "new" Robert. "I work different bases around the city, so I don't see some officers for up to a year.

> *"I buy around the perimeter of the grocery store. There is nothing in the middle aisles for me."*

Recently I walked into a unit, still dressed in my street clothes, and went behind the desk to check the schedule for the day. An officer I work with there started yelling, 'What are you doing? Who are you?' without realizing it was me." But he just laughs at these mistaken identity experiences because Robert has never felt more like himself.

Weight-loss results not typical.

116

Salads

VANILLA BEAN-FRUIT SALAD

**prep: 2 minutes • cook: 11 minutes
other: 30 minutes**

Save time by making the simple syrup first. While it cools, you'll have plenty of time to wash and cut the fruit.

½   cup water
⅓   cup sugar
1   (6-inch) vanilla bean, split lengthwise
2   cups seedless green grapes, halved
1   cup fresh blueberries
1   cup sliced fresh strawberries
1   cup fresh raspberries

1. Combine water and sugar in small saucepan. Scrape seeds from vanilla bean; stir seeds into sugar-water. Bring to a boil; reduce heat and simmer 11 minutes or until reduced to ½ cup, stirring occasionally. Remove from heat; cool completely.
2. While syrup cools, combine fruit in a medium bowl. Pour cooled syrup over fruit, tossing gently to coat fruit. YIELD: 4 servings (serving size: 1 cup).

POINTS value: 3; **Exchanges:** 3 Fruit
Per serving: CAL 179 (3% from fat); PRO 1.5g;
FAT 0.6g (sat 0.1g); CARB 43.7g; FIB 4.4g;
CHOL 0mg; IRON 0.8mg; SOD 3mg;
CALC 25mg

CRANBERRY, PECAN, AND PEAR SALAD

**prep: 8 minutes • cook: 5 minutes
other: 10 minutes**

Transform this salad into an entrée by adding grilled salmon or chicken.

⅓   cup sweetened dried cranberries
3   tablespoons balsamic vinegar
2   tablespoons fat-free, less-sodium chicken broth
2   teaspoons sugar
1   teaspoon Dijon mustard
¼   teaspoon salt
⅛   teaspoon black pepper
¼   cup olive oil
12   cups mixed salad greens
½   cup sweetened dried cranberries
2   Bartlett pears, cored and sliced
⅓   cup chopped pecans, toasted

1. Place ⅓ cup cranberries in a small bowl; cover with warm water. Let stand 10 minutes or until cranberries plump; drain well.
2. Place plump cranberries and next 6 ingredients in a food processor; process until smooth. With processor on, slowly add oil through food chute; process until blended.
3. Divide salad greens evenly among 6 plates. Sprinkle ½ cup dried cranberries evenly over salads; top evenly with pear slices and pecans. Drizzle 1½ tablespoons dressing over each salad. Serve immediately. YIELD: 6 servings.

POINTS value: 5; **Exchanges:** 1 Fruit, 2½ Vegetable, 3 Fat
Per serving: CAL 240 (54% from fat); PRO 2.8g;
FAT 14.4g (sat 1.7g); CARB 29.3g; FIB 5.7g;
CHOL 0mg; IRON 1.9mg; SOD 162mg;
CALC 75mg

ICEBERG WEDGE SALAD

prep: 7 minutes • other: 1 hour

Although serving the creamy dressing over a wedge of iceberg lettuce makes for a stylish presentation, you can serve it over any type of salad. Double the dressing recipe if you'd like, and store it up to 1 week in your refrigerator.

½   cup low-fat buttermilk
¼   cup minced green onions
2   tablespoons light mayonnaise
2   tablespoons low-fat sour cream
½   teaspoon salt
½   teaspoon coarsely ground black pepper
1   garlic clove, minced
½   head iceberg lettuce, cut into 4 wedges
¼   cup (1 ounce) crumbled blue cheese
Coarsely ground black pepper

1. Combine first 7 ingredients in a small bowl; stir with a whisk. Cover and chill at least 1 hour.
2. Spoon dressing over lettuce wedges, and sprinkle with blue cheese and black pepper. YIELD: 4 servings (serving size: 1 lettuce wedge, ¼ cup dressing, and 1 tablespoon blue cheese).

POINTS value: 2; **Exchanges:** 1 Vegetable, 1½ Fat
Per serving: CAL 93 (57% from fat); PRO 3.9g;
FAT 5.8g (sat 2.6g); CARB 6.0g; FIB 1.1g;
CHOL 13mg; IRON 0.3mg; SOD 526mg;
CALC 112mg

WARM FALL SPINACH SALAD

prep: 3 minutes • cook: 13 minutes

2   thick-cut, hickory-smoked bacon slices
2   tablespoons minced shallots (about 1 medium)
⅓   cup sweetened dried cranberries
¼   cup cider vinegar
¼   cup fat-free, less-sodium chicken broth
1   tablespoon extravirgin olive oil
1   teaspoon light brown sugar
1   (6-ounce) package fresh baby spinach
¼   cup chopped pecans, toasted

1. Cook bacon in a nonstick skillet over medium heat until crisp. Remove bacon from pan; drain on paper towels. Discard drippings (do not wipe pan clean). Add shallots to pan; sauté over medium heat 1 minute or until lightly browned. Add cranberries, vinegar, and broth; bring to a simmer, and cook 4 minutes, scraping pan to loosen browned bits. Remove from heat; stir in oil and brown sugar.
2. Place 1½ cups spinach on each of 4 plates; drizzle ¼ cup warm dressing over each salad. Crumble bacon, and sprinkle evenly over salads; top each salad with 1 table-spoon pecans. YIELD: 4 servings.

POINTS value: 4; **Exchanges:** ½ Fruit, 1 Vegetable, 2 Fat
Per serving: CAL 158 (63% from fat); PRO 3.2g; FAT 11.1g (sat 2.0g); CARB 13.4g; FIB 1.7g; CHOL 5mg; IRON 1.6mg; SOD 199mg; CALC 52mg

CREAMY VEGGIE SLAW

prep: 7 minutes

To quickly thaw frozen peas and corn, place in a colander, and run under cold water for 15 seconds or until completely thawed. Shake off excess water, and drain on a paper towel.

2   cups packaged cabbage-and-carrot coleslaw
½   cup thinly sliced celery (about 2 stalks)
½   cup frozen petite green peas, thawed
½   cup frozen whole-kernel corn, thawed
¼   cup light mayonnaise
½   teaspoon salt
½   teaspoon sugar
¼   teaspoon black pepper

1. Combine first 4 ingredients in a large bowl. Combine mayonnaise and next 3 ingredients. Add to cabbage mixture; toss gently to coat. Serve immediately, or cover and chill up to 2 hours. YIELD: 4 servings (serving size: about ½ cup).

POINTS value: 2; **Exchanges:** 2½ Vegetable, 1 Fat
Per serving: CAL 103 (47% from fat); PRO 2.3g; FAT 5.3g (sat 1.1g); CARB 12.7g; FIB 2.5g; CHOL 5mg; IRON 0.8mg; SOD 463mg; CALC 30mg

QUICK COLESLAW

prep: 3 minutes • other: 1 hour

Talk about fast food! You can prepare this side salad in less than 5 minutes. Then chill it while you make the rest of your meal. Fennel seeds add a distinctive licorice flavor to an otherwise basic slaw. The seeds may be omitted, if desired.

1   (16-ounce) package cabbage-and-carrot coleslaw
⅓   cup light mayonnaise
3   tablespoons red wine vinegar
1   teaspoon sugar
½   teaspoon salt
1   teaspoon fennel seeds

1. Place coleslaw in a serving bowl. Combine mayonnaise and next 3 ingredients in a small bowl, stirring well with a whisk. Spoon dressing over coleslaw, and toss well. Sprinkle with fennel seeds. Cover and chill at least 1 hour. YIELD: 4 servings (serving size: 1 cup).

POINTS value: 2; **Exchanges:** 2 Vegetable, 1 Fat
Per serving: CAL 105 (59% from fat); PRO 1.6g; FAT 6.9g (sat 1.4g); CARB 10.2g; FIB 1.1g; CHOL 7mg; IRON 0.8mg; SOD 487mg; CALC 56mg

TANGY CARROT AND BELL PEPPER SALAD

prep: 4 minutes • cook: 7 minutes
other: 1 hour

Fresh dill really brings out the sweetness of the carrots in this eye-catching salad.

2   cups thinly sliced carrots
    (about 3 large)
¼   cup rice vinegar
1   tablespoon sugar
1   tablespoon canola oil
1   teaspoon Dijon mustard
¼   teaspoon salt
1   garlic clove, minced
1   cup thinly sliced red onion
    (about 1 small)
¼   cup chopped fresh dill
1   large red bell pepper, cut into
    thin strips

1. Cook carrots in boiling water 2 minutes or until crisp-tender.
2. While carrots cook, combine vinegar and next 5 ingredients in a medium bowl, and stir well. Drain carrots.
3. Add carrots, onion, dill, and bell pepper to bowl; toss gently to coat. Cover and chill at least 1 hour. YIELD: 5 servings (serving size: ¾ cup).

POINTS value: 2; **Exchanges:** 2½ Vegetable, 1 Fat
Per serving: CAL 81 (35% from fat); PRO 1.1g;
FAT 3.1g (sat 0.2g); CARB 13.3g; FIB 1.8g;
CHOL 0mg; IRON 0.5mg; SOD 178mg;
CALC 27mg

AVOCADO SALAD

prep: 10 minutes

Serve this salad with grilled chicken or pork or as a chunky Southwestern dip.

1   ripe avocado, seeded and diced
½   cup diced English cucumber
½   cup quartered grape or cherry
    tomatoes
2   tablespoons chopped onion
2   tablespoons fresh lime juice
2   teaspoons olive oil
¼   teaspoon ground cumin
¼   teaspoon chili powder
¼   teaspoon freshly ground black
    pepper
⅛   teaspoon salt

1. Combine all ingredients in a medium bowl, tossing gently. Serve at room temperature or chilled. YIELD: 4 servings (serving size: ½ cup).

POINTS value: 2; **Exchanges:** 1 Vegetable, 2 Fat
Per serving: CAL 112 (81% from fat); PRO 1.4g;
FAT 10.1g (sat 1.6g); CARB 6.4g; FIB 3.1g;
CHOL 0mg; IRON 0.7mg; SOD 82mg;
CALC 12mg

SEEDLESS CUCUMBERS

English (or seedless) cucumbers are usually twice the size of regular cucumbers and contain not only fewer seeds but also less water. They're also milder than regular cucumbers and usually more expensive.

WARM FRENCH POTATO SALAD

prep: 16 minutes • cook: 16 minutes

Dressing the potatoes while warm helps them to soak up the tangy vinaigrette. A sprinkle of fresh herbs adds color and flavor.

11 medium red potatoes
    (about 1½ pounds)
3   tablespoons extravirgin
    olive oil
1   tablespoon finely chopped
    shallots
1   tablespoon white wine vinegar
1   teaspoon Dijon mustard
½   teaspoon salt
¼   teaspoon freshly ground black
    pepper
3   tablespoons chopped fresh
    parsley
2   tablespoons chopped fresh
    chives
1   tablespoon chopped fresh
    tarragon

1. Cut each potato in half lengthwise; quarter each potato half. Steam potatoes, covered, 13 to 15 minutes or until tender.
2. While potatoes cook, combine oil and next 5 ingredients in a large bowl; stir well. Drain potatoes. Add warm potatoes to bowl; toss gently to coat. Sprinkle with parsley, chives, and tarragon just before serving. Serve warm or at room temperature. YIELD: 6 servings (serving size: about ¾ cup).

POINTS value: 3; **Exchanges:** 1 Starch, 1 Vegetable, 1 Fat
Per serving: CAL 149 (44% from fat); PRO 2.4g;
FAT 7.3g (sat 1.0g); CARB 18.7g; FIB 2.1g;
CHOL 0mg; IRON 1.0mg; SOD 223mg;
CALC 19mg

SPICY CORN SALAD

(pictured on page 115)
prep: 19 minutes • **other:** 10 minutes

The heat of the poblano and jalapeño peppers in this recipe will add a zesty kick to any fiesta.

1   ripe avocado, seeded and diced
2   cups grape or cherry tomatoes, halved
1   cup frozen whole-kernel corn, thawed
½   cup chopped fresh cilantro
¼   cup finely chopped red onion
¾   teaspoon salt
1   (2.25-ounce) can sliced ripe olives, drained
1   poblano chile, chopped
1   jalapeño pepper, seeded and minced
3   tablespoons cider vinegar
1   teaspoon grated lime rind
2   tablespoons fresh lime juice
Curly leaf lettuce leaves (optional)

1. Combine first 9 ingredients in a large bowl; toss gently.
2. Combine vinegar, lime rind, and juice. Drizzle over salad; toss gently to coat. Let stand 10 minutes. Serve salad in lettuce-lined bowls, if desired.
YIELD: 6 servings (serving size: ¾ cup).

POINTS value: 2; **Exchanges:** 3 Vegetable, 1 Fat
Per serving: CAL 115 (54% from fat); PRO 2.5g; FAT 6.9g (sat 1.1g); CARB 14.4g; FIB 4.0g; CHOL 0mg; IRON 1.5mg; SOD 394mg; CALC 23mg

BARLEY-VEGETABLE SALAD

prep: 20 minutes • **cook:** 52 minutes

Rinsing the barley under cold water removes excess starch so the grains won't be sticky, and it cools the barley quickly so the salad can be tossed together. This salad makes a perfect accompaniment to grilled salmon.

⅔   cup uncooked pearl barley
1   cup frozen petite green peas, thawed
2   tablespoons finely shredded carrot
1   (8-ounce) package sliced mushrooms
¼   cup fresh lemon juice
2   tablespoons diced red onion
1   tablespoon chopped fresh parsley
1   tablespoon chopped fresh mint
2   tablespoons extravirgin olive oil
¼   teaspoon salt
¼   teaspoon freshly ground black pepper

1. Prepare barley according to package directions, omitting salt and fat. Rinse barley with cold water; drain. Combine barley, peas, carrot, and mushrooms in a medium bowl.
2. Combine lemon juice and next 6 ingredients in a small bowl; stir well with a whisk. Pour dressing over salad; toss gently to coat. **YIELD:** 5 servings (serving size: 1 cup).

POINTS value: 3; **Exchanges:** 1 Starch, 2½ Vegetable, 1 Fat
Per serving: CAL 185 (30% from fat); PRO 5.3g; FAT 6.2g (sat 0.9g); CARB 28.7g; FIB 6.0g; CHOL 0mg; IRON 1.8mg; SOD 155mg; CALC 21mg

TABBOULEH

(pictured on page 111)
prep: 34 minutes • **other:** 1 hour

A combination of cilantro and parsley adds interest to this Middle Eastern herb and bulgur salad. If you don't have cilantro on hand, you can double the parsley.

½   cup uncooked bulgur
½   cup boiling water
1   cup chopped tomato (about 2 medium)
¾   cup finely chopped fresh parsley (about 1 bunch)
¾   cup finely chopped fresh cilantro (about 1 bunch)
⅔   cup chopped seeded cucumber
½   cup chopped green onions
¼   cup finely chopped fresh mint
3   tablespoons fresh lemon juice
2   tablespoons extravirgin olive oil
½   teaspoon salt
⅛   teaspoon freshly ground black pepper
Pepperoncini peppers (optional)
Kalamata olives (optional)

1. Combine bulgur and boiling water in a medium bowl. Cover and let stand 30 minutes. Add tomato and next 9 ingredients; stir well. Cover and let stand at room temperature 30 minutes before serving. Garnish with pepperoncini peppers and olives, if desired. **YIELD:** 4 servings (serving size: 1½ cups).

POINTS value: 3; **Exchanges:** 1 Starch, 1 Vegetable, 1 Fat
Per serving: CAL 147 (46% from fat); PRO 3.2g; FAT 7.5g (sat 1.1g); CARB 18.6g; FIB 5.0g; CHOL 0mg; IRON 1.5mg; SOD 307mg; CALC 37mg

ORZO WITH BLACK BEANS AND ASPARAGUS SALAD

prep: 12 minutes • cook: 15 minutes

1   cup uncooked orzo
     (rice-shaped pasta)
1½ cups (1-inch) diagonally cut
     asparagus
1½ cups chopped seeded tomato
1   cup rinsed and drained canned
     black beans
2   tablespoons minced fresh
     cilantro
2   tablespoons balsamic vinegar
1   tablespoon extravirgin
     olive oil
¼   teaspoon salt
⅛   teaspoon black pepper
1   garlic clove, crushed
¼   cup (1 ounce) shredded
     reduced-fat Cheddar cheese

1. Cook orzo according to package
directions, omitting salt and fat.
2. While orzo cooks, steam asparagus, covered, 2 minutes or until
crisp-tender. Rinse asparagus with
cold water; drain well, and pat dry
with paper towels.
3. Drain orzo, reserving 2 tablespoons cooking liquid. Combine
orzo, asparagus, tomato, beans, and
cilantro in a large bowl. Combine
reserved 2 tablespoons cooking liquid, vinegar, oil, and next 3 ingredients in a small bowl; stir with a
whisk. Pour dressing over salad; toss
gently. Sprinkle with cheese. YIELD:
6 servings (serving size: 1 cup).

POINTS value: 3; **Exchanges:** 1 Starch, 3 Vegetable,
½ Fat
Per serving: CAL 177 (20% from fat); PRO 7.7g;
FAT 3.9g (sat 1.1g); CARB 30.4g; FIB 3.3g;
CHOL 3mg; IRON 2.3mg; SOD 173mg; CALC 66mg

COCONUT-SHRIMP SALAD WITH CILANTRO-LIME VINAIGRETTE

prep: 8 minutes • cook: 9 minutes
other: 1 hour

¼   cup fresh lime juice
2   tablespoons chopped fresh
     cilantro
3   tablespoons extravirgin olive oil
1   teaspoon sugar
2   teaspoons honey
½   teaspoon salt
½   teaspoon crushed red pepper
16   jumbo shrimp (1¼ pounds)
1½ cups chopped tomato
1   cup chopped peeled ripe
     avocado
¾   cup chopped peeled mango
½   cup vertically sliced red onion
Cooking spray
1   (5-ounce) package spring mix
     salad greens
½   cup flaked sweetened coconut,
     toasted

1. Combine first 7 ingredients in a
small bowl; stir well with a whisk.
2. Peel shrimp, leaving tails intact.
Devein shrimp, if desired. Combine
shrimp and ¼ cup vinaigrette in an
11 x 7-inch baking dish, stirring to
coat. Cover and chill 1 hour.
3. While shrimp chill, combine
remaining ¼ cup vinaigrette, tomato,
and next 3 ingredients in a bowl,
tossing gently to coat.
4. Prepare grill.
5. Remove shrimp from dish;
discard marinade. Thread 4 shrimp
onto each of 4 (10-inch) skewers.
Place skewers on grill rack coated
with cooking spray; grill 2 to 3
minutes on each side or until shrimp
are done.

6. Place 1 cup salad greens on each
of 4 plates; top each salad with about
1 cup tomato mixture and 1 shrimp
skewer. Sprinkle each salad with 2
tablespoons toasted coconut. YIELD:
4 servings.
Note: If using wooden skewers, soak
in water 30 minutes before grilling.

POINTS value: 7; **Exchanges:** ½ Fruit, 3 Vegetable,
1 Lean Meat, 3 Fat
Per serving: CAL 295 (61% from fat); PRO 8.4g;
FAT 20.1g (sat 5.2g); CARB 23.9g; FIB 4.8g;
CHOL 43mg; IRON 2.0mg; SOD 374mg;
CALC 56mg

ASIAN BEEF SALAD WITH HOISIN DRESSING

prep: 12 minutes • cook: 10 minutes
other: 6 hours

½   cup hoisin sauce
2   tablespoons fresh lime juice
2   tablespoons low-sodium soy
     sauce
2   teaspoons grated peeled fresh
     ginger
1   pound flank steak, trimmed
Cooking spray
1   (6-ounce) package fresh baby
     spinach
1   large cucumber, peeled, halved
     lengthwise, and thinly sliced
     (about 2 cups)
1   yellow bell pepper, cut into
     ½-inch strips (about 1½ cups)
4   thinly sliced radishes (about
     ½ cup)
⅓   cup thinly sliced red onion

1. Combine first 4 ingredients in a
small bowl; stir well. Place steak and
¼ cup hoisin sauce mixture in a
large zip-top plastic bag; seal bag,
and marinate in refrigerator 6 hours,

turning bag occasionally. Cover
remaining ½ cup hoisin sauce mixture,
and refrigerate while steak marinates.

2. Preheat broiler.

3. Remove steak from bag; discard
marinade. Place steak on a broiler
pan coated with cooking spray. Broil
5 minutes on each side or until
desired degree of doneness. Let steak
stand 5 minutes.

4. While steak stands, combine
spinach and next 4 ingredients in a
large bowl. Drizzle with ¼ cup
reserved hoisin sauce mixture; toss
gently to coat. Cut steak diagonally
across grain into thin slices.

5. Place 2½ cups salad on each of 4
plates; divide steak evenly among
salads. Drizzle 1 tablespoon hoisin
sauce mixture over each salad. YIELD:
4 servings.

POINTS value: 5; **Exchanges:** 1 Starch, 1 Vegetable,
3 Lean Meat
Per serving: CAL 254 (28% from fat); PRO 26.1g;
FAT 8.0g (sat 3.0g); CARB 19.7g; FIB 2.2g;
CHOL 45mg; IRON 3.5mg; SOD 708mg;
CALC 84mg

ASIAN NOODLES

Asian noodles vary in width.
They can be as thin as tooth-
picks or as wide as your thumb.
Regardless of width, they are
usually served long and uncut
because in Chinese culture long
noodles symbolize a long life.
And because Asian noodles are
made with hearty ingredients
such as buckwheat flour and
rice, they can handle strong
flavors such as soy sauce,
cilantro, and ginger.

THAI NOODLE CHICKEN SALAD

prep: 35 minutes

1   (6-ounce) package rice sticks
    (rice-flour noodles)
1   large cucumber
2   (6-ounce) packages oven-roasted
    chicken breast cuts (such as
    Louis Rich)
5   cups torn romaine lettuce
1½ cups thin red bell pepper strips
⅓   cup thinly sliced green onions
¼   cup chopped fresh basil
¼   cup fresh lime juice
1   tablespoon light brown sugar
2   tablespoons dark sesame oil
1   tablespoon hot chili sauce (such
    as Sriracha)
4   teaspoons chopped dry-roasted
    cashews or peanuts

1. Prepare noodles according to
package directions.

2. While noodles stand, peel cucumber, and quarter lengthwise; discard
seeds. Thinly slice cucumber.

3. Drain noodles, and place in a
large bowl. Add cucumber, chicken,
lettuce, bell pepper, and green
onions; toss gently.

4. Combine basil and next 4 ingredients in a small bowl; stir well.
Pour dressing over salad; toss well.
Sprinkle each serving with nuts.
Serve immediately. YIELD: 4 servings
(serving size: 2 cups salad and 1 teaspoon nuts).

POINTS value: 8; **Exchanges:** 2 Starch, 4 Vegetable,
1½ Lean Meat, 1 Fat
Per serving: CAL 388 (27% from fat); PRO 24.7g;
FAT 11.7g (sat 2.3g); CARB 50.1g; FIB 3.3g;
CHOL 56mg; IRON 2.9mg; SOD 815mg;
CALC 46mg

GENERAL'S CHINESE CHICKEN SALAD

prep: 25 minutes • cook: 8 minutes

*Uncooked ramen noodles are sprinkled
over this salad for extra crunch.*

¼   cup red wine vinegar
¼   cup low-sodium soy sauce
3   tablespoons minced green
    onions
1   tablespoon minced peeled fresh
    ginger
1   tablespoon hoisin sauce
1   tablespoon dark sesame oil
2   teaspoons honey
1   (3-ounce) package ramen
    noodles
6   cups shredded iceberg lettuce
2   cups shredded cooked chicken
    breast
1   cup shredded carrot (about
    2 medium)
¼   cup slivered almonds, toasted

1. Combine first 7 ingredients in a
small bowl; stir well with a whisk.

2. Discard seasoning packet from
noodles. Break uncooked noodles
into small pieces.

3. Place 1½ cups lettuce on each
of 4 serving plates; top each with
½ cup chicken and ¼ cup shredded
carrot. Divide ramen noodles evenly
over each salad; top each with 1
tablespoon almonds. Spoon 2½
tablespoons dressing evenly over
each salad just before serving.
YIELD: 4 servings.

POINTS value: 7; **Exchanges:** 1 Starch, 3 Vegetable,
2½ Lean Meat, 1 Fat
Per serving: CAL 345 (35% from fat); PRO 27.0g;
FAT 13.4g (sat 2.3g); CARB 30.0g; FIB 4.8g;
CHOL 62mg; IRON 1.7mg; SOD 780mg;
CALC 46mg

SMOKED CHICKEN SAUSAGE AND SUN-DRIED TOMATO PASTA SALAD

prep: 12 minutes • cook: 22 minutes

For simple family meals, toss the salad in the same pot that was used to cook the pasta, and you'll have one less bowl to wash. Feel free to substitute any shaped pasta you have on hand.

1½ cups uncooked penne pasta
Cooking spray
1 (12-ounce) package smoked chicken sausage with sun-dried yellow tomatoes and roasted garlic (such as Gerhard's), thinly sliced
½ cup (2 ounces) shredded part-skim mozzarella cheese
½ cup vertically sliced red onion
½ cup chopped drained oil-packed sun-dried tomato halves
¼ cup chopped fresh basil
¼ cup white balsamic vinegar
1 tablespoon olive oil
¼ teaspoon salt
¼ teaspoon freshly ground black pepper
1 garlic clove, minced

1. Cook pasta according to package directions, omitting salt and fat.
2. While pasta cooks, place a large nonstick skillet coated with cooking spray over medium-high heat. Add sausage; cook 7 minutes or until browned, stirring frequently.
3. Drain pasta. Combine pasta, sausage, cheese, and next 3 ingredients in a large bowl. Combine vinegar and next 4 ingredients in a small bowl; stir well with a whisk. Pour vinaigrette over pasta mixture;

toss gently to coat. YIELD: 7 servings (serving size: 1 cup).

POINTS value: 5; **Exchanges:** 1 Starch, 2 Vegetable, 1 Lean Meat, 1 Fat
Per serving: CAL 219 (37% from fat); PRO 11.5g; FAT 9.2g (sat 2.6g); CARB 24.2g; FIB 2.7g; CHOL 40mg; IRON 1.6mg; SOD 385mg; CALC 68mg

CARIBBEAN GRILLED CHICKEN SALAD WITH HONEY-LIME DRESSING

(pictured on page 113)
prep: 18 minutes • cook: 10 minutes

Enjoy this salad topped with warm strips of grilled, seasoned chicken, or take advantage of some make-ahead tips and serve it cold at a later time.
To get a jump start on the prep, go ahead and grill the chicken and make the dressing. Both will keep well in the refrigerator overnight.

2 teaspoons salt-free Jamaican jerk seasoning, divided
3 (6-ounce) skinless, boneless chicken breast halves
½ teaspoon kosher salt, divided
⅓ cup light mayonnaise
1 tablespoon chopped fresh cilantro
1 tablespoon finely chopped shallots
3 tablespoons honey
2 tablespoons fresh lime juice
3 (6-inch) corn tortillas, cut into ¼-inch strips
Cooking spray
1 (10-ounce) package torn romaine lettuce
⅓ cup (1½ ounces) shredded reduced-fat colby-Jack cheese

1. Preheat oven to 450°. Prepare grill.
2. Rub 1½ teaspoons seasoning over both sides of chicken; cover and chill 30 minutes.
3. While chicken chills, combine ¼ teaspoon kosher salt, mayonnaise, and next 4 ingredients in a small bowl; cover and chill until ready to serve.
4. While chicken and dressing chill, place tortilla strips on a foil-lined baking sheet. Lightly coat tortilla strips with cooking spray, and sprinkle with remaining ½ teaspoon seasoning and remaining ¼ teaspoon kosher salt. Bake at 450° for 8 to 10 minutes or until crisp, tossing strips gently every 2 minutes. Remove from oven, and place strips on a wire rack.
5. Place chicken on grill rack coated with cooking spray; grill 5 to 6 minutes on each side or until chicken is done. Cut chicken diagonally across grain into slices.
6. Place 1¾ cups lettuce on each of 4 plates; divide chicken strips evenly among salads. Sprinkle about 4 teaspoons cheese over each salad, and top evenly with tortilla strips. Drizzle 3 tablespoons dressing over each salad. YIELD: 4 servings.
Note: You may substitute ¼ teaspoon table salt for the ½ teaspoon kosher salt, if desired.

POINTS value: 7; **Exchanges:** 1 Starch, 2 Vegetable, 4 Lean Meat
Per serving: CAL 341 (28% from fat); PRO 33.9g; FAT 10.6g (sat 3.0g); CARB 27.3g; FIB 2.6g; CHOL 86mg; IRON 2.0mg; SOD 726mg; CALC 141mg

Sandwiches

PANINI MARGHERITA

(pictured on page 1)
prep: 10 minutes • cook: 4 minutes

Panini are pressed sandwiches served in Italy. A small appliance called a panini press is available in stores, but a heavy skillet placed on the sandwiches as they cook works just as well. You can even weigh down a lighter skillet with a brick wrapped in foil, a sack of flour, or canned goods.

16 (⅛-inch-thick) slices plum tomato (2 large tomatoes)
8 (1-ounce) slices rustic French bread loaf
¼ teaspoon salt
¼ teaspoon freshly ground black pepper
1 cup (4 ounces) shredded part-skim mozzarella cheese
12 fresh basil leaves
8 teaspoons extravirgin olive oil, divided
Cooking spray

1. Divide tomato slices evenly among 4 bread slices; sprinkle evenly with salt and pepper. Sprinkle cheese evenly over tomatoes. Arrange basil leaves evenly over cheese, and top with remaining 4 bread slices. Drizzle 1 teaspoon olive oil over top of each sandwich, and coat with cooking spray.
2. Place a grill pan or large nonstick skillet over medium-high heat until hot. Place sandwiches, oil sides down, in pan. Drizzle 1 teaspoon oil over top of each sandwich, and coat with cooking spray. Place a piece of foil over sandwiches in pan; place a heavy skillet on top of foil to press sandwiches. Cook 2 minutes or until golden brown. Turn sandwiches over; replace foil and heavy skillet. Cook 2 minutes or until golden brown. Serve immediately. YIELD: 4 servings (serving size: 1 sandwich).

POINTS value: 7; **Exchanges:** 2 Starch, 1 High-Fat Meat, 1 Fat
Per serving: CAL 319 (44% from fat); PRO 12.2g; FAT 15.7g (sat 4.5g); CARB 31.8g; FIB 2.1g; CHOL 16mg; IRON 1.7mg; SOD 625mg; CALC 229mg

ROASTED EGGPLANT AND PESTO SANDWICHES

prep: 12 minutes • cook: 36 minutes

You'll never miss the meat in this cheesy Italian vegetable sandwich.

1 (1-pound) eggplant, peeled and cut into ½-inch-thick slices
Cooking spray
½ teaspoon black pepper, divided
¼ teaspoon salt, divided
1 large red bell pepper, sliced into rings
1 large onion, thinly sliced
1 teaspoon olive oil
2½ teaspoons balsamic vinegar
1 (8-ounce) loaf French bread
2 tablespoons commercial pesto
½ cup (2 ounces) preshredded part-skim mozzarella cheese

1. Preheat oven to 450°.
2. Place eggplant in a single layer on a baking sheet coated with cooking spray. Lightly coat eggplant with cooking spray; sprinkle with ¼ teaspoon black pepper and ⅛ teaspoon salt. Place bell pepper rings and onion slices on another baking sheet coated with cooking spray. Drizzle with oil, and sprinkle with remaining ¼ teaspoon black pepper and ⅛ teaspoon salt.
3. Bake eggplant at 450° for 12 minutes; turn slices over. Add bell pepper and onion to oven with eggplant; bake at 450° for 10 minutes; turn bell pepper and onion slices over. Bake an additional 10 minutes or until vegetables are tender and well browned. Remove pans from oven. Drizzle balsamic vinegar over bell pepper and onion; toss to coat.
4. Cut bread in half horizontally. Place halves, cut sides up, on a baking sheet. Bake at 450° for 3 minutes or until bread is lightly toasted. Remove top half of loaf from pan; set aside.
5. Preheat broiler.
6. Spread 1 tablespoon pesto on each half of bread. Arrange roasted eggplant slices on bottom half of bread; top with bell pepper and onion mixture, and sprinkle with cheese. Broil 1 minute or until cheese melts; replace top half of loaf. Cut sandwich into 4 pieces, and serve immediately. YIELD: 4 servings (serving size: one-fourth loaf).
Note: To roast the vegetables in one oven, use both racks. Start the eggplant on the top rack. When the eggplant slices are turned, move them to the bottom rack, and place the bell pepper and onion on the top rack.

POINTS value: 6; **Exchanges:** 2 Starch, 2½ Vegetable, 1½ Fat
Per serving: CAL 291 (28% from fat); PRO 11.5g; FAT 9.0g (sat 3.0g); CARB 42.5g; FIB 2.5g; CHOL 11mg; IRON 2.3mg; SOD 621mg; CALC 210mg

HUMMUS AND OLIVE WRAPS

prep: 12 minutes

*You can find flatbread sheets in the deli department of your grocery store in a variety of flavors. Or use 4 (8-inch) 96%-fat-free wheat flour tortillas as a substitute. Roll 1 cup filling in each tortilla to make 4 servings. Each tortilla wrap has a **POINTS** value of 5.*

½ cup prepared roasted garlic hummus
2   (12-inch) harvest wheat flatbread sheets (such as Flatout)
4   cups gourmet salad greens
¾ cup (3 ounces) crumbled reduced-fat feta cheese with basil and tomatoes
½ cup pitted kalamata olives, halved
3   tablespoons fat-free red wine vinaigrette

1. Spread ¼ cup hummus over each flatbread sheet.
2. Combine salad greens and next 3 ingredients in a large bowl, tossing well to coat. Top each flatbread sheet with 2 cups salad mixture; roll up, and secure with wooden picks. Cut in half. YIELD: 4 servings (serving size: one-half wrap).

*POINTS value: 5; **Exchanges:** 2 Starch, 1 Lean Meat, 1 Fat*
Per serving: CAL 263 (38% from fat); PRO 12.3g; FAT 11.1g (sat 2.4g); CARB 29.9g; FIB 5.2g; CHOL 8mg; IRON 2.5mg; SOD 993mg; CALC 95mg

GRILLED RATATOUILLE WRAPS

prep: 15 minutes • cook: 15 minutes other: 10 minutes

1   (8-ounce) tub fat-free cream cheese
¼ cup (1 ounce) crumbled reduced-fat feta cheese with basil and tomatoes
2   teaspoons garlic paste (such as Amore)
¼ teaspoon black pepper
2   large red bell peppers
1   large red onion, cut into ½-inch slices
1   small eggplant, cut lengthwise into ½-inch slices
2   small zucchini, cut lengthwise into ½-inch slices
Cooking spray
¼ cup light Caesar dressing (such as Ken's Steak House)
¼ teaspoon salt
1   (14-ounce) package harvest wheat flatbread sheets (such as Flatout)

1. Combine first 4 ingredients in a bowl; stir well. Set aside.
2. Prepare grill.
3. Cut bell peppers in half lengthwise; discard seeds and membranes. Flatten bell peppers with hand. Coat bell pepper halves, onion, eggplant, and zucchini with cooking spray. Place bell pepper halves, skin sides down; onion; eggplant; and zucchini slices on a grill rack. Cover and grill 5 minutes. Turn onion, eggplant, and zucchini slices over (do not turn bell pepper halves); cover and grill 5 minutes or until onion, eggplant, and zucchini are tender. Remove onion, eggplant, and zucchini from grill. Grill bell pepper an additional 5 minutes or until blackened. Place bell pepper halves in a zip-top plastic bag; seal. Let stand 10 minutes. Peel bell peppers, and coarsely chop all vegetables.
4. Combine chopped vegetables, Caesar dressing, and salt in a large bowl; toss gently.
5. Spread about 3 tablespoons cream cheese mixture over each flatbread. Spoon 1 cup vegetable mixture onto 1 short end of each flatbread; roll up wraps. Cut each wrap in half crosswise, and secure with a wooden pick. YIELD: 10 servings (serving size: one-half wrap).

*POINTS value: 4; **Exchanges:** 1 Starch, 3 Vegetable, ½ Fat*
Per serving: CAL 181 (17% from fat); PRO 9.8g; FAT 3.5g (sat 0.7g); CARB 29.2g; FIB 2.0g; CHOL 5mg; IRON 0.4mg; SOD 619mg; CALC 62mg

---

SANDWICH SAVVY

The tried-and-true elements of sandwich-making—bread, deli meat, cheese, mustard, and mayonnaise—really pile on the sodium. Fat-free cheese and reduced-fat condiments help slash fat and calories, but not salt.

Because these sandwiches are high in sodium, we've added vegetables to some of them so that they can be a "one-dish" meal. If you're watching your sodium intake, add low-sodium accompaniments, such as carrot and celery sticks, rather than chips or pickles.

CREOLE CATFISH SANDWICHES

(pictured on page 138)

prep: 15 minutes • cook: 25 minutes
other: 10 minutes

1   teaspoon cornstarch
2   teaspoons lemon juice
½   teaspoon hot sauce
1   large egg white
⅓   cup fresh breadcrumbs
3   tablespoons yellow cornmeal
1   teaspoon Creole seasoning
     (such as Tony Chachere's)
¼   teaspoon black pepper
4   (4-ounce) farm-raised catfish
     fillets
Cooking spray
2   tablespoons reduced-fat
     mayonnaise
2   teaspoons Creole mustard
4   (2½-ounce) Philly-style hoagie
     rolls, toasted
4   curly leaf lettuce leaves
8   (¼-inch-thick) slices tomato

1. Preheat oven to 450°.
2. Combine first 4 ingredients in a shallow dish. Combine breadcrumbs and next 3 ingredients in another shallow dish.
3. Dip fish fillets in egg white mixture. Dredge fish in breadcrumb mixture, pressing firmly to coat. Place fish on a wire rack; let stand 10 minutes. Place jelly-roll pan in oven to heat while fish stands.
4. Coat fish well with cooking spray. Remove hot pan from oven; coat with cooking spray. Place fish on pan in a single layer. Bake at 450° for 25 minutes or until fish flakes easily when tested with a fork.
5. While fish bakes, combine mayonnaise and mustard. Spread mayonnaise mixture evenly on 1 side of each hoagie roll; top each roll with 1 lettuce leaf, 1 catfish fillet, and 2 tomato slices. Top with remaining bread. YIELD: 4 servings (serving size: 1 sandwich).

POINTS value: 8; **Exchanges:** 3 Starch, ½ Vegetable, 2½ Lean Meat
Per serving: CAL 400 (28% from fat); PRO 27.4g; FAT 12.5g (sat 3.3g); CARB 47.5g; FIB 3.3g; CHOL 53mg; IRON 1.2mg; SOD 720mg; CALC 25mg

ASIAN SALMON WRAPS

prep: 10 minutes • cook: 10 minutes

A hint of the East is wrapped up with a spicy, gingered salmon and cabbage blend in this whole wheat sandwich alternative.

Cooking spray
2   tablespoons slivered almonds
2   garlic cloves, minced
1   teaspoon freshly ground black
     pepper
4   (4-ounce) salmon fillets (about
     ½ inch thick)
1   (8-ounce) can sliced water
     chestnuts, drained and chopped
⅓   cup hoisin sauce
1   tablespoon prepared
     horseradish
2   teaspoons grated peeled fresh
     ginger
2   teaspoons orange juice
4   (9-inch) whole wheat flour
     tortillas (such as Toufayan)
4   cups shredded napa (Chinese)
     cabbage

1. Heat a large nonstick skillet coated with cooking spray over medium-high heat. Add almonds and garlic; sauté 3 minutes or until toasted. Spoon into a medium bowl. Return pan to medium-high heat.
2. Sprinkle pepper evenly over both sides of fish. Add fish to pan, and cook 3 minutes on each side or until fish flakes easily when tested with a fork. Break fish into chunks. Add fish and water chestnuts to almond mixture in bowl.
3. Combine hoisin sauce and next 3 ingredients in a small bowl; stir well. Add ¼ cup hoisin sauce mixture to fish mixture, tossing gently to coat.
4. Spread remaining hoisin sauce mixture evenly over tortillas. Spoon 1 cup cabbage and 1¼ cups salmon mixture evenly down center of each tortilla; roll up. YIELD: 4 servings (serving size: 1 wrap).

POINTS value: 8; **Exchanges:** 2 Starch, 1 Vegetable, 3½ Lean Meat
Per serving: CAL 380 (24% from fat); PRO 36.8g; FAT 10.2g (sat 1.4g); CARB 35.0g; FIB 12.9g; CHOL 61mg; IRON 1.4mg; SOD 1,018mg; CALC 102mg

FRESH GINGER

Look for fresh ginger in the produce section of your supermarket. Choose the freshest, youngest-looking ginger you can find. Old rhizomes are fibrous, tough, and flavorless.

Store fresh ginger tightly wrapped in plastic wrap in the vegetable crisper section of the refrigerator for up to 3 weeks. Or store whole fresh ginger in a refrigerated jar of sherry, and use both ginger and sherry in Asian dishes.

WASABI TUNA PITAS

prep: 10 minutes

Wasabi powder, the Japanese version of horseradish, adds sharp, fiery flavor to this tuna salad. Look for this condiment in the Asian section or spice aisle of large supermarkets. If you don't have wasabi, you may substitute 2 teaspoons of horseradish. Or simply omit the wasabi for a traditional tuna salad.

1 (6-ounce) can solid white tuna in water, drained
2 tablespoons light mayonnaise
2 tablespoons sweet pickle relish
2 tablespoons finely chopped red onion
½ teaspoon wasabi powder (dried Japanese horseradish)
2 (6-inch) whole wheat pitas, cut in half
4 red leaf lettuce leaves
4 (¼-inch-thick) slices tomato (about 1 medium)

1. Combine first 5 ingredients in a small bowl; stir well.
2. Line each pita half with a lettuce leaf and tomato slice; fill with ¼ cup tuna salad. YIELD: 4 servings (serving size: 1 pita half).

POINTS value: 3; **Exchanges:** 1 Starch, 1 Vegetable, 1½ Very Lean Meat, ½ Fat
Per serving: CAL 181 (19% from fat); PRO 14.7g; FAT 3.8g (sat 0.6g); CARB 23.4g; FIB 3.2g; CHOL 15mg; IRON 2.0mg; SOD 442mg; CALC 21mg

MEDITERRANEAN TUNA SALAD SANDWICHES

prep: 9 minutes

For a healthy on-the-go lunch, pack the tuna salad in a storage container, and fill the spinach-lined pita when you're ready to eat. Toss a few grapes into your lunch cooler, and the meal is complete.

1 cup rinsed and drained canned chickpeas (garbanzo beans)
½ cup (2 ounces) crumbled reduced-fat feta cheese with basil and tomato
½ cup chopped plum tomato (about 2 tomatoes)
¼ cup chopped pitted kalamata olives
¼ cup light Caesar dressing (such as Ken's Steak House)
1 teaspoon fresh lemon juice
½ teaspoon freshly ground black pepper
1 (6-ounce) can albacore tuna in water, drained
2 (6-inch) whole wheat pitas, cut in half
2 cups fresh baby spinach

1. Place chickpeas in a food processor; pulse 5 times or until chopped. Combine chopped chickpeas, cheese, and next 6 ingredients in a medium bowl; toss well.
2. Line each pita half with ½ cup spinach, and fill with ⅔ cup tuna salad. YIELD: 4 servings (serving size: 1 pita half).

POINTS value: 5; **Exchanges:** 2 Starch, ½ Vegetable, 1½ Medium-Fat Meat
Per serving: CAL 273 (31% from fat); PRO 16.6g; FAT 9.5g (sat 2.0g); CARB 32.8g; FIB 5.8g; CHOL 19mg; IRON 2.8mg; SOD 868mg; CALC 68mg

RANCHERO BURGERS

(pictured on page 134)
prep: 9 minutes • cook: 12 minutes

1 pound ground round
½ cup chopped onion
⅓ cup crushed baked tortilla chips
½ teaspoon ground cumin
¼ teaspoon black pepper
¼ teaspoon salt
1 garlic clove, minced
Cooking spray
1 cup fat-free refried beans
4 teaspoons light mayonnaise
4 (1.6-ounce) light wheat hamburger buns, toasted
½ cup shredded iceberg lettuce
½ cup bottled thick and chunky salsa

1. Combine first 7 ingredients. Divide into 4 equal portions; shape each into a ½-inch-thick patty.
2. Prepare grill.
3. Place patties on a grill rack coated with cooking spray, and grill 6 minutes. Carefully turn patties over, and grill 6 to 7 minutes or until done.
4. Microwave beans in a small bowl at HIGH 1 minute or until warm, stirring after 30 seconds.
5. Spread mayonnaise evenly over bottom halves of buns. Top each with 2 tablespoons lettuce, a burger patty, ¼ cup beans, and 2 tablespoons salsa. Place top halves of buns on each burger. YIELD: 4 servings (serving size: 1 burger).

POINTS value: 6; **Exchanges:** 2½ Starch, 1 Vegetable, 3 Very Lean Meat
Per serving: CAL 327 (21% from fat); PRO 33.8g; FAT 7.6g (sat 1.9g); CARB 40.9g; FIB 8.7g; CHOL 62mg; IRON 5.2mg; SOD 860mg; CALC 98mg

STEAK AND MUSHROOM SANDWICHES

prep: 15 minutes • cook: 20 minutes

Stuffed with steak, vegetables, and cheese, this French dip-style sandwich is a complete one-dish meal.

2   medium onions
½   cup water
1   tablespoon cornstarch
2   teaspoons olive oil, divided
1   garlic clove, minced
¾   teaspoon ground black pepper, divided
1   (10½-ounce) can condensed beef consommé, undiluted
1   pound flank steak, trimmed
¼   teaspoon salt
Cooking spray
1   medium red bell pepper, thinly sliced (about 1½ cups)
1   (8-ounce) package sliced mushrooms
1   (8-ounce) loaf French bread, about 16 inches long
½   cup (2 ounces) shredded fontina cheese

1. Dice enough onion to yield ¼ cup. Slice remaining onion to yield 2 cups; separate slices into rings.
2. Combine water and cornstarch in a small bowl; stir well, and set aside.
3. Heat 1 teaspoon oil in a medium saucepan over medium-high heat. Add diced onion, and sauté 3 minutes or until tender. Add garlic, and sauté 1 minute. Add cornstarch mixture, ¼ teaspoon black pepper, and consommé; bring to a boil. Cook sauce 1 minute or until slightly thick, stirring constantly. Remove from heat; keep warm.

4. Preheat broiler.
5. Sprinkle both sides of steak with ¼ teaspoon black pepper and ¼ teaspoon salt. Place steak on a broiler pan coated with cooking spray; broil 4 to 5 minutes on each side or until desired degree of doneness. Cut steak diagonally across the grain into thin slices.
6. While steak cooks, heat remaining 1 teaspoon oil in a large nonstick skillet over medium-high heat. Add sliced onion, bell pepper, and mushrooms; sauté 10 minutes or until vegetables are tender and liquid evaporates. Add remaining ¼ teaspoon black pepper.
7. Slice bread in half lengthwise, cutting to, but not through, other side. Carefully open bread without separating the halves. Place, cut side up, on a baking sheet. Broil 1 to 2 minutes or until lightly toasted.
8. Place steak slices and vegetables on bottom half of bread; sprinkle cheese evenly over vegetables. Broil 1 to 2 minutes or until cheese melts. Close sandwich, and cut into 5 equal portions. Serve immediately with warm dipping sauce. YIELD: 5 servings (serving size: one-fifth of loaf and about ¼ cup sauce).

POINTS value: 8; **Exchanges:** 2 Starch, 1 Vegetable, 3 Lean Meat, ½ Fat
Per serving: CAL 373 (33% from fat); PRO 27.1g; FAT 13.8g (sat 5.7g); CARB 34.9g; FIB 3.2g; CHOL 51mg; IRON 3.9mg; SOD 832mg; CALC 122mg

PORK WRAPS WITH FRESH TOMATILLO SALSA

(pictured on page 136)
prep: 14 minutes • cook: 9 minutes

2   large tomatillos
½   cup chopped cucumber
¼   cup chopped fresh cilantro
2   tablespoons fresh lime juice
½   teaspoon salt, divided
1   garlic clove, peeled
1   pound boneless pork cutlets, cut into thin strips
1   teaspoon ground cumin
Cooking spray
2   medium poblano chiles, stemmed, seeded, and cut into thin strips
1   medium onion, vertically sliced
4   (8-inch) fat-free flour tortillas
½   cup low-fat sour cream

1. Discard husks and stems from tomatillos. Combine tomatillos, cucumber, cilantro, lime juice, ¼ teaspoon salt, and garlic in a blender. Process until finely chopped, and set aside.
2. Sprinkle pork with cumin. Place a large nonstick skillet coated with cooking spray over medium-high heat until hot. Add pork; cook 3 minutes or until no longer pink in center, stirring occasionally. Remove from pan; keep warm.
3. Coat pan with cooking spray; add chiles and onion. Coat vegetables with cooking spray; cook 4 minutes or until onion begins to brown, stirring frequently.
4. Meanwhile, heat tortillas according to package directions.
5. Return pork to pan; add remaining ¼ teaspoon salt, and cook 30

seconds or until the pork mixture is thoroughly heated, stirring constantly. **6.** Divide pork mixture evenly among tortillas. Top each with about ⅓ cup salsa; roll up. Serve with sour cream. YIELD: 4 servings (serving size: 1 wrap and 2 tablespoons sour cream).

POINTS value: 6; **Exchanges:** 2 Starch, 1 Vegetable, 2 Lean Meat
Per serving: CAL 325 (19% from fat); PRO 29.0g; FAT 6.8g (sat 2.9g); CARB 36.2g; FIB 2.9g; CHOL 84mg; IRON 3.1mg; SOD 761mg; CALC 86mg

BARBECUED PORK ROLL-UPS

prep: 10 minutes • cook: 20 minutes
other: 8 hours and 15 minutes

This sandwich uses bottled barbecue sauce to flavor the pork. Coleslaw mix and preshredded carrots save time and combine for a quick coleslaw.

½ cup plus 2 tablespoons barbecue sauce, divided
3 tablespoons red wine vinegar, divided
2 tablespoons water
1 garlic clove, minced
1 (12-ounce) pork tenderloin
Cooking spray
¼ cup light mayonnaise
1 teaspoon sugar
¼ teaspoon freshly ground black pepper
⅛ teaspoon salt
2½ cups packaged coleslaw
¾ cup preshredded carrot
2 tablespoons chopped fresh parsley
4 (6-inch) flour tortillas

1. Combine ½ cup barbecue sauce, 2 tablespoons vinegar, water, and garlic

in a large zip-top plastic bag. Add pork; seal bag, and marinate in refrigerator 8 hours, turning bag occasionally.
2. Preheat oven to 400°.
3. Remove pork from bag; discard marinade. Heat a large ovenproof skillet coated with cooking spray over medium-high heat. Add pork; cook 2 to 3 minutes, browning on all sides. Remove from heat, and place pan in oven. Bake at 400° for 13 minutes or until a thermometer registers 145°. Brush tenderloin with remaining 2 tablespoons barbecue sauce; bake an additional 5 minutes or until thermometer registers 155°. Remove from oven; let stand 15 minutes. Cut in half crosswise. Slice each half lengthwise into ¼-inch-thick slices.
4. Meanwhile, combine remaining 1 tablespoon vinegar, mayonnaise, and next 3 ingredients in a medium bowl. Add coleslaw, carrot, and parsley; toss well to coat. Set aside.
5. Divide pork evenly among tortillas. Top each with ½ cup slaw mixture; roll up tortillas. Serve immediately. YIELD: 4 servings (serving size: 1 roll-up).

POINTS value: 6; **Exchanges:** 1½ Starch, 1 Vegetable, 2 Lean Meat, 1 Fat
Per serving: CAL 295 (33% from fat); PRO 21.6g; FAT 10.8g (sat 2.3g); CARB 27.4g; FIB 2.1g; CHOL 61mg; IRON 2.2mg; SOD 787mg; CALC 63mg

HAWAIIAN CALZONES

prep: 9 minutes • cook: 28 minutes

1 cup diced 96%-fat-free ham
½ cup drained canned pineapple tidbits in juice
½ cup chopped red bell pepper
⅓ cup chopped fresh mushrooms
1 (11-ounce) can refrigerated French bread dough
½ cup tomato-basil pasta sauce
¼ cup (1 ounce) shredded part-skim mozzarella cheese
Cooking spray
2 tablespoons grated Parmesan cheese

1. Preheat oven to 350°.
2. Combine first 4 ingredients in a small bowl.
3. Unroll dough on a lightly floured surface. Cut into 4 (6½-inch) squares. Spread 2 tablespoons pasta sauce evenly over each square, leaving a ½-inch border. Spoon ½ cup ham mixture onto each square, and sprinkle each with 1 tablespoon mozzarella cheese. Fold the dough over the filling to form a triangle, pressing edges to seal.
4. Place calzones on a baking sheet coated with cooking spray. Press edges with a fork to seal. Coat tops of calzones with cooking spray; sprinkle with Parmesan cheese.
5. Bake at 350° for 28 minutes or until golden brown. YIELD: 4 servings (serving size: 1 calzone).

POINTS value: 6; **Exchanges:** 2 Starch, 2 Vegetable, 1 Medium-Fat Meat
Per serving: CAL 290 (20% from fat); PRO 16.7g FAT 6.4g (sat 3.1g); CARB 41.3g; FIB 2.1g; CHOL 27mg; IRON 2.5mg; SOD 1,051mg; CALC 98mg

GRILLED CHICKEN AND SWISS PANINI

prep: 2 minutes • cook: 5 minutes

Smoked turkey and ham make tasty substitutes for the smoked chicken in these pressed Italian sandwiches.

¼ pound thinly sliced smoked chicken breast
2 (¾-ounce) slices reduced-fat, reduced-sodium Swiss cheese (such as Alpine Lace)
4 (0.5-ounce) slices very thin white bread
Butter-flavored cooking spray

1. Divide chicken and cheese evenly between 2 bread slices. Top with remaining bread slices.
2. Coat tops of sandwiches with cooking spray. Place sandwiches, coated sides down, in a grill pan or large nonstick skillet over medium heat. Coat tops of sandwiches with cooking spray. Place a piece of foil over sandwiches in pan; place a heavy skillet on top of foil to press sandwiches. Cook 3 minutes or until lightly browned. Turn sandwiches over; replace foil and heavy skillet. Cook 2 minutes or until lightly browned. Cut sandwiches in half, and serve immediately. YIELD: 2 sandwiches (serving size: 1 sandwich).
Note: We used a smaller skillet weighted with 2 canned goods to press the sandwiches, but a cast-iron skillet would also do the trick.

POINTS value: 3; **Exchanges:** 1 Starch, 2½ Very Lean Meat
Per serving: CAL 161 (17% from fat); PRO 19.2g; FAT 3.1g (sat 1.3g); CARB 14.6g; FIB 1.2g; CHOL 36mg; IRON 1.2mg; SOD 796mg; CALC 253mg

PROVOLONE CHICKEN SANDWICHES

prep: 12 minutes • cook: 2 minutes

Rotisserie chicken is a real time-saver when preparing this yummy sandwich.

2 tablespoons light mayonnaise
2 teaspoons stone-ground or Dijon mustard
1 (12-ounce) loaf French bread
2½ cups chopped cooked chicken
1 (7-ounce) bottle roasted red bell peppers, drained and chopped
5 (¾-ounce) slices smoked provolone cheese (such as Boar's Head)
10 fresh basil leaves

1. Combine mayonnaise and mustard in a small bowl; stir well.
2. Cut bread in half horizontally. Spread mayonnaise mixture evenly over cut sides of bread. Place bread halves, cut sides up, on a baking sheet. Place chicken on bottom half of bread; top with bell pepper and cheese slices, overlapping cheese slices as necessary.
3. Preheat broiler.
4. Broil sandwich 2 minutes or until cheese melts. Place basil leaves over melted cheese; replace top half of loaf. Cut sandwich into 6 equal portions. YIELD: 6 servings (serving size: one-sixth of loaf).

POINTS value: 8; **Exchanges:** 2 Starch, 3 Lean Meat, ½ Fat
Per serving: CAL 353 (32% from fat); PRO 26.5g; FAT 12.6g (sat 4.9g); CARB 31.4g; FIB 1.8g; CHOL 66mg; IRON 2.3mg; SOD 723mg; CALC 189mg

OPEN-FACED TURKEY, BACON, AND CHEDDAR SANDWICHES

prep: 4 minutes • cook: 4 minutes

Apple butter offers a sweet contrast to sharp Cheddar cheese and smoky bacon in these fork-and-knife sandwiches.

3 (2-ounce) ciabatta rolls, cut in half horizontally
Cooking spray
6 tablespoons apple butter
1 pound thinly sliced 47%-less-sodium deli turkey (such as Boar's Head)
9 precooked bacon slices, halved
¾ cup (3 ounces) shredded reduced-fat sharp Cheddar cheese

1. Preheat broiler.
2. Place rolls, cut sides up, on a baking sheet. Lightly coat cut sides of rolls with cooking spray. Broil 2 minutes or until toasted.
3. Spread 1 tablespoon apple butter over each roll half. Divide turkey evenly among roll halves. Place 3 half-slices of bacon over turkey; sprinkle evenly with cheese. Broil 2 minutes or until cheese melts. Serve immediately. YIELD: 6 servings (serving size: 1 open-faced sandwich).

POINTS value: 6; **Exchanges:** 1½ Starch, 3 Lean Meat
Per serving: CAL 288 (28% from fat); PRO 25.8g; FAT 8.9g (sat 3.5g); CARB 23.8g; FIB 0.8g; CHOL 48mg; IRON 1.1mg; SOD 995mg; CALC 104mg

Someday Is Now

SARAH STILLE • **HEIGHT** 5'8" • **BEFORE** 307 LBS. • **AFTER** 207 LBS.

Advice: "Kick the excuses and start making it happen—today."

Sarah Stille was overweight all her life, but she dreamed that someday she wouldn't be. "Even in my baby pictures, I was too heavy. And until the age of 24, I was the largest person in all of my classes," she says. "Yet I don't ever recall being hurt by anyone treating me differently. I just hurt inside."

Rather than blaming genetics, Sarah makes no excuses. "I may have been genetically prone, but I also overate," she admits.

Sarah's "appetite" had nothing to do with food. "I ate, not because I was hungry, but for comfort," she now realizes. "I didn't know what it felt like to be hungry, but I certainly knew what it felt like to be full!"

> *"Someday I want to get hit on, date, marry, and have a family."*

As a teen, Sarah continued to overeat and gain, yet she remained popular. She was homecoming queen—at size 18—and achieved All-State in softball, basketball, and track. "I think almost everyone liked me, not for what I looked like, but for the person I was inside," she says. "The only person who ever said anything about my weight was my doctor."

It was not until age 25, when Sarah wrote her "someday" dreams in a letter to a friend, that she began to realize them. She wrote, "Someday I want to be in pictures and not try to hide myself in the back. I want to fit into a 'normal' bridesmaid dress. I want to climb Torres National Park (again) but not be out of breath. And someday I want to get hit on, date, marry, and have a family."

The letter writing proved both a therapeutic experience and an awakening. "Realizing and rejecting the path I was taking, where someday obesity would determine my life and health, I decided to define 'someday' myself, and I joined *Weight Watchers*."

Sarah lost 12 pounds the first week, then 5 pounds consistently every week until she lost a total of 80 pounds.

Eventually, Sarah lost over 100 pounds and maintained the weight loss for over two years until her most recent challenge—a career change. Her former job as an instructor at Health, Physical Education, and Leisure Services included opportunities for exercise. But her new position as event manager came without workouts and led to a 20-pound weight gain. "So now I drive to the gym at 5:00 a.m. for muscle and strength training, run two miles after work, and play in a local volleyball league," she explains.

Today Sarah is comfortable—but not fully content—with her weight. "My new goal is to lose 31 more pounds. And my new 'someday' dream is to educate, motivate, and inspire others to kick the excuses and start making it happen—today."

Ranchero Burger,
page 129

Oven-Roasted Sweet
Potato Wedges,
page 145

Pork Wraps with Fresh
Tomatillo Salsa,
page 130

Lemon-Basil Orzo
with Parmesan,
page 149

Green Beans in
Vinaigrette with Feta,
page 144

Creole Catfish
Sandwich,
page 128

Grilled Asparagus with
Balsamic Vinaigrette,
page 142

Cajun Black-Eyed Peas
and Greens,
page 144

Dating Again

ANN JAMES • **HEIGHT** 5'9" • **BEFORE** 273 LBS. • **AFTER** 180 LBS.
PHILLIP JAMES • **HEIGHT** 5'11" • **BEFORE** 275 LBS. • **AFTER** 180 LBS.

Appreciation: "We already had a good relationship, but this experience brought us much closer together."

Approaching their 50th birthdays, Ann and Phillip James fulfilled a lifelong dream—buying their own boat. With their children grown, they envisioned spending their days together relaxing on the lake.

But rather than sailing off into the sunset, the 100 pounds each had gained since their wedding day made their boat rides a rocky experience. "Both of us struggled getting up and down the boat's ladder," Phillip recalls. So before enjoying their boat, they realized that they would first have to do something else together—lose weight.

Ann and Phillip joined *Weight Watchers* because they wanted more than a diet. They wanted a lifestyle change. "A diet is something that you do for a short time. But this can really never be over," Ann explains.

Phillip lost 10 pounds the first week, but it took Ann two weeks to lose five pounds. "Men have more muscle mass than women, making it easier to lose weight. And he had not yo-yo dieted through the years like I had, which slowed my metabolism," she explains.

"In some ways, that was nice. And in some, it wasn't," Phillip laughs. "Almost all of the people at our *Weight Watchers* meetings were female. While I lost three to five pounds

each week, they might lose half of a pound. Although they were happy for me, I had to wonder if they were thinking, 'Men!'"

Phillip lost 85 pounds and met his goal in nine months. Ann persevered and met her goal 10 months after her husband.

Ironically, it was their *Weight Watchers* experience, rather than the boat, that brought them closer together. "Wednesday nights were not only for *Weight Watchers* meetings; we made it date night," he says. "After weighing in, we would go to our favorite Mexican restaurant for dinner, but we would stay within our **POINTS**."

"Wednesday nights were not only for Weight Watchers *meetings; we made it date night."*

Weight Watchers remains an integral part of Ann's and Phillip's lives. "This has been about so much more than food," Ann says. "We already had a good relationship, but this experience brought us much closer together. It has been a spiritual journey."

Sides

GRILLED ASPARAGUS WITH BALSAMIC VINAIGRETTE

(pictured on page 139)
prep: 8 minutes • cook: 4 minutes

If your plans for dinner don't involve the grill, this asparagus is also delicious roasted. Place the asparagus spears on a jelly-roll pan, and roast at 450° for 5 to 7 minutes.

2   pounds asparagus spears
Olive oil-flavored cooking spray
2   tablespoons balsamic vinegar
1   tablespoon extravirgin olive oil
½   teaspoon kosher salt or
      ¼ teaspoon table salt
½   teaspoon freshly ground black
      pepper
⅓   cup (1⅓ ounces) shredded
      fresh Parmigiano-Reggiano or
      Parmesan cheese

1. Preheat grill.
2. Snap off tough ends of asparagus. Coat asparagus with cooking spray; place on grill rack, and grill 4 minutes or until crisp-tender, turning frequently. Place asparagus on a serving platter.
3. Combine vinegar and oil in a small bowl; stir with a whisk. Drizzle over asparagus; sprinkle with salt, pepper, and cheese. Serve immediately. YIELD: 6 servings (serving size: ⅙ of asparagus).

POINTS value: 1; **Exchanges:** 1 Vegetable, 1 Fat
Per serving: CAL 60 (57% from fat); PRO 3.5g;
FAT 3.8g (sat 1.2g); CARB 4.1g; FIB 1.5g;
CHOL 4mg; IRON 0.8mg; SOD 237mg;
CALC 69mg

ORANGE-BALSAMIC BEETS WITH BASIL

prep: 13 minutes • cook: 1 hour

The aroma of fresh orange fills the air as olive oil is infused with orange rind. The infused oil adds a touch of sweetness to the beets.

8   small beets (about 1¾ pounds)
1   tablespoon olive oil
1   tablespoon grated orange rind
1   tablespoon chopped fresh basil
1   tablespoon balsamic vinegar
⅛   teaspoon salt
⅛   teaspoon black pepper

1. Leave root and 1 inch of stem on beets; scrub with a brush. Place in a large Dutch oven; cover with water. Bring to a boil; cover, reduce heat, and simmer 45 minutes or until tender. Drain and rinse under cold water; drain.
2. Place oil and orange rind in a small nonstick skillet, and cook over low heat 5 minutes or until oil is fragrant. Remove from heat.
3. Trim off beet roots. Rub off skins, and cut each beet into 4 wedges. Combine beets, infused oil, basil, and remaining ingredients in a bowl, tossing gently to coat. Serve immediately, or cover and chill. YIELD: 4 servings (serving size: about ½ cup).

POINTS value: 1; **Exchanges:** 2½ Vegetable, ½ Fat
Per serving: CAL 91 (36% from fat); PRO 2.2g;
FAT 3.6g (sat 0.5g); CARB 13.7g; FIB 3.9g;
CHOL 0mg; IRON 1.2mg; SOD 178mg;
CALC 26mg

BROCCOLI WITH BROWNED BUTTER AND BREADCRUMBS

prep: 3 minutes • cook: 5 minutes

Look for panko breadcrumbs in the Asian section of large supermarkets or in Asian markets. They're ideal for an extracrunchy topping for the broccoli.

1   (12-ounce) package fresh
      broccoli florets
¼   cup panko (Japanese)
      breadcrumbs or fresh
      breadcrumbs
1½ tablespoons butter
¼   teaspoon kosher salt or
      ⅛ teaspoon table salt
¼   teaspoon freshly ground black
      pepper
Dash of ground red pepper

1. Steam broccoli, covered, 4 to 5 minutes or until crisp-tender.
2. While broccoli steams, place breadcrumbs in a large skillet; cook over medium heat 3 minutes or until lightly browned, stirring frequently. Remove from skillet, and set aside.
3. Add butter to skillet, and cook over medium heat 1 to 2 minutes or until butter is lightly browned, stirring constantly. Remove from heat.
4. Drain broccoli. Add broccoli, salt, and peppers to skillet, tossing to coat broccoli with butter. Place in a serving bowl; sprinkle with breadcrumbs. Serve immediately. YIELD: 3 servings (serving size: 1 cup).

POINTS value: 2; **Exchanges:** 2 Vegetable, 1 Fat
Per serving: CAL 101 (56% from fat); PRO 4.1g;
FAT 6.3g (sat 3.7g); CARB 9.4g; FIB 3.5g;
CHOL 15mg; IRON 1.0mg; SOD 202mg;
CALC 57mg

SESAME BROCCOLI RABE

prep: 5 minutes • cook: 10 minutes

This dish is also delicious served cold as a healthy vegetable salad or tossed with cold soba or Asian rice noodles.

2   bunches (about 1⅓ pounds) broccoli rabe (rapini)
1   tablespoon kosher salt or 1½ teaspoons table salt
2   tablespoons minced shallots (1 large)
2   tablespoons seasoned rice vinegar
1   tablespoon peanut oil, divided
1   teaspoon dark sesame oil, divided
½   teaspoon freshly ground black pepper
¼   teaspoon kosher salt or ⅛ teaspoon table salt
1   large garlic clove, pressed
1   tablespoon sesame seeds, toasted

1. Trim ends of broccoli rabe stalks. Bring 8 cups water and 1 tablespoon kosher salt to a boil in a large saucepan. Add broccoli rabe; cook 1 minute. Drain and plunge broccoli rabe into ice water; drain.
2. Combine shallots, vinegar, 1½ teaspoons peanut oil, ½ teaspoon sesame oil, pepper, and ¼ teaspoon salt in a small bowl; stir well with a whisk.
3. Heat remaining 1½ teaspoons peanut oil and remaining ½ teaspoon sesame oil in a large nonstick skillet over medium-high heat. Add garlic; sauté 1 minute. Add broccoli rabe; sauté 1½ minutes or until thoroughly heated. Remove from heat.

Drizzle with shallot mixture; toss gently to coat. Sprinkle with toasted sesame seeds. YIELD: 4 servings (serving size: 1 cup).

POINTS value: 2; **Exchanges:** 2 Vegetable, 1 Fat
Per serving: CAL 105 (47% from fat); PRO 5.9g; FAT 5.5g (sat 0.9g); CARB 9.8g; FIB 0.5g; CHOL 0mg; IRON 1.6mg; SOD 340mg; CALC 78mg

BRUSSELS SPROUTS WITH LEMON-BUTTER SAUCE

prep: 1 minute • cook: 9 minutes

Frozen Brussels sprouts work well in this recipe, and they require no washing or trimming.

1   (16-ounce) package frozen Brussels sprouts
2   tablespoons butter
1   tablespoon lemon juice
1   teaspoon Worcestershire sauce
½   teaspoon salt

1. Steam Brussels sprouts, covered, 8 minutes or until tender. Drain, and set aside.
2. Add butter and next 3 ingredients to pan; cook over medium-high heat 1 minute or until butter melts. Add Brussels sprouts; toss gently to coat. YIELD: 3 servings (serving size: 1 cup).

POINTS value: 3; **Exchanges:** 2½ Vegetable, 1½ Fat
Per serving: CAL 131 (56% from fat); PRO 5.8g; FAT 8.2g (sat 4.9g); CARB 12.7g; FIB 5.8g; CHOL 20mg; IRON 1.5mg; SOD 422mg; CALC 44mg

CABBAGE SAUTÉ WITH APPLES

prep: 4 minutes • cook: 16 minutes

This simple sauté is the perfect accompaniment to dress up your smoked turkey sausage, pork chop, or brat.

2   teaspoons butter
2   teaspoons olive oil
1¼   cups vertically sliced red onion
1   teaspoon chopped fresh thyme
2   teaspoons Dijon mustard
½   teaspoon fennel seeds
½   teaspoon salt
1   large Granny Smith apple, cored and chopped (1¼ cups)
1   (10-ounce) package angel hair slaw
¼   cup apple juice
3   tablespoons cider vinegar
1   teaspoon sugar
½   teaspoon ground white pepper

1. Heat butter and oil in a large nonstick skillet over medium-high heat until butter melts. Add onion and next 4 ingredients; sauté 3 minutes or until onion is tender. Add apple and slaw; sauté 2 minutes or until cabbage begins to wilt. Stir in apple juice and remaining ingredients. Bring to a boil; reduce heat to medium, and simmer 10 minutes or until liquid evaporates, stirring occasionally. YIELD: 5 servings (serving size: ½ cup).

POINTS value: 2; **Exchanges:** 1½ Fruit, 1 Vegetable, ½ Fat
Per serving: CAL 85 (38% from fat); PRO 1.2g; FAT 3.6g (sat 1.2g); CARB 13.0g; FIB 2.4g; CHOL 4mg; IRON 0.4mg; SOD 298mg; CALC 16mg

LEMON-HONEY
GLAZED CARROTS

prep: 2 minutes • cook: 8 minutes

Lemon juice and honey create a sweet and tangy sauce for this simple side that's ready to serve from the microwave in minutes.

1   (16-ounce) package fresh baby carrots
2   tablespoons honey
1   tablespoon light stick butter
2   teaspoons lemon juice
¼   teaspoon salt

1. Combine all ingredients in a medium microwave-safe dish. Cover and microwave at HIGH 8 to 10 minutes or until tender, stirring after 4 minutes. YIELD: 4 servings (serving size: about ½ cup).

POINTS value: 1; **Exchanges:** ½ Starch, 2 Vegetable
Per serving: CAL 85 (18% from fat); PRO 1.0g; FAT 1.7g (sat 1.0g); CARB 18.3g; FIB 2.1g; CHOL 5mg; IRON 1.1mg; SOD 234mg; CALC 37mg

---

CARROTS

Carrots are the Fort Knox of beta-carotene, and the deeper the orange, the more there is. Beta-carotene is a form of vitamin A and appears to help reduce the risk of cancer. Carrots are a healthful food choice, whether eaten raw or cooked. However, cooking carrots makes it easier for the body to absorb the beta-carotene.

GREEN BEANS IN
VINAIGRETTE WITH FETA

(pictured on page 137)
prep: 3 minutes • cook: 12 minutes

Washed and trimmed fresh green beans are a real time-saver. Cook them and toss with a homemade vinaigrette to liven up any dinner plate.

2   (12-ounce) packages ready-to-eat fresh green beans
1   tablespoon olive oil
1   teaspoon bottled minced garlic
2   teaspoons balsamic vinegar
1   teaspoon Dijon mustard
½   teaspoon salt
¼   cup (1 ounce) crumbled feta cheese with basil and sun-dried tomatoes

1. Bring 8 cups water to a boil in a Dutch oven. Add green beans, and cook 4 minutes or until crisp-tender.
2. While beans are cooking, heat oil in a small saucepan over medium heat. Add garlic; sauté 3 minutes or until lightly browned. Remove from heat; add vinegar, mustard, and salt, stirring well with a whisk.
3. Drain beans, and return to pan. Pour vinaigrette over beans; toss gently to coat. Sprinkle with feta cheese. Serve immediately. YIELD: 6 servings (serving size: about ¾ cup).

POINTS value: 1; **Exchanges:** 1½ Vegetable, 1 Fat
Per serving: CAL 75 (44% from fat); PRO 2.3g; FAT 3.7g (sat 1.2g); CARB 7.6g; FIB 4.1g; CHOL 6mg; IRON 0.6mg; SOD 285mg; CALC 87mg

---

CAJUN BLACK-EYED PEAS
AND GREENS

(pictured on page 139)
prep: 5 minutes • cook: 1 hour and 23 minutes • other: 1 hour

The full, rich flavor of this classic Southern fare begins with soaking the peas, so plan ahead. It's well worth the effort.

8   ounces dried black-eyed peas (1¼ cups)
2   teaspoons canola oil
⅔   cup chopped onion (1 medium)
½   cup chopped red bell pepper (½ medium)
10 garlic cloves, pressed
1   (1-pound) package chopped fresh collard greens
2   teaspoons Cajun seasoning
1   teaspoon freshly ground black pepper
1   (32-ounce) carton fat-free, less-sodium chicken broth
1   bay leaf

1. Sort and wash peas; place in a large Dutch oven. Cover with water to 2 inches above peas; bring to a boil, and cook 2 minutes. Remove from heat; cover and let stand 1 hour. Drain peas. Wipe pan dry with a paper towel.
2. Heat oil in pan over medium-high heat. Add onion, bell pepper, and garlic; sauté 2 minutes. Add collard greens, seasoning, and black pepper; cover and cook 2 minutes or until collard greens begin to wilt. Add peas, broth, and bay leaf. Bring to a boil; cover, reduce heat to medium-low, and simmer 1 hour and 15 minutes or until peas are

tender. Discard bay leaf. Serve with a slotted spoon. YIELD: 7 servings (serving size: 1 cup).

POINTS value: 1; **Exchanges:** 3 Vegetable
Per serving: CAL 85 (19% from fat); PRO 4.8g;
FAT 1.8g (sat 0.2g); CARB 14.2g; FIB 4.2g;
CHOL 0mg; IRON 0.6mg; SOD 512mg;
CALC 146mg

PARSNIP MASHED POTATOES

prep: 9 minutes • cook: 26 minutes

There is just enough parsnip in this dish to give everyday mashed potatoes a flavor boost. Serve them with roasted pork or chicken.

1   pound baking potatoes, peeled and cubed
¾   cup cubed peeled parsnip (about 1 large)
⅓   cup fat-free, less-sodium chicken broth
⅓   cup 1% low-fat milk
2   tablespoons butter
½   teaspoon salt
1   tablespoon chopped fresh parsley

1. Place potato and parsnip in a medium saucepan; add water to cover. Bring to a boil; reduce heat, and simmer, uncovered, 18 minutes or until tender. Drain.
2. Return potato mixture to pan. Add broth and next 3 ingredients; beat with a mixer at medium speed until smooth. Stir in parsley. YIELD: 6 servings (serving size: ½ cup).

POINTS value: 2; **Exchange:** 1 Starch
Per serving: CAL 90 (23% from fat); PRO 2.3g;
FAT 2.3g (sat 1.4g); CARB 16.3g; FIB 1.8g;
CHOL 7mg; IRON 0.4mg; SOD 240mg;
CALC 27mg

ENGLISH-STYLE BAKED CHIPS

prep: 16 minutes • cook: 18 minutes
other: 10 minutes

Soaking the potato slices in hot water speeds up the cooking process and washes away excess starch, resulting in crispier chips.

1   (12-ounce) baking potato
3   cups very hot water
1   teaspoon canola oil
Cooking spray
1   teaspoon lemon pepper
½   teaspoon kosher salt or ¼ teaspoon table salt

1. Preheat oven to 400°.
2. Scrub potato with a brush. Cut potato crosswise into 40 very thin slices using a mandoline slicer.
3. Combine potato slices and hot water in a large bowl; let stand 10 minutes. Drain. Arrange potato slices on a layer of paper towels; pat dry.
4. Coat 2 (15 x 10-inch) jelly-roll pans evenly with oil. Arrange potato slices in a single layer on pans. Coat potato slices with cooking spray, and sprinkle evenly with lemon pepper and salt. Bake at 400° for 18 minutes or until lightly browned. YIELD: 4 servings (serving size: 10 chips).
Note: Watch chips carefully, and quickly remove individual chips from the pan as they become lightly browned.

POINTS value: 2; **Exchanges:** 1½ Starch
Per serving: CAL 104 (11% from fat); PRO 2.0g;
FAT 1.3g (sat 0.1g); CARB 21.6g; FIB 2.1g;
CHOL 0mg; IRON 1.2mg; SOD 357mg;
CALC 9mg

OVEN-ROASTED SWEET POTATO WEDGES

(pictured on page 135)
prep: 6 minutes • cook: 30 minutes

Be sure your sweet potatoes are spread in a single layer in the roasting pan. This insures that the potatoes get nicely browned and do not steam.

4   medium sweet potatoes (about 2½ pounds), each cut into 6 wedges
1   tablespoon chopped fresh rosemary
2   tablespoons olive oil
1   teaspoon salt
1   teaspoon cracked black pepper
½   teaspoon garlic powder

1. Preheat oven to 450°.
2. Combine all ingredients in a large bowl; toss well. Arrange potatoes in a single layer in a roasting pan.
3. Bake at 450° for 20 minutes. Gently stir potatoes, and bake an additional 10 minutes or until lightly browned and tender. YIELD: 6 servings (serving size: 4 wedges).

POINTS value: 2; **Exchanges:** 1½ Starch
Per serving: CAL 129 (31% from fat); PRO 1.4g;
FAT 4.5g (sat 0.6g); CARB 22.5g; FIB 2.8g;
CHOL 0mg; IRON 0.3mg; SOD 418mg;
CALC 16mg

GRILLED RADICCHIO WITH GORGONZOLA CRUMBLES

prep: 5 minutes • cook: 6 minutes

If you don't have Gorgonzola on hand, drizzle each grilled radicchio half with 1 tablespoon refrigerated light blue cheese dressing for a **POINTS** *value of 3.*

2 tablespoons olive oil
1 tablespoon balsamic vinegar
¼ teaspoon salt
½ teaspoon freshly ground black pepper
Olive oil-flavored cooking spray
2 (8-ounce) heads radicchio, halved
½ cup (2 ounces) crumbled Gorgonzola cheese

1. Preheat grill.
2. Combine first 4 ingredients in a small bowl; stir well with a whisk. Coat grill rack with cooking spray. Place radicchio, cut sides up, on grill rack; brush with vinaigrette. Grill 3 minutes on each side or until slightly blackened, brushing with vinaigrette after turning. Place radicchio halves, cut sides up, on plates; top with Gorgonzola cheese. YIELD: 4 servings (serving size: one-half radicchio head and 2 tablespoons cheese).

POINTS value: 3; **Exchanges:** *2 Starch, 1 ½ Vegetable* **Per serving:** *CAL 139 (72% from fat); PRO 4.7g; FAT 11.1g (sat 4.0g); CARB 6.3g; FIB 1.6g; CHOL 13mg; IRON 0.7mg; SOD 361mg; CALC 99mg*

CREAMED SPINACH WITH TOMATOES

prep: 5 minutes • cook: 10 minutes

Using two kinds of spinach provides texture and plenty of flavor.

1 (10-ounce) package frozen creamed spinach (such as Green Giant)
2 tablespoons all-purpose flour
1 cup 1% low-fat milk
1½ tablespoons light stick butter
½ cup (2 ounces) shredded part-skim mozzarella cheese
1 (10-ounce) package frozen chopped spinach, thawed, drained, and squeezed dry
1 (14.5-ounce) can diced tomatoes with garlic and onion, undrained

1. Cook creamed spinach according to package directions; set aside.
2. While spinach cooks, place flour in a small bowl; gradually add milk, stirring with a whisk until well blended. Melt butter in a medium saucepan over medium heat. Add milk mixture, stirring constantly with a whisk. Cook 5 minutes or until mixture begins to thicken. Remove from heat. Add cheese; stir until cheese melts.
3. Stir in creamed spinach, chopped spinach, and tomatoes. Bring to a simmer over medium-low heat, and cook 5 minutes or until thoroughly heated. YIELD: 8 servings (serving size: about ⅔ cup).

POINTS value: 2; **Exchanges:** *2 Vegetable, 1 Fat* **Per serving:** *CAL 97 (38% from fat); PRO 6.2g; FAT 4.1g (sat 2.2g); CARB 10.9g; FIB 2.0g; CHOL 9mg; IRON 1.6mg; SOD 489mg; CALC 160mg*

BALSAMIC GRILLED SQUASH

prep: 4 minutes • cook: 8 minutes
other: 1 hour

We tested this recipe with light and regular balsamic vinaigrette. Our taste-testing panel preferred the full flavor of the regular dressing.

¼ cup balsamic vinaigrette
2 tablespoons chopped fresh basil
1 garlic clove, minced
4 medium yellow squash (about 1¼ pounds), each cut in half lengthwise
Cooking spray
¼ teaspoon salt
⅛ teaspoon freshly ground black pepper

1. Combine first 3 ingredients in a large zip-top plastic bag. Add squash; seal bag, and let stand 1 hour, turning bag occasionally.
2. Prepare grill.
3. Remove squash from bag, reserving marinade. Place squash on grill rack coated with cooking spray; cover and grill 4 to 6 minutes on each side or until squash is tender. Place squash on a serving platter; sprinkle with salt and pepper. Drizzle with reserved marinade. YIELD: 4 servings (serving size: 2 squash halves).

POINTS value: 1; **Exchanges:** *2 Vegetable* **Per serving:** *CAL 48 (0% from fat); PRO 1.8g; FAT 0g (sat 0g); CARB 9.0g; FIB 1.8g; CHOL 0mg; IRON 0.2mg; SOD 174mg; CALC 6mg*

SAUTÉED SUMMER SQUASH WITH ROSEMARY AND GARLIC

prep: 7 minutes • cook: 7 minutes

Here's a superquick side dish that lets you take advantage of garden-fresh rosemary, squash, and zucchini. Substitute any fresh herb you have on hand.

2   teaspoons olive oil
1½ cups (¼-inch) sliced zucchini (about 1 large)
1½ cups (¼-inch) sliced yellow squash (about 2 medium)
2   garlic cloves, minced
2   teaspoons chopped fresh rosemary
¼   teaspoon salt
¼   teaspoon freshly ground black pepper

1. Heat oil in a large nonstick skillet over medium-high heat. Add zucchini and squash; sauté 4 minutes or until lightly browned. Add garlic; sauté 1 minute. Reduce heat to low. Add rosemary, salt, and pepper; sauté 1 minute. Serve immediately. **YIELD:** 2 servings (serving size: 1 cup).

POINTS value: 1; **Exchanges:** 1½ Vegetable, 1 Fat
Per serving: CAL 73 (60% from fat); PRO 2.3g;
FAT 4.9g (sat 0.7g); CARB 7.0g; FIB 2.1g;
CHOL 0mg; IRON 0.7mg; SOD 302mg;
CALC 34mg

OVEN-FRIED ZUCCHINI WITH LEMON DIPPING SAUCE

prep: 15 minutes • cook: 15 minutes

This two-for-one recipe not only serves as an exciting side dish, but the crispy rounds of zucchini also make a delightful appetizer.

3   cups (¼-inch) sliced zucchini (2 large)
2   tablespoons fat-free Italian dressing
¼   cup Italian-seasoned breadcrumbs
1   tablespoon grated Parmesan cheese
½   teaspoon paprika
    Cooking spray
1   teaspoon olive oil
    Lemon Dipping Sauce

1. Preheat oven to 450°.
2. Combine zucchini and Italian dressing in a medium bowl; toss well to coat.
3. Combine breadcrumbs, cheese, and paprika in a shallow dish. Dredge zucchini slices in breadcrumb mixture, and place on a jelly-roll pan lined with foil and coated with cooking spray. Drizzle zucchini evenly with olive oil.
4. Bake at 450° for 15 minutes. Serve immediately with Lemon Dipping Sauce. **YIELD:** 4 servings (serving size: about ⅔ cup zucchini and 2 tablespoons sauce).

POINTS value: 3; **Exchanges:** ½ Starch, 1 Vegetable, 1 Fat
Per serving: CAL 117 (47% from fat); PRO 3.7g;
FAT 6.1g (sat 1.9g); CARB 12.5g; FIB 1.6g;
CHOL 11mg; IRON 0.7mg; SOD 707mg;
CALC 83mg

LEMON DIPPING SAUCE

⅓   cup low-fat sour cream
2   tablespoons light mayonnaise
1   tablespoon lemon juice
1   tablespoon fat-free milk
½   teaspoon salt

1. Combine all ingredients in a small bowl. Serve with zucchini.
YIELD: 4 servings (serving size: 2 tablespoons).

POINTS value: 1; **Exchange:** 1 Fat
Per serving: CAL 54 (68% from fat); PRO 0.9g;
FAT 4.1g (sat 1.4g); CARB 3.2g; FIB 0.0g;
CHOL 9mg; IRON 0.0mg; SOD 400mg; CALC 45mg

ZUCCHINI

Zucchini have thin, edible skins and soft seeds. The flesh is tender, has a mild flavor, and doesn't require a long cooking time. It's used in almost everything, including salads, breads, and gratins.

Zucchini's mild taste and cool flavor make it perfect for blending with other ingredients or for using in simple preparations highlighting the taste of fresh herbs. Zucchini are at their peak from June through late August but are available at most supermarkets throughout the year.

CONFETTI BARLEY PILAF

prep: 15 minutes • cook: 17 minutes

Bits of vegetables and herbs add specks of festive color to this hearty pilaf. To save time, toast the almonds while you chop the vegetables and parsley.

1   tablespoon olive oil
½   cup chopped yellow bell pepper
½   cup chopped carrot
½   cup chopped red onion
1   cup uncooked quick-cooking barley
½   teaspoon salt
1   (14-ounce) can fat-free, less-sodium chicken broth
1   small bay leaf
1   fresh thyme sprig
½   cup chopped tomato
⅓   cup slivered almonds, toasted
¼   cup chopped fresh parsley
⅛   teaspoon freshly ground black pepper

1. Heat oil in a medium saucepan over medium-high heat. Add bell pepper, carrot, and onion; sauté 5 minutes or until onion is almost tender. Add barley; sauté 1 minute. Add salt, broth, bay leaf, and thyme sprig. Bring to a boil; cover, reduce heat, and simmer 10 minutes or until barley is tender and liquid is absorbed. Discard bay leaf and thyme sprig. Remove from heat; stir in tomato and next 3 ingredients. YIELD: 5 servings (serving size: ¾ cup).

POINTS value: 4; **Exchanges:** 2 Starch, 1 Fat
Per serving: CAL 205 (36% from fat); PRO 6.7g;
FAT 8.1g (sat 0.8g); CARB 29.1g; FIB 4.9g;
CHOL 0mg; IRON 1.3mg; SOD 457mg;
CALC 46mg

TOMATO-BASIL BASMATI PILAF

prep: 5 minutes • cook: 19 minutes
other: 5 minutes

The hot rice brings out the flavor of the fresh basil and tomato as the pilaf is tossed. The better the tomatoes, the tastier the pilaf will be. This dish is the perfect partner for grilled chicken.

1¾ cups water
1   cup uncooked basmati rice
1   teaspoon salt
1½ tablespoons light stick butter
½   cup chopped onion
⅔   cup chopped tomato (about 1 medium)
1   tablespoon lemon juice
½   cup chopped fresh basil

1. Bring water to a boil in a medium saucepan. Add rice and salt; cover, reduce heat, and simmer 15 minutes. Remove from heat, and let stand, covered, 5 minutes or until liquid is absorbed.
2. While rice stands, melt butter in a small skillet. Add onion; sauté 4 minutes or until tender. Remove from heat; stir in tomato and lemon juice. Add tomato mixture and basil to hot cooked rice; toss gently. Serve immediately. YIELD: 7 servings (serving size: ½ cup).

POINTS value: 2; **Exchanges:** 1 Starch, 2½ Vegetable
Per serving: CAL 123 (10% from fat); PRO 2.1g;
FAT 1.4g (sat 0.9g); CARB 28.1g; FIB 1.3g;
CHOL 4mg; IRON 1.0mg; SOD 334mg;
CALC 9mg

EASY HOPPIN' JOHN

prep: 1 minute • cook: 21 minutes
other: 15 minutes

1¾ cups water
1¼ teaspoons concentrated ham base (such as Better Than Bouillon)
1⅓ cups frozen black-eyed peas
½   cup uncooked basmati rice
2   center-cut bacon slices
½   cup chopped green onions (about 4 onions)

1. Bring water and ham base to a boil in a medium saucepan. Add peas and rice; return to a boil. Cover, reduce heat, and simmer 15 minutes or until peas and rice are tender. Remove from heat; let stand, covered, 15 minutes or until liquid is absorbed.
2. While rice mixture stands, cook bacon in a large skillet over medium heat until crisp. Remove bacon from pan to a paper towel-lined plate, reserving 1 teaspoon drippings in pan. Increase heat to medium-high. Add green onions to reserved drippings in skillet; sauté 2 minutes. Add green onions to rice mixture. Crumble bacon; add to rice mixture, tossing gently. YIELD: 6 servings (serving size: ½ cup).

Note: Substitute 1 (0.1-ounce) packet ham-flavored bouillon granules (such as Goya), if desired. The sodium is higher in this product.

POINTS value: 2; **Exchanges:** 1½ Starch, ½ Vegetable
Per serving: CAL 124 (7% from fat); PRO 5.0g;
FAT 1.0g (sat 0.3g); CARB 24.9g; FIB 2.6g;
CHOL 2mg; IRON 1.3mg; SOD 190mg; CALC 9mg

WINTER SQUASH AND RICE GRATIN

prep: 10 minutes • cook: 1 hour and 20 minutes • other: 5 minutes

To cut winter squash, microwave at HIGH 1 minute. This will soften the squash so you can easily cut through the thick shell.

1   (2-pound) butternut squash, cut into 4 pieces
½   cup uncooked long-grain rice
2   tablespoons butter
¼   cup finely chopped shallots
3   garlic cloves, minced
3   tablespoons all-purpose flour
1½   cups fat-free milk
¼   cup chopped fresh parsley
1   tablespoon chopped fresh sage
¾   teaspoon salt
¾   teaspoon black pepper
½   teaspoon ground nutmeg
½   cup (2 ounces) shredded fontina cheese
Cooking spray

1. Place squash in a Dutch oven; cover with water. Bring to a boil. Cover, reduce heat, and simmer 35 minutes or until tender. Drain.
2. Preheat oven to 400°.
3. Cook rice according to package directions, omitting salt and fat.
4. While squash and rice cook, melt butter in a medium, heavy saucepan over medium heat. Add shallots and garlic; sauté 2 minutes or until tender. Add flour; cook 1 minute, stirring constantly with a whisk. Gradually add milk; cook 5 minutes or until mixture is thick, stirring constantly. Remove from heat; stir in parsley and next 4 ingredients.

5. Scoop out squash pulp; discard squash peel. Combine squash, cheese, and garlic-butter sauce in a large bowl; beat with a mixer at medium speed until well blended. Stir in rice. Pour squash mixture into a 1½-quart casserole coated with cooking spray.
6. Bake at 400° for 45 minutes or until edges are golden and top is set. Let stand 5 minutes before serving. YIELD: 6 servings (serving size: ½ cup).

POINTS value: 5; **Exchanges:** 1½ Starch, 3 Vegetable, 1 Fat
Per serving: CAL 232 (28% from fat); PRO 7.8g; FAT 7.1g (sat 4.3g); CARB 36.5g; FIB 3.1g; CHOL 22mg; IRON 2.3mg; SOD 398mg; CALC 185mg

NUTTY BASMATI RICE

prep: 3 minutes • cook: 22 minutes
other: 5 minutes

Serve this simple, nutty rice alongside your family's favorite chicken or pork dish. We preferred the flavor of curly leaf parsley in this recipe rather than flat-leaf parsley. Toast the walnuts while the rice simmers so the nuts can be stirred in when the rice is done.

1   (14-ounce) can fat-free, less-sodium chicken broth
2   tablespoons light stick butter
¾   teaspoon salt
¼   teaspoon freshly ground black pepper
1   cup uncooked basmati rice
¼   cup chopped walnuts, toasted
¼   cup chopped fresh parsley

1. Bring first 4 ingredients to a boil in a medium saucepan. Add rice; cover, reduce heat, and simmer 18 minutes or until rice is tender

and liquid is absorbed. Remove from heat; let stand, covered, 5 minutes. Add walnuts and parsley, and fluff with a fork. YIELD: 6 servings (serving size: ⅔ cup).

POINTS value: 4; **Exchanges:** 2 Starch, ½ Fat
Per serving: CAL 175 (27% from fat); PRO 3.8g; FAT 5.3g (sat 1.6g); CARB 31.4g; FIB 1.3g; CHOL 7mg; IRON 1.3mg; SOD 466mg; CALC 9mg

LEMON-BASIL ORZO WITH PARMESAN

(pictured on page 137)
prep: 6 minutes • cook: 16 minutes

¾   cup uncooked orzo
2   teaspoons olive oil
2   teaspoons grated lemon rind
2   garlic cloves, minced
¼   cup chopped fresh basil
2   tablespoons (½ ounce) grated Parmigiano-Reggiano cheese
¼   teaspoon salt
¼   teaspoon black pepper
Basil sprigs (optional)

1. Cook the orzo according to package directions, omitting the salt and fat. Drain.
2. While orzo cooks, heat oil in a medium nonstick skillet over medium-high heat. Add lemon rind and garlic; sauté 1 minute. Remove from heat. Add orzo, chopped basil, and next 3 ingredients; toss well. Garnish with basil sprigs, if desired. Serve immediately. YIELD: 4 servings (serving size: ½ cup).

POINTS value: 3; **Exchanges:** 1½ Starch, ½ Fat
Per serving: CAL 154 (21% from fat); PRO 5.1g; FAT 3.6g (sat 0.7g); CARB 24.8g; FIB 1.4g; CHOL 2mg; IRON 0.2mg; SOD 184mg; CALC 36mg

CREAMY POLENTA

prep: 3 minutes • cook: 8 minutes

A favorite in Northern Italy, this quick side dish takes the place of mashed potatoes, rice, or noodles at the dinner table. Soft polenta is best served immediately while it's still creamy. But leftover polenta can be chilled in a pan until firm and then cut into squares and pan-seared for a side dish at another meal.

1¾   cups 1% low-fat milk
½   teaspoon salt
1   (14-ounce) can fat-free, less-sodium chicken broth
1   cup instant dry polenta
¼   cup (1 ounce) preshredded Parmesan, Romano, Asiago cheese blend (such as DiGiorno)
1   tablespoon butter
¼   teaspoon black pepper

1. Bring first 3 ingredients to a boil in a medium saucepan. Reduce heat to low, and slowly add polenta, stirring constantly with a whisk. Cook 3 minutes or until thick, stirring frequently. Remove from heat, and add cheese, butter, and pepper, stirring until cheese melts. Serve immediately. YIELD: 8 servings (serving size: ½ cup).

POINTS value: 2; **Exchanges:** 1 Starch, 1 Fat
Per serving: CAL 124 (23% from fat); PRO 6.1g;
FAT 3.1g (sat 2.0g); CARB 13.3g; FIB 1.9g;
CHOL 8mg; IRON 0mg; SOD 375mg;
CALC 126mg

SPINACH AND GARLIC COUSCOUS

prep: 5 minutes • cook: 8 minutes
other: 5 minutes

This tasty accompaniment combines both a vegetable and a starch for a great "one-dish" side.

1   teaspoon olive oil
½   cup finely chopped onion
1   (10-ounce) package frozen chopped spinach, thawed, drained, and squeezed dry
1   tablespoon bottled minced garlic
¾   teaspoon salt
½   teaspoon freshly ground black pepper
1   (14-ounce) can fat-free, less-sodium chicken broth
2   tablespoons light stick butter
1   (10-ounce) package couscous

1. Heat oil in a large saucepan over medium-high heat. Add onion; sauté 4 minutes or until tender. Add spinach and next 3 ingredients; sauté 1 minute. Add broth and butter; bring to a boil, and stir in couscous. Remove from heat; cover and let stand 5 minutes. Fluff with a fork. Serve immediately. YIELD: 8 servings (serving size: ¾ cup).

POINTS value: 3; **Exchanges:** 2 Starch, ½ Fat
Per serving: CAL 175 (14% from fat); PRO 6.9g;
FAT 2.8g (sat 1.2g); CARB 30.7g; FIB 3.0g;
CHOL 5mg; IRON 1.1mg; SOD 379mg;
CALC 66mg

COUSCOUS WITH CRANBERRIES AND PINE NUTS

prep: 2 minutes • cook: 5 minutes
other: 5 minutes

Using broth instead of water gives this dish added flavor without additional fat. Use this tip when cooking rice and mashed potatoes, too. It's a great way to punch up the flavor.

1¼   cups fat-free, less-sodium chicken broth
1   teaspoon olive oil
¼   teaspoon salt
1   cup uncooked whole wheat couscous
¼   cup sweetened dried cranberries
2   tablespoons pine nuts, toasted
2   tablespoons chopped fresh flat-leaf parsley

1. Bring first 3 ingredients to a boil in a medium saucepan. Stir in couscous and cranberries. Remove from heat; cover and let stand 5 minutes. Add pine nuts and parsley; fluff with a fork. Serve immediately. YIELD: 4 servings (serving size: ¾ cup).

POINTS value: 3; **Exchanges:** 1½ Starch, ½ Fruit, ½ Fat
Per serving: CAL 172 (25% from fat); PRO 5.6g; FAT 4.7g (sat 0.4g); CARB 29.7g; FIB 4.2g; CHOL 0mg; IRON 1.3mg; SOD 340mg; CALC 14mg

Soups & Stews

CHINESE HOT AND SOUR SOUP

prep: 15 minutes • cook: 21 minutes

Serve this soup as a light meal, or pair it with Shrimp Fried Rice with Edamame on page 58 for an Asian-inspired meal with a total **POINTS** *value of 9.*

3   cups fat-free, less-sodium chicken broth
1   tablespoon low-sodium soy sauce
1½ teaspoons chili garlic sauce (such as Lee Kum Kee)
1   (4-ounce) package gourmet blend mushrooms (baby bella, shiitake, and oyster mushrooms), sliced
½   (16-ounce) package firm tofu, drained and cubed
¼   cup drained sliced bamboo shoots, cut into julienne strips
¼   cup rice wine vinegar
¼   teaspoon ground white pepper
¼   cup water
1½ tablespoons cornstarch
1   large egg, lightly beaten
1   teaspoon sesame oil
Sliced green onions (optional)

1. Bring first 4 ingredients to a boil in a Dutch oven. Reduce heat, and simmer, uncovered, 10 minutes. Add tofu and next 3 ingredients. Bring to a boil; reduce heat, and simmer, uncovered, 5 minutes.
2. Combine water and cornstarch in a small bowl; stir well with a whisk. Add cornstarch mixture to soup. Bring to a boil, and cook 1 minute or until soup begins to thicken. Reduce heat to medium.

3. Pour egg in a slow, steady stream into simmering soup. Stir in sesame oil. Garnish with green onions, if desired. Serve immediately. YIELD: 5 servings (serving size: 1 cup).

POINTS value: 2; **Exchanges:** 1½ Vegetable, 1 Lean Meat
Per serving: CAL 88 (33% from fat); PRO 7.3g; FAT 3.2g (sat 0.6g); CARB 7.5g; FIB 0.6g; CHOL 42mg; IRON 1.2mg; SOD 596mg; CALC 22mg

POTATO AND PARSNIP SOUP WITH BACON

prep: 18 minutes • cook: 40 minutes

Fresh parsnips are available year-round, but their peak seasons are fall and winter. Parsnips add a slight sweetness to this hearty soup.

2   thick-cut bacon slices
1   cup diced onion (about 1 medium)
⅓   cup diced celery (about 1 stalk)
2½ cups fat-free, less-sodium chicken broth
1   cup diced peeled parsnip (about 2 small)
3½ cups diced peeled Yukon gold potato (about 1½ pounds)
1   cup 1% low-fat milk
½   teaspoon salt
¼   teaspoon black pepper
2   tablespoons chopped fresh parsley

1. Cook bacon in a Dutch oven over medium-high heat until crisp. Remove bacon from pan, reserving 2 teaspoons drippings in pan. Crumble bacon; set aside.
2. Place pan over medium-high heat. Add onion and celery to

drippings in pan; sauté 5 minutes or until tender. Stir in broth and parsnip; bring to a boil. Cover, reduce heat, and simmer 5 minutes. Stir in potato; cover and simmer 19 minutes or until vegetables are tender. Remove from heat; stir in milk, salt, and pepper.
3. Spoon 3 cups soup into a large bowl; mash vegetables with a potato masher, and return soup to pan. Stir in parsley. Ladle soup into bowls, and sprinkle each with crumbled bacon. YIELD: 6 servings (serving size: 1 cup soup and 1 teaspoon bacon).

POINTS value: 4; **Exchanges:** 1 Starch, 2½ Vegetable, 1 Fat
Per serving: CAL 192 (29% from fat); PRO 7.0g; FAT 6.3g (sat 2.2g); CARB 27.0g; FIB 2.7g; CHOL 10mg; IRON 1.2mg; SOD 593mg; CALC 69mg

TORTELLINI-TOMATO SOUP

prep: 6 minutes • cook: 26 minutes

2   teaspoons olive oil
1¼ cups chopped onion (about 1 medium)
2   garlic cloves, minced
2   (14-ounce) cans fat-free, less-sodium chicken broth
1   (28-ounce) can crushed tomatoes
½   cup water
1   teaspoon sugar
1   teaspoon dried basil
¼   teaspoon black pepper
1   (9-ounce) package refrigerated three-cheese tortellini
¼   cup (1 ounce) preshredded fresh Parmesan cheese

1. Heat oil in a Dutch oven over medium-high heat. Add onion; sauté

5 minutes or until tender. Add garlic; sauté 1 minute. Add broth and next 5 ingredients. Bring to a boil; cover, reduce heat, and simmer 10 minutes. Add tortellini; simmer, uncovered, 5 to 7 minutes or until pasta is tender. Ladle soup into bowls; sprinkle with Parmesan cheese. YIELD: 6 servings (serving size: 1¼ cups soup and 2 teaspoons cheese).

POINTS value: 4; Exchanges: 1 Starch, 4 Vegetable, 1 Fat
Per serving: CAL 227 (23% from fat); PRO 11.3g; FAT 5.9g (sat 2.4g); CARB 34.8g; FIB 3.9g; CHOL 20mg; IRON 2.6mg; SOD 728mg; CALC 165mg

SUMMER VEGETABLE SOUP

prep: 18 minutes • cook: 21 minutes

Substitute frozen corn for fresh and 2 (14.5-ounce) cans diced tomatoes, drained, for fresh summer tomatoes, if desired.

2   teaspoons olive oil
1½   cups diced onion (about 1 large)
1   garlic clove, minced
3   (14-ounce) cans fat-free, less-sodium chicken broth
2¼   cups (1-inch) sliced fresh green beans (about 8 ounces)
1¼   cups diced zucchini (about 1 small)
1¼   cups diced yellow squash (about 1 small)
1   cup fresh corn kernels (about 2 ears)
2   large tomatoes (about 1½ pounds), chopped
½   cup chopped fresh basil
¼   teaspoon salt
¼   teaspoon black pepper

1. Heat olive oil in a large Dutch oven over medium heat. Add onion; sauté 5 minutes. Add garlic; sauté 1 minute. Add chicken broth; bring to a boil. Stir in green beans, and bring to a boil; cook 3 minutes. Add zucchini, yellow squash, and corn. Bring to a boil, and cook 4 minutes or until vegetables are tender. Stir in tomatoes; bring to a boil. Remove from heat; stir in basil, salt, and pepper. YIELD: 6 servings (serving size: about 1⅓ cups).

POINTS value: 2; Exchanges: 3½ Vegetable, ½ Fat
Per serving: CAL 99 (19% from fat); PRO 5.8g; FAT 2.1g (sat 0.3g); CARB 16.9g; FIB 3.2g; CHOL 0mg; IRON 1.0mg; SOD 639mg; CALC 41mg

ZUCCHINI AND AVOCADO SOUP WITH CUCUMBER SALSA

(pictured on page 159)
prep: 18 minutes • cook: 7 minutes
other: 2 hours and 30 minutes

3   cups chopped zucchini (about 2 medium)
½   cup thinly sliced green onions, divided
1   (14-ounce) can vegetable broth (such as Swanson)
1¼   cups diced seeded peeled cucumber (about 1 large)
1   tablespoon chopped fresh cilantro
3   tablespoons fresh lime juice, divided
½   teaspoon salt, divided
¾   cup diced peeled avocado (1 medium)
¾   cup low-fat buttermilk
¼   teaspoon ground cumin

1. Combine zucchini, ¼ cup green onions, and broth in a large saucepan; bring to a boil. Cover, reduce heat, and simmer 5 to 7 minutes or until zucchini is tender. Remove from heat; cool 30 minutes.
2. While zucchini mixture cools, combine remaining ¼ cup green onions, cucumber, cilantro, 1 tablespoon lime juice, and ¼ teaspoon salt in a small bowl; toss well. Cover and chill.
3. Place remaining 2 tablespoons lime juice, remaining ¼ teaspoon salt, zucchini mixture, avocado, buttermilk, and cumin in a blender, and process until mixture is smooth. Cover and chill at least 2 hours. Pour soup into bowls, and top with cucumber salsa. Serve chilled. YIELD: 4 servings (serving size: 1 cup soup and ¼ cup salsa).

POINTS value: 2; Exchanges: 2½ Vegetable, 1½ Fat
Per serving: CAL 123 (54% from fat); PRO 5.1g; FAT 7.3g (sat 1.5g); CARB 13.0g; FIB 5.1g; CHOL 2mg; IRON 0.6mg; SOD 768mg; CALC 76mg

VERSATILE DUTCH OVEN

A Dutch oven is neither Dutch nor an oven; rather, it's a deep pot with a tight-fitting lid that can go from cooktop to oven. It usually holds 3 to 6 quarts. Some versions come with a long handle, like a skillet.

Dutch ovens are frequently used for braising and for making soups, stews, chili, pot roasts, and pasta. They're also great for cooking large amounts of greens, such as spinach.

BLACK BEAN SOUP

prep: 9 minutes • cook: 27 minutes
other: 15 minutes

It's hard to beat the cool cucumber-laced cream on top of this soup, but you can top each serving with 1 tablespoon shredded reduced-fat sharp Cheddar cheese and 1 teaspoon chopped fresh cilantro instead. Served with cheese, each bowl has a POINTS value of 3.

Cucumber-Cilantro Cream
1   teaspoon olive oil
1½   cups chopped onion (about
     1 large)
1¼   cups chopped red bell pepper
     (about 1 small)
2   garlic cloves, minced
2   (15-ounce) cans black beans,
     rinsed and drained
2   (14-ounce) cans fat-free,
     less-sodium chicken broth
1   (14½-ounce) can petite-cut
     diced tomatoes with jalapeños,
     undrained
1   tablespoon chili powder
1   teaspoon ground cumin

1. Prepare the Cucumber-Cilantro Cream.
2. Heat oil in a Dutch oven over medium-high heat. Add onion, bell pepper, and garlic; sauté 5 minutes or until vegetables are tender. Add beans and next 4 ingredients; bring to a boil. Reduce heat, and simmer, uncovered, 15 minutes. Remove from heat; cool slightly.
3. Place 2 cups soup in a blender; process until smooth. Return pureed soup to pan; stir well. Ladle soup into bowls, and top with Cucumber-Cilantro Cream.

YIELD: 6 servings (serving size: 1⅓ cups soup and about 2 tablespoons Cucumber-Cilantro Cream).

POINTS value: 3; **Exchanges:** 1 Starch, 3 Vegetable
Per serving: CAL 162 (16% from fat); PRO 9.3g;
FAT 2.8g (sat 1.2g); CARB 31.1g; FIB 8.6g;
CHOL 5mg; IRON 3.0mg; SOD 977mg;
CALC 91mg

CUCUMBER-CILANTRO CREAM

½   cup grated seeded peeled
     cucumber (about 1 medium)
⅓   cup reduced-fat sour cream
2   tablespoons chopped fresh
     cilantro
2   teaspoons fresh lime juice
⅛   teaspoon salt

1. Combine all ingredients in a small bowl; stir well. Cover and chill until ready to serve. YIELD: ¾ cup (serving size: 2 tablespoons).

POINTS value: 1; **Exchange:** ½ Fat
Per serving: CAL 20 (73% from fat); PRO 0.5g;
FAT 1.6g (sat 1.0g); CARB 1.0g; FIB 0.1g;
CHOL 5mg; IRON 0.0mg; SOD 54mg;
CALC 16mg

VEGGIE TIPS

To keep vitamins and minerals as intact as possible, cut vegetables just before cooking, and keep the pieces reasonably large (small pieces expose more surface area and therefore increase nutrient loss). Boiling zaps nutrients the most, followed by steaming and microwaving. If you use the liquid that the vegetables are cooked in and don't overcook, you retain the nutrients.

YELLOW-GREEN SPLIT PEA SOUP

prep: 18 minutes • cook: 52 minutes
other: 15 minutes

Using yellow and green split peas makes a stunning presentation, but the soup is just as tasty with only one color pea. Pick your favorite color and use 1½ cups peas; then there's no need to divide the ingredients and cook them in separate pans. You'll need a Dutch oven when cooking all of the ingredients together to make a single-colored soup.

2   tablespoons olive oil
2   cups chopped onion
     (about 2 medium)
¾   cup chopped carrot (about
     1 large)
½   teaspoon salt, divided
2   garlic cloves, minced
¾   cup yellow split peas
3   cups water, divided
3   cups fat-free, less-sodium
     chicken broth, divided
1   tablespoon low-sodium soy
     sauce, divided
¾   cup green split peas
¼   teaspoon freshly ground black
     pepper, divided
2   tablespoons sour cream
1   tablespoon buttermilk
Chopped fresh chives (optional)

1. Heat oil in a large saucepan over medium heat. Add onion and carrot; sauté 5 minutes. Stir in ¼ teaspoon salt and garlic; sauté 1 minute.
2. Remove half of onion mixture to another large saucepan. Add yellow peas to 1 pan; add ⅛ teaspoon salt, 1½ cups water, 1½ cups broth, and 1½ teaspoons soy sauce.

3. Add green peas, remaining ⅛ teaspoon salt, remaining 1½ cups water, remaining 1½ cups broth, and remaining 1½ teaspoons soy sauce to onion mixture in second pan. Bring both pans to a boil; cover, reduce heat, and simmer 45 minutes or just until peas are tender. Stir ⅛ teaspoon pepper into each pan. Cool slightly.

4. Pour yellow pea soup into blender; process on low speed until smooth. Return to pan. Repeat procedure with green pea soup, returning to other pan. Carefully pour about ⅔ cup each of yellow pea soup and green pea soup into individual bowls at the same time, so that soup pours evenly from each side, creating 2 colors in each bowl.

5. Combine sour cream and buttermilk; stir well with a whisk. Drizzle sour cream mixture over each serving. Garnish with chopped chives, if desired. Serve immediately.

YIELD: 6 servings (serving size: about 1¼ cups soup and 1½ teaspoons sour cream mixture).

POINTS value: 6; **Exchanges:** 2½ Starch, 1 Vegetable, 1 Fat
Per serving: CAL 267 (19% from fat); PRO 15.4g; FAT 5.8g (sat 1.3g); CARB 39.7g; FIB 1.5g; CHOL 2mg; IRON 2.0mg; SOD 609mg; CALC 28mg

ZESTY PROVENÇALE BOUILLABAISSE WITH PISTOU

prep: 16 minutes • cook: 52 minutes

A favorite in Provence, this seafood stew is often ladled over thick slices of French bread. The pistou, France's version of pesto, kicks the flavor up a notch. The stew mellows as it stands, so it can even be made ahead.

6   whole allspice
2   (2 x 1-inch) orange rind strips
1   thyme sprig
1   bay leaf
1   dried hot red chile
1   teaspoon olive oil
Cooking spray
2   cups chopped onion (about 1 large)
¾   cup chopped celery (about 2 stalks)
2   garlic cloves, minced
½   cup dry white wine or fat-free, less-sodium chicken broth
1   (28-ounce) can diced tomatoes, undrained
1   (8-ounce) bottle clam juice
1   cup fat-free, less-sodium chicken broth
½   teaspoon fennel seeds
⅛   teaspoon saffron threads
½   cup loosely packed fresh basil leaves
3   tablespoons olive oil
⅛   teaspoon salt
⅛   teaspoon black pepper
2   garlic cloves, peeled and halved
6   ounces halibut fillet, cut into pieces
6   ounces sea scallops
6   ounces medium shrimp, peeled and deveined

1. Place first 5 ingredients on a double layer of cheesecloth. Gather edges of cheesecloth together; tie securely.

2. Heat 1 teaspoon oil in a large Dutch oven coated with cooking spray over medium-high heat. Add onion and celery; sauté 3 minutes or until tender. Add garlic; sauté 1 minute. Add wine, and cook 1 to 2 minutes or until liquid evaporates, scraping pan to loosen browned bits. Add cheesecloth bag, tomatoes, and next 4 ingredients; bring to a boil. Reduce heat to low, and simmer, uncovered, 35 minutes.

3. While stew simmers, combine basil and next 4 ingredients in a food processor; process until smooth. Spoon pistou into a small bowl; set aside.

4. Remove cheesecloth bag from stew, and discard. Bring stew to a boil. Stir in fish and scallops; cover and cook 2 minutes. Stir in shrimp; cover and cook 3 minutes or until seafood is done. Ladle soup into bowls, and top with pistou. YIELD: 4 servings (serving size: 1¾ cups stew and 1 tablespoon pistou).

POINTS value: 7; **Exchanges:** 4 Vegetable, 3 Lean Meat, 1 Fat
Per serving: CAL 319 (38% from fat); PRO 28.5g; FAT 13.5g (sat 1.9g); CARB 21.7g; FIB 4.7g; CHOL 94mg; IRON 2.9mg; SOD 780mg; CALC 137mg

MEATBALL SOUP WITH SPINACH

(pictured on page 158)
prep: 25 minutes • cook: 30 minutes

1	large onion
1	(1.2-ounce) slice white bread
1	pound ground sirloin
½	teaspoon black pepper, divided
1	large egg white
2	teaspoons olive oil
1	cup diced carrot
1	cup water
3	(10½-ounce) cans condensed beef consommé, undiluted
1	(14½-ounce) can diced tomatoes with basil, garlic, and oregano, undrained
1	(6-ounce) package fresh baby spinach, coarsely chopped
¼	cup (1 ounce) grated fresh Parmesan cheese

1. Grate 2 tablespoons onion; place in a large bowl. Chop remaining onion to measure 2 cups; set aside. Place bread in a food processor; pulse 10 times or until coarse crumbs measure ⅓ cup. Add the breadcrumbs, meat, ¼ teaspoon pepper, and egg white to grated onion in bowl; mix with hands until well blended. Shape mixture into 42 (1-inch) meatballs; set aside.
2. Heat oil in a large Dutch oven over medium heat. Add 2 cups chopped onion and carrot; sauté 5 minutes or until vegetables are tender. Add water, consommé, and tomatoes; bring to a boil. Reduce heat to medium. Carefully add meatballs to soup; simmer 20 minutes or until meatballs are no longer pink. Stir in remaining ¼ teaspoon pepper and spinach. Ladle soup into bowls, and sprinkle with Parmesan cheese.
YIELD: 8 servings (serving size: about 1⅓ cups soup and 1½ teaspoons Parmesan cheese).

POINTS value: 3; **Exchanges:** 2½ Vegetable, 2 Lean Meat
Per serving: CAL 169 (24% from fat); PRO 19.5g; FAT 4.6g (sat 1.6g); CARB 13.7g; FIB 2.1g; CHOL 32mg; IRON 3.0mg; SOD 994mg; CALC 97mg

SPICY ASIAN BEEF AND NOODLE SOUP

(pictured on page 159)
prep: 18 minutes • cook: 30 minutes

1	pound flank steak, trimmed
2	teaspoons dark sesame oil, divided
¼	cup minced shallots (about 2)
3	tablespoons minced peeled fresh ginger
4	cups water
¼	cup rice vinegar
¼	teaspoon crushed red pepper
3	(14-ounce) cans less-sodium beef broth
8	ounces uncooked whole wheat angel hair pasta
5	whole star anise
2	(3-inch) cinnamon sticks
2	(3½-ounce) packages fresh shiitake mushrooms
2	cups diagonally cut fresh snow peas
¼	cup fish sauce
1	cup thinly sliced fresh basil leaves
1	cup bean sprouts
¼	cup diagonally sliced green onions (about 2 onions)
8	lime wedges

1. Cut steak diagonally across grain into thin slices.
2. Heat 1 teaspoon oil in a large Dutch oven over high heat. Add steak, and stir-fry 4 minutes or until browned. Remove steak from pan; set aside. Reduce heat to medium. Add remaining 1 teaspoon oil, shallots, and ginger, and stir-fry 1 to 2 minutes. Add water and next 6 ingredients. Bring to a boil; cover, reduce heat, and simmer 15 minutes.
3. While soup simmers, remove and discard stems from mushrooms. Slice mushroom caps into thin strips; set aside. Stir mushrooms, snow peas, and fish sauce into soup; cook 2 minutes or until peas are crisp-tender. Return beef to pan; cook 2 minutes or until thoroughly heated. Remove from heat; stir in basil. Discard cinnamon sticks and star anise. Ladle soup into bowls; top with bean sprouts and green onions. Serve with lime wedges. YIELD: 8 servings (serving size: 1½ cups soup, 2 tablespoons bean sprouts, 1½ teaspoons green onions, and 1 lime wedge).

POINTS value: 4; **Exchanges:** 1 Starch, 2½ Vegetable, 2 Lean Meat
Per serving: CAL 233 (19% from fat); PRO 20.5g; FAT 5.0g (sat 1.7g); CARB 27.8g; FIB 4.9g; CHOL 22mg; IRON 2.9mg; SOD 773mg; CALC 41mg

Walk This Way

KATHI BURGESS • **HEIGHT** 5'3" • **BEFORE** 215 LBS. • **AFTER** 160 LBS.

Philosophy: "Weight loss is not a destination. It is a journey."

A visit with her 105-year-old grandmother inspired Kathi Burgess to rediscover her "old" self. "As I celebrated my grandmother's birthday, I realized that I was a 5'3" 'shrinking' 200-pounder hampered by chronic diseases and pain at the age of 45," she says. "And if I was going to live as long as my grandmother, I had to get back to my former weight."

Like many women, Kathi's weight problem began as "baby fat" left from her pregnancies. "After my children were born, I had no life other than their activities, where I was a spectator, not a participant," she explains. "I went to baby swim class, but I wasn't the one swimming. And I sat on the sidelines watching them play baseball and perform martial arts." With her children almost grown, Kathi was left with 50 extra pounds and weight-related health issues.

"My doctor said that I needed to lose 50 pounds by age 50. Five years

"We are all in this race of a lifetime together, and I love being on the Weight Watchers team."

to lose 50 pounds. That was 10 pounds each year, which seemed like no problem," she recalls. But two years later, instead of losing 20 pounds, Kathi found that she had gained 15. "And then I had three years to lose 65 pounds!"

Realizing that she could not do this alone, Kathi joined *Weight Watchers* and followed in the footsteps of her parents, who were Lifetime members. She also began walking—building up to 12-mile hikes—with her husband, Dennis. Although she lost less than 1 pound each week, over a period of two years, she went from a women's petite size 20 to a size 6 or 8.

After losing 76 pounds, Kathi met her *Weight Watchers* goal of 140 pounds and made Lifetime. But soon afterwards, her father died. "When my beloved dad passed away, depression set in for this 'daddy's girl,'" she says. "My willpower and self-discipline went right out the door. Then my doctor prescribed mood elevators and sleeping aids, and soon my weight shot up 20 pounds above the goal I'd just met!"

Her grief was compounded by an inheritance of her father's *Weight Watchers* records. "I couldn't attend the weekly meetings because they made me think of my dad and start crying. But after six months, I finally realized that this was not what my father would have wanted. He would not have wanted me to gain the weight back. So I got control of myself and my life," she says.

Kathi found her way back to the weekly meetings, where she rediscovered her *Weight Watchers* friends and established new ones. "Weight loss is not a destination. It is a journey," she explains. "We are all in this race of a lifetime together, and I love being on the *Weight Watchers* team."

157

Meatball Soup with Spinach,
page 156

Zucchini and Avocado Soup
with Cucumber Salsa,
page 153

Spicy Asian Beef
and Noodle Soup,
page 156

Southern Supper,
page 166

CURRIED LAMB AND SWEET POTATO STEW

prep: 40 minutes • cook: 1 hour and 2 minutes

3   pounds sweet potatoes, peeled and cut into 1-inch pieces (about 8¾ cups)
4   teaspoons dark sesame oil, divided
½   teaspoon salt, divided
Cooking spray
1   pound boneless leg of lamb, trimmed and cut into bite-sized pieces
1½   tablespoons curry powder
1   cup chopped onion (about 1 medium)
4   garlic cloves, minced
1   (14-ounce) can fat-free, less-sodium chicken broth, divided
2   cups fat-free half-and-half
¼   teaspoon ground red pepper

1. Preheat oven to 450°.
2. Combine sweet potato, 2 teaspoons oil, and ¼ teaspoon salt in a shallow roasting pan coated with cooking spray; toss to coat. Spread into a single layer. Bake at 450° for 40 minutes or until tender and edges begin to blacken.
3. Sprinkle lamb with remaining ¼ teaspoon salt and curry powder; toss well to coat evenly. Heat ½ teaspoon oil in a large Dutch oven over medium-high heat. Add half of lamb; cook 6 to 7 minutes or until browned, stirring occasionally. Remove lamb from pan; keep warm. Repeat procedure with ½ teaspoon oil and remaining half of lamb. Add remaining 1 teaspoon oil to pan. Add onion, garlic, and ½ cup broth; cook 4 minutes or until onion is tender, scraping pan to loosen browned bits.
4. Place half of roasted sweet potatoes and remaining broth in a food processor or blender; process until smooth. Add pureed mixture to onion mixture in pan. Stir in remaining half of roasted sweet potatoes, lamb, half-and-half, and ground red pepper, and cook over medium heat 5 minutes or until thoroughly heated. YIELD: 5 servings (serving size: 1½ cups).

POINTS value: 8; **Exchanges:** 2½ Starch, 1 Fat-Free Milk, 1 Medium-Fat Meat, ½ Fat
Per serving: CAL 385 (20% from fat); PRO 21.6g; FAT 8.7g (sat 2.2g); CARB 49.4g; FIB 6.6g; CHOL 52mg; IRON 3.0mg; SOD 640mg; CALC 152mg

POSOLE

prep: 7 minutes • cook: 1 hour and 2 minutes

Traditionally served at Christmastime, posole (also pozole) is a thick, hearty soup originating from Mexico's Pacific Coast region. It consists of pork, broth, hominy, onion, garlic, and cilantro.

Cooking spray
1   pound pork loin, trimmed and cut into ½-inch cubes
2   cups chopped onion (about 1 large)
4   garlic cloves, minced
1½   tablespoons chili powder
1   (14-ounce) can fat-free, less-sodium chicken broth
1   (15.5-ounce) can golden hominy, drained
¾   teaspoon ground cumin
⅛   teaspoon salt
Chopped fresh cilantro

1. Heat a Dutch oven coated with cooking spray over medium-high heat. Add pork; cook 4 minutes or just until pork begins to brown, stirring constantly. Remove pork from pan; set aside.
2. Place pan over medium heat. Recoat pan with cooking spray. Add onion and garlic; sauté 3 minutes. Add chili powder; cook 15 seconds. Add pork and broth; bring to a boil. Cover, reduce heat, and simmer 30 minutes. Add hominy, cumin, and salt; simmer, uncovered, 20 minutes. Ladle soup into bowls, and sprinkle with fresh cilantro. YIELD: 4 servings (serving size: 1¼ cups).

POINTS value: 4; **Exchanges:** ½ Starch, 2 Vegetable, 3½ Very Lean Meat
Per serving: CAL 226 (19% from fat); PRO 27.2g; FAT 4.6g (sat 1.5g); CARB 18.2g; FIB 4.5g; CHOL 74mg; IRON 2.4mg; SOD 770mg; CALC 51mg

POSOLE DAY

Traditionally, posole, a hearty pork and hominy stew, was made with a pig's head. Although the dish originated in Jalisco (the middle of Mexico's Pacific Coast region), each region has its own version of posole. It comes in the colors of the Mexican flag: red, white, and green, depending on the varieties of chiles used.

In certain parts of Mexico, one day a week is designated "posole day." Shops close early, work comes to a stop, and people go to posole restaurants to eat this rich soup that is often served in earthenware bowls.

PORK AND BUTTERNUT SQUASH STEW

(pictured on back cover)
prep: 20 minutes • **cook:** 39 minutes

Warm up a cold winter's night with a steaming bowl of stew and crusty bread from the oven. Bright orange squash and dark green kale add more than just color to this soup—these winter-garden veggies also add plenty of vitamins and fiber.

2   teaspoons olive oil
1   pound boneless pork loin, trimmed and cut into ¾-inch cubes
½   teaspoon salt
¾   teaspoon freshly ground black pepper, divided
1½   cups chopped onion
1   teaspoon ground coriander
2   garlic cloves, minced
6   cups coarsely chopped fresh kale (about 1 pound)
5   cups cubed peeled butternut squash (about 2¼ pounds)
2   tablespoons tomato paste
3   (14-ounce) cans fat-free, less-sodium chicken broth
1   (14½-ounce) can diced tomatoes, undrained

1. Heat oil in a large Dutch oven over medium heat. Add pork, salt, and ½ teaspoon pepper; cook 9 minutes or until pork is browned, stirring occasionally. Remove pork from pan; set aside.
2. Add onion to pan; sauté 5 minutes or until tender. Add coriander and garlic; sauté 1 minute. Return pork to pan. Add remaining ¼ teaspoon pepper, kale, and remaining ingredients; bring to a boil. Cover, reduce heat, and simmer 20 minutes or until vegetables are tender. **YIELD:** 8 servings (serving size: 1½ cups).

POINTS value: 4; **Exchanges:** 6 Vegetable, 1 Lean Meat
Per serving: CAL 212 (18% from fat); PRO 17.4g; FAT 4.2g (sat 1.1g); CARB 30.0g; FIB 5.6g; CHOL 32mg; IRON 2.9mg; SOD 658mg; CALC 163mg

PORTUGUESE KALE AND SAUSAGE SOUP

prep: 20 minutes • **cook:** 39 minutes

*This hearty soup is a lighter version of caldo verde, a traditional Portuguese soup. We love the flavor, and with a **POINTS** value of 3 per serving, it can't be beat.*

1   tablespoon olive oil
1½   cups coarsely chopped onion
6   garlic cloves, chopped
½   teaspoon salt, divided
4   cups water
3   large red potatoes (about 1¼ pounds), peeled and cut into ½-inch pieces
3   cups fat-free, less-sodium chicken broth
¼   teaspoon crushed red pepper
8   ounces low-fat smoked kielbasa (such as Healthy Choice), thinly sliced
6   cups thinly sliced kale (about 1 pound)

1. Heat oil in a large Dutch oven over medium heat. Add onion, and sauté 3 minutes. Add garlic, and sauté 1 minute. Stir in ¼ teaspoon salt.
2. Add water and potato; bring to a boil. Reduce heat, and simmer, uncovered, 8 to 10 minutes or until potato is tender. Add broth, crushed red pepper, and sausage; bring to a boil. Reduce heat, and simmer, uncovered, 10 minutes. Stir in remaining ¼ teaspoon salt and kale, and simmer 8 to 10 minutes or until kale is tender. **YIELD:** 6 servings (serving size: 1⅓ cups).

POINTS value: 3; **Exchanges:** 1 Starch, 1 Vegetable, 1 Fat
Per serving: CAL 162 (25% from fat); PRO 8.1g; FAT 4.6g (sat 0.8g); CARB 23.1g; FIB 2.8g; CHOL 10mg; IRON 1.9mg; SOD 650mg; CALC 98mg

COCONUT CHICKEN AND RICE SOUP

prep: 10 minutes • **cook:** 10 minutes

We used deli rotisserie chicken to make this Thai-style soup, but any leftover chicken you have on hand will work.

1   (3½-ounce) bag uncooked boil-in-bag long-grain rice
2   (14-ounce) cans fat-free, less-sodium chicken broth
1   (13.5-ounce) can light coconut milk
2   tablespoons minced peeled fresh ginger
2   tablespoons low-sodium soy sauce
1   teaspoon grated lime rind
1   garlic clove, minced
2   cups shredded cooked chicken
½   cup sliced green onions (about 4 onions)
3   tablespoons fresh lime juice
Chopped fresh cilantro (optional)

1. Cook rice according to package directions, omitting salt and fat.

2. While rice cooks, bring broth and next 5 ingredients to a boil in a Dutch oven. Add chicken; reduce heat, and simmer, uncovered, 2 minutes. Stir in cooked rice, green onions, and lime juice. Ladle soup into bowls, and garnish with cilantro, if desired. YIELD: 5 servings (serving size: 1½ cups).

POINTS value: 5; **Exchanges:** 1 Starch, 1 ½ Vegetable, 2 Lean Meat
Per serving: CAL 242 (29% from fat); PRO 21.0g; FAT 7.9g (sat 4.6g); CARB 22.1g; FIB 0.9g; CHOL 50mg; IRON 2.0mg; SOD 702mg; CALC 18mg

SPICY BARBECUE CHICKEN SOUP

prep: 6 minutes • cook: 16 minutes

Cooking spray
1   cup chopped onion (about 1 medium)
2   tablespoons chili powder
1   teaspoon curry powder
½   teaspoon salt
2   garlic cloves, minced
1   jalapeño pepper, minced
2   cups fat-free half-and-half
2   cups chopped cooked chicken
1   cup spicy barbecue sauce (such as KC Masterpiece)
2   (15-ounce) cans black beans, rinsed and drained
2   (10¾-ounce) cans condensed reduced-fat, reduced-sodium tomato soup, undiluted
1   (14-ounce) can fat-free, less-sodium chicken broth
½   cup reduced-fat sour cream

1. Coat a large Dutch oven with cooking spray; place over medium-high heat until hot. Add onion and next 5 ingredients; sauté 4 minutes or until tender, adding water, 1 tablespoon at a time, to prevent scorching, if necessary. Stir in half-and-half and next 5 ingredients. Bring to a boil; reduce heat, and simmer, uncovered, 8 minutes or until thoroughly heated. Ladle soup into bowls; top with sour cream. YIELD: 8 servings (serving size: about 1½ cups soup and 1 tablespoon sour cream).

POINTS value: 5; **Exchanges:** 2 Starch, 1 ½ Vegetable, 1 Lean Meat
Per serving: CAL 277 (19% from fat); PRO 17.4g; FAT 6.0g (sat 2.2g); CARB 37.2g; FIB 4.6g; CHOL 44mg; IRON 2.5mg; SOD 987mg; CALC 101mg

ROASTED CHICKEN WITH WILD RICE SOUP

prep: 16 minutes • cook: 42 minutes

1   (6-ounce) box long-grain and wild rice mix (such as Uncle Ben's)
1   tablespoon olive oil
1½ cups chopped red onion
1   cup chopped celery
1   cup chopped carrot
2   garlic cloves, chopped
1   (8-ounce) package mushrooms, halved
¼   cup all-purpose flour
½   teaspoon dried tarragon
¼   teaspoon dried thyme
2   cups water
2   tablespoons dry sherry
2   (14-ounce) cans fat-free, less-sodium chicken broth
1   (12-ounce) can fat-free evaporated milk
3   cups shredded cooked chicken

1. Cook rice according to package directions, omitting salt and fat.
2. While rice cooks, heat oil in a large Dutch oven over medium-high heat. Add chopped onion and next 4 ingredients, and sauté 6 minutes or until onion is tender.
3. Lightly spoon flour into a dry measuring cup, and level with a knife. Stir flour, tarragon, and thyme into onion mixture, and cook 1 minute, stirring frequently. Add 2 cups water, sherry, broth, and evaporated milk; bring mixture to a boil, stirring occasionally. Reduce heat, and simmer 20 minutes or until slightly thick, stirring occasionally. Stir in cooked rice and chicken; cook 10 minutes or until thoroughly heated. YIELD: 8 servings (serving size: 1½ cups).

POINTS value: 5; **Exchanges:** 2 Starch, 1 ½ Lean Meat
Per serving: CAL 246 (22% from fat); PRO 16.4g; FAT 6.0g (sat 1.9g); CARB 31.2g; FIB 2.1g; CHOL 43mg; IRON 2.2mg; SOD 690mg; CALC 173mg

Ladies Luncheon

Serves 6 • Total **POINTS** value: 12

Creamy Carrot Soup • Chicken-Spinach Salad
Strawberry-Chocolate Mousse Parfaits

GAME PLAN

1. Prepare **Strawberry-Chocolate Mousse Parfaits** up to 3 days in advance.

2. Prepare vinaigrette, and marinate chicken for **Chicken-Spinach Salad.**

3. While chicken marinates, prepare and cook other ingredients for **Chicken-Spinach Salad.**

4. Prepare **Creamy Carrot Soup,** and keep warm.

5. Grill the chicken for **Chicken-Spinach Salad,** and assemble each salad.

CREAMY CARROT SOUP

prep: 26 minutes • cook: 33 minutes • other: 15 minutes

2   teaspoons olive oil
2   teaspoons butter
3   cups diced carrot (about 6 medium carrots)
1   cup chopped onion
1   tablespoon grated peeled fresh ginger
2   cups fat-free, less-sodium chicken broth, divided
1   teaspoon grated orange rind
¼   cup fresh orange juice
1½ tablespoons honey
½   teaspoon salt
½   teaspoon ground turmeric
⅛   teaspoon ground red pepper
1   cup fat-free half-and-half
¼   cup reduced-fat sour cream

1. Heat oil and butter in a Dutch oven over medium heat. Add carrot and onion; sauté 8 minutes or until carrot begins to brown and onion is tender. Add ginger; sauté 30 seconds.

Add 1 cup broth; bring to a boil. Cover, reduce heat, and simmer 15 minutes or until carrot is tender. Remove from heat; cool 15 minutes.
2. Place carrot mixture in a blender or food processor; process until smooth. Add remaining 1 cup broth; process until smooth.
3. Return puree to pan. Stir in orange rind and next 5 ingredients. Place over medium heat; cook 5 minutes. Stir in half-and-half, and cook 2 minutes or until soup is thoroughly heated. Ladle into bowls; top each serving with sour cream. YIELD: 6 servings (serving size: about 1 cup soup and 2 teaspoons sour cream).

POINTS value: 3; **Exchanges:** ½ Starch, 2½ Vegetable, 1 Fat
Per serving: CAL 135 (31% from fat); PRO 2.2g; FAT 4.7g (sat 2.0g); CARB 19.7g; FIB 2.4g; CHOL 9mg; IRON 0.4mg; SOD 319mg; CALC 71mg

CHICKEN-SPINACH SALAD

prep: 9 minutes • cook: 25 minutes
other: 3 hours and 30 minutes

*A vinegar reduction is used to create a
honey-Dijon vinaigrette that doubles as
a marinade for the chicken and a
flavorful dressing for the salad.*

2 tablespoons olive oil, divided
Cooking spray
½ cup finely chopped onion
2 garlic cloves, minced
⅔ cup balsamic vinegar
⅔ cup fat-free, less-sodium
    chicken broth
2 tablespoons Dijon mustard
2 tablespoons honey
¼ teaspoon salt
¼ teaspoon black pepper
1½ pounds skinless, boneless chicken
    breast halves
1 pound asparagus spears
1 (7-ounce) package fresh baby
    spinach (about 10 cups)
1 cup grape tomatoes, halved
2 hard-cooked large eggs, thinly
    sliced
3 bacon slices, cooked and
    crumbled

1. Heat 1 teaspoon oil in a large
nonstick skillet coated with cooking
spray over medium-high heat. Add
onion and garlic, and sauté 3 minutes or until tender. Add remaining 5
teaspoons oil, vinegar, and next 5
ingredients; bring to a boil. Reduce
heat; simmer 8 minutes or until mixture is reduced to 1 cup. Remove
from heat; cool 30 minutes.

2. Pour ½ cup vinegar mixture into
a small bowl; cover and chill. Pour
remaining ½ cup mixture into a
large zip-top plastic bag. Add chicken;
seal bag. Marinate in refrigerator 3
hours, turning bag occasionally.
3. Prepare grill.
4. Remove chicken from bag; discard marinade. Place chicken on grill
rack coated with cooking spray;
cover and grill 5 minutes on each
side or until chicken is done.
5. While chicken cooks, snap off
tough ends of asparagus, and cut
spears into 2-inch pieces. Steam
asparagus, covered, 5 minutes or until
crisp-tender. Drain and plunge
asparagus into ice water; drain.
6. Cut chicken into thin slices.
Divide spinach evenly among 6
plates; top evenly with chicken,
asparagus, tomatoes, egg slices, and
bacon. Drizzle 4 teaspoons reserved
vinegar mixture over each salad.
YIELD: 6 servings.

POINTS value: 6; **Exchanges:** 3 Vegetable,
4 Lean Meat
Per serving: CAL 282 (32% from fat); PRO 33.1g;
FAT 9.9g (sat 2.1g); CARB 15.8g; FIB 0.8g;
CHOL 140mg; IRON 4.1mg; SOD 401mg;
CALC 92mg

*Quick Tip: Rather than
heating up the grill, use a
grill pan. It gives the food
a grilled appearance, and
it provides nice browning.
The cooking time will be
about the same as for
a regular grill.*

STRAWBERRY-CHOCOLATE MOUSSE PARFAITS

prep: 26 minutes • other: 1 hour

2 (2.8-ounce) packages
    European-style dark chocolate
    mousse mix (such as Nestlé)
1⅓ cups 1% chocolate low-fat milk
1 (10-ounce) package frozen
    strawberry halves in light
    syrup, thawed and undrained
4 cups frozen reduced-calorie
    whipped topping, thawed
Fresh strawberries (optional)

1. Combine mousse mix and chocolate milk in a medium bowl; beat
with a mixer at medium speed for
1 minute, scraping sides of bowl as
necessary. Beat at high speed 2 to
3 minutes or until thick and light
in color.
2. Place strawberries and juice in a
blender or food processor; process
until smooth. Pour into a medium
bowl; fold whipped topping into
strawberry puree.
3. Spoon about 3 tablespoons
chocolate mousse into each of
8 (1-cup) champagne flutes or
glasses; top each with ¼ cup strawberry cream. Repeat layers once,
ending with strawberry cream.
Garnish with fresh strawberries, if
desired. Cover and chill at least 1
hour. YIELD: 8 servings (serving size:
1 parfait).
Note: Cover any leftover parfaits, and
refrigerate up to 3 days.

POINTS value: 3; **Exchanges:** 1 Starch, 1 Fruit,
1½ Fat
Per serving: CAL 176 (35% from fat); PRO 4.5g;
FAT 6.9g (sat 3.7g); CARB 26.4g; FIB 3.0g;
CHOL 22mg; IRON 0.3mg; SOD 45mg;
CALC 46mg

Southern Supper

Serves 4 • Total **POINTS** value: 15

**Buttermilk "Fried" Chicken • Smashed Potatoes with Green Onions
Okra, Corn, and Tomatoes • Cornmeal Biscuits**

GAME PLAN

1. Marinate chicken for **Buttermilk "Fried" Chicken.**

2. While chicken marinates, slice green onions and mince garlic for **Smashed Potatoes with Green Onions.** Cook bacon, chop onion, slice okra, and thaw corn for **Okra, Corn, and Tomatoes.** Measure ingredients for **Cornmeal Biscuits.**

3. Bake **Buttermilk "Fried" Chicken.**

4. While chicken bakes, prepare **Smashed Potatoes with Green Onions** and **Okra, Corn, and Tomatoes.** Cut out **Cornmeal Biscuits.**

5. Remove chicken from oven, and keep warm. Bake **Cornmeal Biscuits** at 450°.

BUTTERMILK "FRIED" CHICKEN

(pictured on page 160)
prep: 20 minutes • cook: 45 minutes • other: 6 hours

*Hot sauce and ground red pepper add extra flavor to this
Southern favorite, while crushed melba toast adds crunch to the coating.*

1   cup low-fat buttermilk
1   small onion, halved and thinly sliced
½   teaspoon hot sauce
2   chicken breast halves (about 1 pound), skinned
2   chicken drumsticks (about ½ pound), skinned
2   chicken thighs (about ½ pound), skinned
1   (5¼-ounce) package whole grain melba toast rounds, coarsely crushed
1   teaspoon paprika
½   teaspoon dried basil
¼   teaspoon dried thyme
¼   teaspoon garlic powder
¼   teaspoon onion powder
⅛   teaspoon ground red pepper
½   teaspoon salt
Cooking spray

1. Combine first 3 ingredients in a large heavy-duty zip-top plastic bag.

Add chicken; seal bag, and shake gently to coat chicken. Marinate in refrigerator at least 6 hours.

2. Preheat oven to 400°.

3. Combine melba toast crumbs and next 6 ingredients in a shallow dish. Remove chicken from bag, and discard marinade. Sprinkle chicken with salt. Dredge chicken in crumb mixture, pressing crumbs gently onto chicken to coat.

4. Line a baking sheet with foil, and coat foil with cooking spray. Place chicken on prepared pan. Bake at 400° for 45 minutes or until the chicken is done. YIELD: 4 servings (serving size: 1 breast half or 1 thigh and 1 drumstick).

POINTS value: 7; Exchanges: 1 Starch, 7 Very Lean Meat, ½ Fat
Per serving: CAL 353 (16% from fat); PRO 52.1g; FAT 6.4g (sat 1.6g); CARB 18.1g; FIB 1.6g; CHOL 157mg; IRON 3.0mg; SOD 476mg; CALC 58mg

SMASHED POTATOES
WITH GREEN ONIONS

(pictured on page 160)
prep: 8 minutes • **cook:** 20 minutes

These potatoes are supposed to be lumpy rather than smoothly creamed. A potato masher works best for coarsely mashing the potatoes.

1¾ pounds red potatoes, each cut into eighths
2 tablespoons butter
½ cup sliced green onions (about 3 onions)
1 large garlic clove, minced
¼ cup 1% low-fat milk
¼ cup fat-free sour cream
½ teaspoon salt
¼ teaspoon black pepper

1. Place potatoes in a large saucepan, and cover with water; bring to a boil. Cover, reduce heat, and simmer 12 minutes or until tender.
2. While potatoes cook, melt butter in a large nonstick skillet over medium-high heat. Add green onions and garlic; sauté 3 minutes or until tender. Remove from heat; set aside.
3. Drain potatoes, and return to pan. Add milk, sour cream, salt, and pepper. Mash potatoes with a potato masher until desired consistency. Stir in green onion mixture. YIELD: 6 servings (serving size: ⅔ cup).

POINTS value: 3; **Exchanges:** 1½ Starch, ½ Fat
Per serving: CAL 147 (26% from fat); PRO 3.4g; FAT 4.2g (sat 2.6g); CARB 24.0g; FIB 2.6g; CHOL 11mg; IRON 1.0mg; SOD 217mg; CALC 43mg

OKRA, CORN, AND
TOMATOES

(pictured on page 160)
prep: 4 minutes • **cook:** 23 minutes

Freshly picked small, tender okra pods will cook more quickly than larger pods or pods that have not been recently picked.

2 bacon slices
1 cup chopped onion
1 pound fresh okra, cut into ½-inch slices (about 4⅓ cups)
1 (14.5-ounce) can diced tomatoes with basil, garlic, and oregano, undrained
1 cup frozen whole-kernel corn, thawed
¼ teaspoon salt
⅛ teaspoon black pepper

1. Cook bacon in a large nonstick skillet over medium heat until crisp. Remove bacon from pan, reserving drippings in pan. Crumble bacon, and set aside. Add onion to drippings in pan; sauté 4 minutes or until onion is tender. Add okra; sauté 4 minutes. Add tomatoes, corn, salt, and pepper; cook 5 minutes or until okra is tender, stirring occasionally. Stir in crumbled bacon. YIELD: 5 servings (serving size: ¾ cup).

POINTS value: 2; **Exchanges:** 4½ Vegetable
Per serving: CAL 116 (11% from fat); PRO 5.3g; FAT 1.4g (sat 0.4g); CARB 23.5g; FIB 4.7g; CHOL 3mg; IRON 1.4mg; SOD 519mg; CALC 79mg

CORNMEAL BISCUITS

(pictured on page 160)
prep: 13 minutes • **cook:** 11 minutes

Cornmeal adds a slight crunch to these airy biscuits. Plan on rerolling the dough to get a yield of 9.

1½ cups all-purpose flour
½ cup yellow cornmeal
2 teaspoons baking powder
½ teaspoon salt
¼ teaspoon baking soda
¼ cup chilled butter, cut into small pieces
¾ cup low-fat buttermilk
Cooking spray

1. Preheat oven to 450°.
2. Lightly spoon flour into dry measuring cups; level with a knife. Combine flour and next 4 ingredients in a large bowl. Cut in butter with a pastry blender or 2 knives until mixture resembles coarse meal. Add buttermilk; stir with a fork just until moist.
3. Turn dough out onto a lightly floured surface, and knead 3 to 4 times. Roll dough to ½-inch thickness; cut with a 2½-inch biscuit cutter. Place biscuits on a baking sheet coated with cooking spray. Bake at 450° for 11 minutes or until lightly browned. YIELD: 9 biscuits (serving size: 1 biscuit).

POINTS value: 3; **Exchanges:** 1½ Starch, 1 Fat
Per serving: CAL 157 (32% from fat); PRO 3.5g; FAT 5.6g (sat 3.4g); CARB 23.1g; FIB 1.1g; CHOL 14mg; IRON 1.2mg; SOD 295mg; CALC 89mg

Supper Club

Serves 8 • Total *POINTS* value: 14

Seared Beef Tenderloin with Herbed Shallot Gravy
Strawberry-Apple Salad with Apple Cider Vinaigrette
Broccolini with Garlic and Asiago • Chocolate-Peanut Butter Cup Pie

GAME PLAN

1. Prepare **Chocolate-Peanut Butter Cup Pie,** and freeze.

2. Make **Apple Cider Vinaigrette,** slice strawberries, and toast almonds.

3. Trim broccolini, mince garlic, grate cheese and lemon rind, and juice lemon.

4. Prepare Steps 1 and 2 of **Seared Beef Tenderloin with Herbed Shallot Gravy.**

5. While steaks cook, toss together **Strawberry-Apple Salad with Apple Cider Vinaigrette,** and cook **Broccolini with Garlic and Asiago.**

6. Prepare sauce for steaks.

SEARED BEEF TENDERLOIN WITH HERBED SHALLOT GRAVY

prep: 3 minutes • cook: 35 minutes

1	teaspoon onion powder
½	teaspoon salt
¼	teaspoon black pepper
8	(4-ounce) beef tenderloin steaks (about 1 inch thick)
2	teaspoons olive oil
½	cup Marsala or less-sodium beef broth
1	(14-ounce) can less-sodium beef broth
2	shallots, halved and thinly sliced (about ¾ cup)
1	tablespoon chopped fresh rosemary
1	tablespoon chopped fresh thyme
1	tablespoon all-purpose flour
1	teaspoon water
2	tablespoons light stick butter
¼	teaspoon black pepper

1. Combine first 3 ingredients in a small bowl; stir well. Sprinkle seasoning mixture evenly over steaks.
2. Heat oil in a large nonstick skillet over medium-high heat. Add steaks, and cook 6 minutes on each side or until desired degree of doneness. Remove steaks from skillet; keep warm. Add Marsala, broth, and shallots to pan, stirring to loosen browned bits. Stir in rosemary and thyme. Bring to a boil; reduce heat, and simmer 15 minutes or until shallots are tender and mixture is reduced to 1½ cups.
3. Place flour in a small bowl; add water, stirring with a whisk. Stir flour mixture into broth mixture, and cook 4 minutes or until slightly thick, stirring occasionally. Remove from heat; add butter and ¼ teaspoon pepper, stirring just until butter melts. Serve sauce over steaks.
YIELD: 8 servings (serving size: 1 steak and 3 tablespoons sauce).

POINTS value: 4; **Exchanges:** ½ Vegetable, 3 Lean Meat
Per serving: CAL 185 (46% from fat); PRO 20.6g; FAT 9.5g (sat 3.7g); CARB 3.7g; FIB 0.3g; CHOL 62mg; IRON 2.8mg; SOD 309mg; CALC 14mg

STRAWBERRY-APPLE SALAD WITH APPLE CIDER VINAIGRETTE

prep: 7 minutes • cook: 6 minutes

The thin consistency and light, refreshing flavor of this vinaigrette make it ideal for dressing this salad of delicate greens and fruit.

¼ cup apple cider
2 tablespoons cider vinegar
2 tablespoons vegetable oil
1 tablespoon honey
1 tablespoon lemon juice
¼ teaspoon salt
1 (5-ounce) package spring mix salad greens with herbs
2 cups sliced strawberries
1½ cups chopped Granny Smith apple (about 1 large)
¼ cup sliced almonds, toasted

1. Combine first 6 ingredients in a small bowl; stir well with a whisk.
2. Combine salad greens and next 3 ingredients in a large bowl. Pour vinaigrette over salad; toss gently to coat. YIELD: 8 servings (serving size: about 1 cup).

POINTS value: 2; **Exchanges:** 2 Vegetable, 1 Fat
Per serving: CAL 88 (53% from fat); PRO 1.7g; FAT 5.2g (sat 0.5g); CARB 10.8g; FIB 2.4g; CHOL 0mg; IRON 0.9mg; SOD 84mg; CALC 38mg

BROCCOLINI WITH GARLIC AND ASIAGO

prep: 10 minutes • cook: 12 minutes

Broccolini is a cross between broccoli and Chinese kale. Not only is it tender and sweet, but it's also a nutritional powerhouse. It has as much vitamin C as orange juice, and it provides a substantial amount of folate, vitamin A, and potassium. It will also give you iron, calcium, vitamin B, and fiber.

2 pounds broccolini, trimmed
1 tablespoon olive oil
6 garlic cloves, minced
Olive oil-flavored cooking spray
½ cup (2 ounces) grated Asiago cheese
1 teaspoon grated lemon rind
1 teaspoon fresh lemon juice
½ teaspoon salt
½ teaspoon freshly ground black pepper

1. Preheat oven to 450°.
2. Combine first 3 ingredients in a large bowl, and toss to coat. Arrange broccolini in a single layer on a jelly-roll pan, and coat with cooking spray. Sprinkle with Asiago cheese and remaining ingredients.
3. Bake at 450° for 12 minutes or until broccolini is lightly browned and Asiago cheese melts. Serve immediately. YIELD: 8 servings (serving size: about ⅔ cup).

POINTS value: 2; **Exchanges:** 1½ Vegetable, ½ Medium-Fat Meat
Per serving: CAL 81 (41% from fat); PRO 5.2g; FAT 3.7g (sat 1.5g); CARB 7.2g; FIB 1.1g; CHOL 7mg; IRON 0.8mg; SOD 189mg; CALC 133mg

CHOCOLATE-PEANUT BUTTER CUP PIE

prep: 13 minutes • other: 6 hours

Layers of chocolate ice cream, hot fudge topping, and peanut butter cups fill a chocolate cookie crust in this heavenly four-ingredient dessert. It's no wonder this pie received our Test Kitchens' highest rating and became a staff favorite.

4 cups no-sugar-added chocolate ice cream
½ cup chopped miniature peanut butter cups (about 11 candies), divided
1 (6-ounce) cream-filled chocolate sandwich cookie pie crust (such as Oreo)
¼ cup fat-free hot fudge topping

1. Let ice cream stand at room temperature 5 minutes or until slightly softened.
2. Combine ice cream and ¼ cup chopped candy in a large bowl. Spoon ice cream mixture into bottom of pie crust. Sprinkle remaining ¼ cup candy over top. Cover and freeze at least 6 hours or until firm. Drizzle each slice with hot fudge topping. YIELD: 8 servings (serving size: 1 slice and 1½ teaspoons hot fudge topping).

POINTS value: 6; **Exchanges:** 3 Starch, 1½ Fat
Per serving: CAL 279 (37% from fat); PRO 5.4g; FAT 11.6g (sat 2.4g); CARB 40.0g; FIB 4.3g; CHOL 1mg; IRON 1.3mg; SOD 223mg; CALC 10mg

Tailgate

Serves 8 • Total **POINTS** value: 12

Touchdown Chili • Fresh Fruit Salsa with Cinnamon Chips
Ooey-Gooey Brownies

GAME PLAN

1. Prepare **Cinnamon Chips** up to 2 days in advance, and store in airtight container.

2. Prepare **Fresh Fruit Salsa** up to 1 day in advance, omitting banana.

3. Prepare Steps 1 and 2 of **Ooey-Gooey Brownies.** Let cool.

4. While brownies cool, prepare **Touchdown Chili.**

5. While chili simmers, frost brownies and add banana to fruit salsa.

TOUCHDOWN CHILI

prep: 4 minutes • cook: 1 hour and 5 minutes

If you're looking for a warm, quick classic that everyone will enjoy on game day, this chili scores big. It's not too spicy, so the kids will like it, too. Serve with hot sauce for those who like more heat.

2   pounds ground sirloin
1½   cups chopped red onion (about 1 large)
3   (14½-ounce) cans zesty chili-style diced tomatoes, undrained
½   cup water
¼   cup chili powder
1   teaspoon sugar
½   teaspoon salt
⅛   teaspoon ground red pepper
2   (16-ounce) cans chili beans in mild sauce (such as Bush's), undrained

1. Cook beef and onion in a large Dutch oven over medium-high heat until browned, stirring to crumble. Drain well, and return to pan. Stir in tomatoes and next 5 ingredients; bring to a boil. Reduce heat, and simmer, uncovered, 45 minutes, stirring occasionally. Stir in beans; cook 10 minutes or until thoroughly heated. YIELD: 8 servings (serving size: about 1⅓ cups chili).

POINTS value: 5; **Exchanges:** 1 Starch, 2 Vegetable, 3 Very Lean Meat
Per serving: CAL 288 (21% from fat); PRO 29.2g; FAT 6.8g (sat 2.6g); CARB 29.2g; FIB 8.4g; CHOL 60mg; IRON 5.2mg; SOD 867mg; CALC 83mg

CHILI TOPPERS

Dress up a bowl of chili with any of these tasty toppings.

• ¼ cup oyster crackers (*POINTS* value: 1)
• ¼ cup diced zucchini (*POINTS* value: 0)
• 2 tablespoons shredded reduced-fat Cheddar cheese (*POINTS* value: 1)
• 1 tablespoon low-fat sour cream (*POINTS* value: 0)
• 1 tablespoon chopped onion (*POINTS* value: 0)

FRESH FRUIT SALSA WITH CINNAMON CHIPS

prep: 17 minutes • **cook:** 9 minutes
other: 1 hour

While this refreshing fruit salsa chills, you'll have plenty of time to prepare the sweet crunchy chips. Or you can make the chips up to 2 days before serving and store them in an airtight container. The salsa can be made up to 1 day ahead—just dice the banana, and stir it in right before serving.

2   tablespoons light brown sugar
1   teaspoon grated lime rind
2   tablespoons fresh lime juice
1   teaspoon grated orange rind
2   tablespoons fresh orange juice
1   tablespoon honey
¼   teaspoon ground cinnamon
2   cups diced fresh pineapple
1½ cups diced firm ripe banana
      (about 2 medium)
1   cup diced strawberries
1   cup blueberries
¾   cup diced peeled kiwifruit
      (about 2 kiwifruit)
½   cup coarsely chopped orange
      sections (about 1 large navel
      orange)
Cinnamon Chips

1. Combine first 7 ingredients in a small bowl; stir well.
2. Combine pineapple and next 5 ingredients in a large bowl. Add dressing, tossing gently to coat. Cover and chill 1 to 4 hours. Serve with Cinnamon Chips. YIELD: 8 servings (serving size: ¾ cup salsa and about 5 chips).

CINNAMON CHIPS

½   cup sugar
1   teaspoon ground cinnamon
20 won ton wrappers, each cut in
      half diagonally
Butter-flavored cooking spray

1. Preheat oven to 375°.
2. Combine sugar and cinnamon in a medium bowl; stir well.
3. Coat both sides of won ton wrappers with cooking spray, and dredge in cinnamon-sugar. Arrange won ton wrappers in a single layer on baking sheets coated with cooking spray. Bake at 375° for 9 minutes or until crisp and golden. YIELD: 40 chips.

POINTS value: 3; **Exchanges:** 1 Starch, 2 Fat
Per serving: CAL 191 (2% from fat); PRO 3.1g; FAT 0.4g (sat 0.1g); CARB 47.0g; FIB 3.8g; CHOL 0mg; IRON 1.0mg; SOD 102mg; CALC 29mg

OOEY-GOOEY BROWNIES

prep: 10 minutes • **cook:** 28 minutes
other: 1 hour

Fudgy brownies are topped with a rich chocolate frosting to satisfy any chocolate lover's dream.

1   (13.7-ounce) package fat-free
      fudge brownie mix (such as
      No Pudge!)
1   (6-ounce) container vanilla
      low-fat yogurt
⅓   cup light stick butter, softened
1   teaspoon vanilla extract
½   teaspoon fat-free milk
1   cup powdered sugar
½   cup semisweet chocolate chips,
      melted

1. Preheat oven to 350°.
2. Prepare brownie mix according to package directions, using yogurt. Spread batter into a foil-lined 8-inch square baking pan. Bake at 350° for 28 minutes or until a wooden pick inserted in center comes out clean. Cool completely in pan on a wire rack.
3. Place butter, vanilla, and milk in a medium bowl, and beat with a mixer at medium speed until smooth and creamy. Add powdered sugar, beating at low speed 1 minute or until spreading consistency. Gradually add melted chocolate, beating until smooth. Spread frosting evenly over brownies. Remove brownies from pan by lifting foil. Remove foil; cut into 16 squares. YIELD: 16 servings (serving size: 1 brownie).

POINTS value: 4; **Exchanges:** 2 Starch
Per serving: CAL 168 (20% from fat); PRO 3.0g; FAT 3.7g (sat 2.3g); CARB 32.7g; FIB 0.3g; CHOL 7mg; IRON 1.2mg; SOD 118mg; CALC 59mg

Quick Tip: To easily transport the brownies, remove them from the pan using the foil, and cut into 16 squares. Then return the brownies with the foil to the pan, and cover the pan. When you're ready to serve the brownies, lift out the foil, and move the cut brownies to a serving plate.

Vegetarian Dinner

Serves 6 • Total **POINTS** value: 11

Mushroom and Smoked Provolone Pizza • Roasted Red Pepper-White Bean Dip • Italian Greens with Fennel and Artichokes Chocolate-Cappuccino Meringue Cookies

GAME PLAN

1. Prepare **Chocolate-Cappuccino Meringue Cookies.**

2. Prepare the **Roasted Red Pepper-White Bean Dip.**

3. Prepare vinaigrette, slice fennel bulb, drain artichokes, chop parsley, and shave cheese for **Italian Greens with Fennel and Artichokes.** Chill vinaigrette and salad ingredients separately.

4. Prepare **Mushroom and Smoked Provolone Pizza.**

5. While pizza stands, toss salad with vinaigrette.

MUSHROOM AND SMOKED PROVOLONE PIZZA

prep: 11 minutes • cook: 35 minutes • other: 5 minutes

1   (1-pound) loaf frozen white bread dough
Cooking spray
2   teaspoons olive oil, divided
3   (4-ounce) packages gourmet blend mushrooms (about 6 cups), thinly sliced
1   teaspoon butter
½   cup chopped onion
1   teaspoon minced garlic
2   tablespoons dry red wine
1   teaspoon dried thyme
½   teaspoon salt
½   cup bottled sun-dried tomato pasta sauce (such as Classico)
5   ounces thinly sliced smoked provolone cheese

1. Preheat oven to 400°.
2. Wrap frozen dough loosely with plastic wrap. Microwave on LOW (10% power) 5 to 6 minutes, rotating dough a quarter-turn every 2 minutes. Place dough on a baking sheet coated with cooking spray. Pat dough into a 12 x 9-inch rectangle. Brush with 1 teaspoon olive oil. Bake at 400° for 15 minutes or until lightly browned.

3. While crust bakes, place a large nonstick skillet coated with cooking spray over medium-high heat until hot. Add mushrooms; sauté 6 minutes. Remove from pan; set aside.
4. Heat remaining 1 teaspoon olive oil and butter in pan over medium-high heat. Add onion and garlic; sauté 3 minutes or until tender. Add red wine, thyme, and salt; cook 5 minutes or until most of liquid evaporates. Stir in reserved mushrooms.
5. Spread pasta sauce over pizza crust, leaving a ½-inch border; top with mushroom mixture. Arrange cheese slices over mushrooms. Bake at 400° for 15 minutes or until cheese melts. Remove from oven; let stand 5 minutes. Cut pizza into 6 slices.
YIELD: 6 servings (serving size: 1 slice).
Note: The bread dough can also be thawed overnight in the refrigerator or in 1 to 2 hours at room temperature.

POINTS value: 7; **Exchanges:** 2½ Starch, 1 Vegetable, 1½ Medium-Fat Meat
Per serving: CAL 344 (33% from fat); PRO 16.3g; FAT 12.8g (sat 4.8g); CARB 44.5g; FIB 3.4g; CHOL 18mg; IRON 3.6mg; SOD 899mg; CALC 216mg

ROASTED RED PEPPER-WHITE BEAN DIP

prep: 10 minutes

Cool, crisp cucumber slices make tasty low-cal dippers for this dip, but crunchy breadsticks and melba toasts are delicious, too.

1   (19-ounce) can cannellini beans or other white beans, rinsed and drained
½   cup sliced bottled roasted red bell pepper
1   garlic clove, peeled and halved
2   tablespoons vegetable broth (such as Swanson) or water
2   teaspoons lemon juice
1   teaspoon olive oil
¼   teaspoon salt
⅛   teaspoon ground red pepper
¼   cup (1 ounce) grated Asiago cheese
2   tablespoons chopped fresh basil
2   large cucumbers, sliced

1. Place first 3 ingredients in a food processor or blender; process until smooth, stopping to scrape down sides as necessary. Add broth and next 4 ingredients; process until well blended. Spoon dip into a serving bowl; stir in cheese and basil. Serve with cucumber slices. YIELD: 12 servings (serving size: 2 tablespoons dip and about 4 cucumber slices).

POINTS value: 1; **Exchange:** ½ Starch
Per serving: CAL 54 (21% from fat); PRO 2.7g; FAT 1.3g (sat 0.5g); CARB 7.7g; FIB 2.1g; CHOL 2mg; IRON 0.8mg; SOD 175mg; CALC 43mg

ITALIAN GREENS WITH FENNEL AND ARTICHOKES

prep: 17 minutes

2   tablespoons vegetable broth (such as Swanson)
1   tablespoon orange juice
¼   teaspoon grated lemon rind
2   tablespoons fresh lemon juice
2   teaspoons extravirgin olive oil
1   teaspoon honey
1   teaspoon Dijon mustard
⅛   teaspoon freshly ground black pepper
1   garlic clove, minced
1   small fennel bulb
1   (4-ounce) package organic fresh herb salad (such as Earthbound Farms)
1   (14-ounce) can quartered artichoke hearts, drained
¼   cup coarsely chopped fresh flat-leaf parsley
1   ounce shaved Asiago cheese

1. Combine first 9 ingredients in a small bowl; stir well with a whisk.
2. Remove and discard stalks from fennel bulb. Cut bulb in half vertically, and discard core. Cut each half crosswise into thin slices to measure ½ cup. Reserve remaining fennel for another use.
3. Combine ½ cup fennel, salad greens, artichokes, and parsley in a bowl. Pour vinaigrette over salad; toss gently to coat. Sprinkle cheese over salad. YIELD: 6 servings (serving size: 1⅓ cups).

POINTS value: 1; **Exchanges:** 2½ Vegetable, ½ Fat
Per serving: CAL 86 (32% from fat); PRO 4.8g; FAT 3.0g (sat 1.1g); CARB 12.6g; FIB 3.9g; CHOL 4mg; IRON 0.4mg; SOD 489mg; CALC 67mg

CHOCOLATE-CAPPUCCINO MERINGUE COOKIES

(pictured on page 4)
prep: 8 minutes • cook: 5 minutes
other: 30 minutes

⅓   cup semisweet chocolate chips
8   cappuccino-flavored meringue cookies (such as Miss Meringue)
2½ tablespoons finely chopped pecans, toasted

1. Place chocolate chips in a 1-cup glass measure. Microwave at HIGH 30 to 45 seconds or until morsels are softened, stirring until smooth.
2. Dip tops of each cookie in melted chocolate; sprinkle evenly with pecans. Let stand at least 30 minutes or until chocolate is set. YIELD: 8 servings (serving size: 1 cookie).
Note: Look for meringue cookies in the produce department or on the cookie aisle of supermarkets.

POINTS value: 2; **Exchanges:** ½ Starch, ½ Fat
Per serving: CAL 70 (49% from fat); PRO 0.8g; FAT 3.8g (sat 1.4g); CARB 9.7g; FIB 0.6g; CHOL 0mg; IRON 0.6mg; SOD 9mg; CALC 8mg

MICROWAVES

Microwave ovens vary in wattage, ranging from 600 watts to 1,200 watts. All foods cooked in a microwave oven are cooked on either HIGH (100% power), MEDIUM-HIGH (70% power), MEDIUM (50% power), MEDIUM-LOW (30% power), or LOW (10% power). Varying the power level enables you to essentially control the "heat" the oven is producing.

One day's menu provides at least two servings of dairy and at least five servings of fruits and/or vegetables.

	MONDAY	TUESDAY	WEDNESDAY	THURSDAY
BREAKFAST	**high-fiber toast,** 1 slice, with 1 tablespoon peanut butter **blueberries,** 1 cup **orange-mango fat-free yogurt,** 1 (6-ounce) carton	**fruit-and-nut trail mix bar,** 1 **fat-free milk,** 1 cup **orange juice,** ½ cup	**Cranberry-Walnut Oatmeal** (Stir 2 tablespoons each of sweetened dried cranberries and chopped walnuts and 1 tablespoon brown sugar into 1 cup hot cooked oatmeal - ***POINTS* value: 6.**) **fat-free milk,** 1 cup	**high-fiber toast,** 1 slice, with 2 teaspoons light butter **scrambled egg,** 1 large egg **strawberry fat-free yogurt,** 1 (6-ounce) carton
LUNCH	**Roast Beef and Swiss Sandwich** (Top 1 slice high-fiber bread with 2 teaspoons fat-free mayonnaise, 1 teaspoon Dijon mustard, 2 ounces extralean roast beef, 1 [¾-ounce] slice Swiss cheese, lettuce, tomato slice, and another bread slice - ***POINTS* value: 6.**) **celery sticks,** 1 cup, with 2 tablespoons fat-free Ranch dressing **pear,** 1 medium	**low-fat supreme pizza,** frozen, 1 single-serving size **lemon chiffon fat-free yogurt,** 1 (6-ounce) carton **cantaloupe chunks,** 1 cup	**Tortellini-Tomato Soup,** page 152, 1 serving **Swiss Cheese Toast** (Place 1 [¾-ounce] slice Swiss cheese on 1 slice high-fiber bread. Broil until cheese melts - ***POINTS* value: 3.**) **celery sticks,** 1 cup	**Spinach Salad with Beef and Feta** (Combine 2 cups torn spinach leaves; ½ cup diced tomato; 2 ounces thinly sliced extralean roast beef, cut into thin strips; and 2 tablespoons crumbled feta cheese. Drizzle with 2 tablespoons light vinaigrette - ***POINTS* value: 4.**) **melba toast,** 6 rounds **fat-free milk,** 1 cup
DINNER	**boiled shrimp,** 6 ounces peeled **boiled corn on the cob,** 1 small ear **steamed new potatoes,** 4 ounces, with 2 teaspoons light butter	**Grilled Two-Mustard Pork Tenderloin,** page 93, 1 serving **Oven-Roasted Sweet Potato Wedges,** page 145, 1 serving **Broccoli with Browned Butter and Breadcrumbs,** page 142, 1 serving	**Salad Pizzas with Feta,** page 62, 1 serving **blueberries,** 1 cup **fat-free milk,** 1 cup	**Broiled Salmon with Curried Honey Glaze,** page 54, 1 serving **mashed potatoes,** ½ cup **steamed green beans,** 1 cup
SNACK	**Almond Meringues,** page 32, 3 cookies **fat-free milk,** 1 cup	**mixed berry fat-free yogurt smoothie,** 1 (7-ounce) container	**vanilla light ice cream,** ½ cup, with 1 tablespoon fat-free caramel sundae syrup	**vanilla light ice cream,** ½ cup, with 1 tablespoon fat-free caramel sundae syrup
POINTS VALUE	***POINTS* value for the day: 26**	***POINTS* value for the day: 26**	***POINTS* value for the day: 27**	***POINTS* value for the day: 26**

	FRIDAY	SATURDAY	SUNDAY
BREAKFAST	**Artichoke Omelets, page 73,** 1 serving **cantaloupe chunks,** 1 cup **vanilla fat-free yogurt,** 1 (6-ounce) carton	**Honey-Walnut Oatmeal** (Stir 1½ tablespoons chopped walnuts and 1 tablespoon honey into 1 cup hot cooked oatmeal - *POINTS* value: **4**.) **orange juice,** ½ cup	**Blueberry-Lemon Muffins, page 26,** 1 serving **fat-free milk,** 1 cup
LUNCH	**New England clam chowder,** low-fat canned, 1 cup **melba toast,** 6 rounds **mixed salad greens,** 2 cups, with 2 tablespoons light vinaigrette dressing	**Chicken Salad with Cranberries** (Combine ½ cup chopped grilled chicken breast; 3 tablespoons fat-free mayonnaise; and 2 tablespoons each of diced celery, dried cranberries, and chopped walnuts. Serve over 1 cup salad greens - *POINTS* value: **5**.) **melba toast,** 6 rounds **sliced tomato,** 1 **fat-free milk,** 1 cup	**Hot Roast Beef Melt** (Spread 1 slice high-fiber bread with 1 teaspoon Dijon mustard; top with 2 ounces extralean roast beef, 1 [¾-ounce] slice Swiss cheese, and another bread slice. Spread 1 teaspoon light butter over each side of sandwich. Place a nonstick skillet over medium heat. Add sandwich, and cook until both sides of sandwich are toasted - *POINTS* value: **6**.) **cantaloupe chunks,** 1 cup **celery sticks,** 1 cup
DINNER	**grilled skinless, boneless chicken breast half,** 4 ounces **Creamy Polenta, page 150,** 1 serving **Green Beans in Vinaigrette with Feta, page 144,** 1 serving	**Filet Mignon with Three-Herb Gremolata, page 84,** 1 serving **cooked Parmesan couscous (such as Near East),** ½ cup **Roasted Asparagus** (Coat 12 asparagus spears with olive oil-flavored cooking spray; toss with 1 garlic clove, minced, and ⅛ teaspoon salt. Place on a baking sheet, and bake at 450° for 8 minutes - *POINTS* value: **0**.)	**Cajun Black-Eyed Peas and Greens, page 144,** 1 serving **sliced tomato,** 1 **corn bread,** 1 (2-inch) square, with 2 teaspoons light butter
SNACK	**fruit-and-nut trail mix bar,** 1 **fat-free milk,** 1 cup	**Caramel-Apple Galette, page 37,** 1 serving **fat-free milk,** 1 cup	**fruit-and-nut trail mix bar,** 1 **fat-free milk,** 1 cup
POINTS VALUE	*POINTS* value for the day: 25	*POINTS* value for the day: 25	*POINTS* value for the day: 23

One day's menu provides at least two servings of dairy and at least five servings of fruits and/or vegetables.

	MONDAY	TUESDAY	WEDNESDAY	THURSDAY
BREAKFAST	**bran flakes,** 1 cup **fat-free milk,** 1 cup **blueberries,** 1 cup	**whole wheat bagel,** 1 small, with 2 tablespoons light cream cheese **peach,** 1 medium **fat-free milk,** 1 cup	**bran flakes,** 1 cup **fat-free milk,** 1 cup **banana,** 1 small	**Blueberry-Banana Smoothie** (Combine 1 small banana, 1 cup blueberries, 1 cup ice cubes, and 1 [6-ounce] carton vanilla fat-free yogurt in a blender; process until smooth - ***POINTS* value: 4.**)
LUNCH	**bean and ham soup,** canned, 1 cup **cucumber slices,** ½ cup, with 2 tablespoons fat-free Ranch dressing **apple,** 1 small **peach-passion fruit fat-free yogurt smoothie,** 1 (7-ounce) carton	**Pita Pizza** (Spread 2 tablespoons tomato sauce over 1 small pita; sprinkle with 2 tablespoons each of grated Parmesan cheese and chopped black olives. Top with ¼ cup diced tomato and 1 tablespoon crumbled feta cheese. Bake at 350° for 5 minutes or until thoroughly heated - ***POINTS* value: 4.**) **raspberry fat-free yogurt,** 1 (6-ounce) carton **honeydew chunks,** 1 cup	**Chicken Caesar Salad** (Combine 2 cups torn romaine lettuce, ½ cup cucumber slices, and 6 cherry tomatoes. Top with 4 ounces thinly sliced baked chicken breast and 2 tablespoons each of grated Parmesan cheese and reduced-calorie Caesar dressing - ***POINTS* value: 7.**)	**Ham and Honey-Mustard Sandwich** (Spread 1 tablespoon honey mustard on 1 slice high-fiber bread, and top with 2 ounces extralean ham, lettuce, tomato slices, and another bread slice - ***POINTS* value: 5.**) **peach,** 1 medium **celery sticks,** 1 cup **fat-free milk,** 1 cup
DINNER	**Fish Tacos, page 53,** 1 serving **honeydew chunks,** 1 cup	**baked skinless, boneless chicken breast half,** 4 ounces **prepared refrigerated mashed sweet potatoes (such as Simply Potatoes),** ⅔ cup **steamed sugar snap peas,** 1 cup	**Lemon-Mint Lamb Chops, page 86,** 1 serving **cooked roasted garlic and olive oil couscous (such as Near East),** ¾ cup **steamed asparagus,** 12 spears	**Mozzarella-Rotini Skillet Supper, page 74,** 1 serving **Spinach Salad** (Combine 2 cups torn spinach leaves, 6 cherry tomatoes, and 2 tablespoons each of grated Parmesan cheese and light vinaigrette dressing - ***POINTS* value: 2.**) **soft breadstick,** 1
SNACK	**Coconut-Almond Chocolate Ice Cream, page 49,** 1 serving	**high-fiber toast,** 1 slice, with 1 tablespoon peanut butter **fat-free milk,** 1 cup	**apple,** 1 small, with 1 tablespoon peanut butter **fat-free milk,** 1 cup	**Coconut-Almond Chocolate Ice Cream, page 49,** 1 serving
POINTS VALUE	***POINTS* value for the day: 24**	***POINTS* value for the day: 27**	***POINTS* value for the day: 27**	***POINTS* value for the day: 25**

	FRIDAY	SATURDAY	SUNDAY
BREAKFAST	**whole wheat bagel,** 1 small, with 2 tablespoons light cream cheese **blueberries,** 1 cup	**Sticky Orange Rolls, page 27,** 1 serving **fat-free milk,** 1 cup	**Peanut Butter and Banana Bagel** (Spread 1 tablespoon peanut butter on 1 small whole wheat bagel, toasted. Top with 1 small banana, sliced - *POINTS* **value: 6.**)
LUNCH	**bean burrito,** 1 fast food **apple,** 1 small **fat-free milk,** 1 cup	**low-fat spicy sausage pizza,** frozen, 1 single-serving size **cucumber slices,** ½ cup, with 2 tablespoons fat-free Ranch dressing **white chocolate-raspberry fat-free yogurt,** 1 (6-ounce) carton	**Quick Tuna Salad Sandwich** (Combine 4 ounces drained tuna packed in water, ¼ cup chopped celery, 1 tablespoon fat-free mayonnaise, and a dash of pepper; stir well. Spread mixture between 2 slices high-fiber bread - *POINTS* **value: 4.**) **blueberries,** 1 cup **cherry tomatoes,** 6, with 2 tablespoons fat-free Ranch dressing **fat-free milk,** 1 cup
DINNER	**grilled salmon fillet,** 6 ounces **cooked wild rice,** ½ cup **Lemon-Butter Broccoli** (Steam 1½ cups broccoli until desired degree of doneness. Combine 1 tablespoon melted light butter and 1 teaspoon lemon juice; drizzle over broccoli, and sprinkle with salt and pepper, if desired - *POINTS* **value: 1.**)	**General's Chinese Chicken Salad, page 123,** 1 serving **honeydew chunks,** 1 cup	**Horseradish-Turkey Meat Loaf, page 106,** 1 serving **mashed potatoes,** ½ cup **steamed green beans,** 1 cup **fat-free milk,** 1 cup
SNACK	**mixed berry fat-free yogurt smoothie,** 1 (7-ounce) container **peach,** 1 medium	**Double Peach Parfait** (Layer ½ [6-ounce] carton peach fat-free yogurt; ½ peach, peeled and sliced; and 1 tablespoon fat-free whipped topping in a parfait glass. Repeat layers - *POINTS* **value: 3.**)	**Coconut-Almond Chocolate Ice Cream, page 49,** 1 serving
POINTS VALUE	*POINTS* **value for the day: 27**	*POINTS* **value for the day: 27**	*POINTS* **value for the day: 27**

One day's menu provides at least two servings of dairy and at least five servings of fruits and/or vegetables.

	MONDAY	TUESDAY	WEDNESDAY	THURSDAY
BREAKFAST	**cooked oatmeal,** 1 cup, with 1 tablespoon brown sugar **strawberries,** 1½ cups **fat-free milk,** 1 cup	**Breakfast Grilled Cheese** (Place 1 [¾-ounce] slice reduced-fat sharp Cheddar processed cheese between 2 slices high-fiber bread. Spread 1 teaspoon light butter over each side of sandwich. Place a nonstick skillet over medium heat. Add sandwich; cook until cheese melts - **POINTS value: 5.**) **banana,** 1 small	**cooked oatmeal,** 1 cup, with 1 tablespoon honey **fat-free milk,** 1 cup	**high-fiber toast,** 1 slice, with 2 teaspoons light butter **scrambled egg,** 1 large egg **strawberries,** 1½ cups
LUNCH	**low-fat cheese lasagna,** frozen, 1 entrée **celery sticks,** 1 cup, with 2 tablespoons fat-free Ranch dressing	**Tuna-Stuffed Tomato** (Combine 4 ounces drained tuna packed in water, ¼ cup chopped celery, 1 tablespoon fat-free mayonnaise, 1 teaspoon Dijon mustard, and a dash of pepper; stir well. Cut a tomato into 4 wedges, cutting to, but not through bottom; spoon tuna mixture into tomato - **POINTS value: 2.**) **pita,** 1 small, cut into wedges **pineapple chunks,** 1 cup	**Veggie-Hummus Pita Pocket** (Cut a small pita in half; spread 1 tablespoon Kalamata Hummus (page 14) in each pita half. Toss together 1 cup lettuce; 6 cherry tomatoes, halved; ½ cup cucumber slices; and 2 tablespoons each of crumbled feta cheese and light vinaigrette dressing. Divide mixture evenly between pita halves - **POINTS value: 5.**) **strawberries,** 1½ cups **peach fat-free yogurt,** 1 (6-ounce) carton	**Black Bean Soup, page 154,** 1 serving **pineapple chunks,** 1 cup **coleslaw,** ½ cup **fat-free milk,** 1 cup
DINNER	**Texas Flank Steak with Pico de Gallo, page 83,** 1 serving **cooked black beans and rice,** ½ cup **mixed salad greens,** 2 cups, tossed with 3 tablespoons fat-free Ranch dressing and 1 tablespoon salsa	**grilled snapper,** 6 ounces **baked potato,** 1 medium, with 2 teaspoons light butter **Sautéed Summer Squash with Rosemary and Garlic, page 147,** 1 serving **fat-free milk,** 1 cup	**Rosemary-Feta Chicken with Cherry Tomato-Olive Sauce, page 101,** 1 serving **cooked toasted pine nut couscous** (such as Near East), ½ cup **sautéed spinach,** 1 cup	**Hawaiian Calzones, page 131,** 1 serving **mixed salad greens,** 2 cups, with 2 tablespoons fat-free Ranch dressing
SNACK	**Kalamata Hummus, page 14,** 2 servings (includes pitas for dipping) **baby carrots,** 1 cup **fat-free milk,** 1 cup	**Peanut Butter-Chocolate Cookies, page 33,** 3 cookies **fat-free milk,** 1 cup	**cappuccino,** prepared with fat-free milk, 1 grande (16 ounces) **chocolate biscotti,** 1	**tropical fruit fat-free yogurt smoothie,** 1 (7-ounce) container
POINTS VALUE	**POINTS value for the day: 28**	**POINTS value for the day: 26**	**POINTS value for the day: 25**	**POINTS value for the day: 23**

	FRIDAY	SATURDAY	SUNDAY
BREAKFAST	**high-fiber toast,** 1 slice **fat-free milk,** 1 cup **banana,** 1 small	**Pumpkin-Walnut Biscuits, page 26,** 1 serving, with 1 tablespoon honey **fat-free milk,** 1 cup	**Spinach, Mushroom, and Feta Frittata, page 73,** 1 serving **strawberries,** 1½ cups
LUNCH	**Artichoke and Tomato Pasta, page 74,** 1 serving **pineapple chunks,** 1 cup **baby carrots,** 1 cup **fat-free milk,** 1 cup	**chicken nuggets,** fast food, 6 pieces **green salad,** fast food, 1 small **light Italian dressing,** 1 packet **fat-free milk,** 1 cup	**French Bread Pizza** (Split 1 [2-ounce] piece of French bread in half lengthwise. Spoon 2 tablespoons tomato sauce on each cut side of bread; top each side with ¼ cup each of chopped bell pepper, sliced mushrooms, and part-skim mozzarella cheese. Bake at 350° for 6 minutes or until cheese melts - *POINTS* value: 6.) **fat-free milk,** 1 cup
DINNER	**Shrimp and Sausage Jambalaya, page 60,** 1 serving **French bread,** 1 ounce, with 2 teaspoons light butter **coleslaw,** ½ cup	**grilled pork tenderloin,** 3 ounces **Nutty Basmati Rice, page 149,** 1 serving **Greek Salad** (Combine 2 cups salad greens, 2 tablespoons crumbled feta cheese, and 6 each of cherry tomatoes and kalamata olives. Drizzle with 2 tablespoons light vinaigrette - *POINTS* value: 3.)	**roasted turkey breast,** 4 ounces **prepared corn bread stuffing,** ½ cup **steamed green beans,** 1 cup **fat-free milk,** 1 cup
SNACK	**fat-free butterscotch pudding,** 1 snack cup **frozen fat-free whipped topping,** thawed, 2 tablespoons	**Kalamata Hummus, page 14,** 1 serving (includes pitas for dipping) **baby carrots,** 1 cup	**fat-free butterscotch pudding,** 1 snack cup **frozen fat-free whipped topping,** thawed, 2 tablespoons
POINTS VALUE	*POINTS* value for the day: 27	*POINTS* value for the day: 28	*POINTS* value for the day: 25

One day's menu provides at least two servings of dairy and at least five servings of fruits and/or vegetables.

	MONDAY	TUESDAY	WEDNESDAY	THURSDAY
BREAKFAST	**Breakfast PB&J** (Spread 1 tablespoon peanut butter and 1 tablespoon all-fruit spread on cut sides of 1 [2-ounce] English muffin - *POINTS* value: **5**.) **fat-free milk,** 1 cup	**English muffin,** 1 (2-ounce), with 1 tablespoon all-fruit spread **raspberries,** 1 cup	**fat-free cottage cheese,** ½ cup **cantaloupe chunks,** 1 cup **turkey bacon,** 2 slices **fat-free milk,** 1 cup	**Egg and Cheese Muffinwich** (Scramble 1 large egg. Place egg on 1 half of a [2-ounce] English muffin, toasted, and top with 1 [¾-ounce] slice reduced-fat sharp Cheddar processed cheese and remaining half of muffin - *POINTS* value: **6**.)
LUNCH	**tomato-basil soup,** canned, 1½ cups **thin cheese crackers (such as Cheese Nip 100 Calorie Packs),** 1 package **fat-free milk,** 1 cup **mixed salad greens,** 2 cups, with 2 tablespoons light vinaigrette dressing	**Turkey-Pesto Sandwich** (Combine 2 teaspoons fat-free mayonnaise and 2 teaspoons commercial pesto; spread mixture on 1 slice of high-fiber bread. Top with 2 ounces lean deli turkey, 1 [¾-ounce] slice part-skim mozzarella cheese, lettuce, tomato, and another bread slice - *POINTS* value: **7**.) **baby carrots,** 1 cup **fat-free milk,** 1 cup	**Raspberry-Chicken Salad** (Combine 2 cups salad greens, 3 ounces thinly sliced grilled chicken, ⅓ cup raspberries, and 2 tablespoons each of crumbled Gorgonzola cheese and reduced-fat raspberry vinaigrette - *POINTS* value: **6**.) **thin cheese crackers (such as Cheese Nip 100 Calorie Packs),** 1 package **fat-free milk,** 1 cup	**cheeseburger,** fast food, 1 small **pear,** 1 medium **strawberry fat-free yogurt,** 1 (6-ounce) carton
DINNER	**Curried Pork Chops with Mango Sauce, page 87,** 1 serving **cooked herbed chicken couscous (such as Near East),** ½ cup **sautéed zucchini,** 1 cup **grapes,** 1 cup	**grilled chicken tenders,** 3 ounces **steamed new potatoes,** 4 ounces **Grilled Radicchio with Gorgonzola Crumbles, page 146,** 1 serving **fat-free milk,** 1 cup	**Coconut-Curry Tofu Stir-Fry, page 79,** 1 serving **apple,** 1 small	**Grilled Grouper with Cucumber Salsa, page 52,** 1 serving **cooked basmati rice,** ½ cup **steamed sugar snap peas,** 1 cup **fat-free milk,** 1 cup
SNACK	**Bananas Foster Sundae, page 40,** 1 serving	**thin cheese crackers (such as Cheese Nip 100 Calorie Packs),** 1 package **orange,** 1 medium	**vanilla light ice cream,** ¾ cup, with 2 tablespoons fat-free chocolate syrup	**Homemade Green Goddess Dip, page 12,** 1 serving **baby carrots,** 1 cup
POINTS VALUE	*POINTS* value for the day: **28**	*POINTS* value for the day: **27**	*POINTS* value for the day: **29**	*POINTS* value for the day: **28**

	FRIDAY	SATURDAY	SUNDAY	
BREAKFAST	**scrambled egg,** 1 large **turkey bacon,** 2 slices **high-fiber toast,** 1 slice, with 2 teaspoons light butter **cantaloupe,** 1 cup	**Apple-Wheat Germ Pancakes, page 29,** 1 serving, with 2 tablespoons maple syrup **fat-free milk,** 1 cup	**fat-free cottage cheese,** ½ cup **raspberries,** 1 cup **turkey bacon,** 2 slices **fat-free milk,** 1 cup	
LUNCH	**low-fat macaroni and cheese,** frozen, 1 entrée **sliced tomato,** 1 **grapes,** 1 cup **fat-free milk,** 1 cup	**Beef and Gorgonzola over Greens** (Combine 2 cups salad greens, 3 ounces thinly sliced grilled flank steak, 6 cherry tomatoes, and 2 tablespoons each of crumbled Gorgonzola cheese and light raspberry vinaigrette - **POINTS value: 6.**) **grapes,** 1 cup **thin cheese crackers (such as Cheese Nip 100 Calorie Packs),** 1 package	**Turkey Melt** (Spread 1 slice high-fiber bread with 2 teaspoons fat-free mayonnaise and 1 teaspoon Dijon mustard; top with 2 ounces thinly sliced deli turkey, 1 [¾-ounce] slice part-skim mozzarella cheese, and another bread slice. Spread 1 teaspoon light butter over each side of sandwich. Place a nonstick skillet over medium heat. Add sandwich; grill both sides - **POINTS value: 7.**) **fat-free milk,** 1 cup **baby carrots,** 1 cup	
DINNER	**grilled flank steak,** 4 ounces **Oven-Fried Potatoes** (Cut a small baking potato into 6 wedges. Toss with 1 teaspoon olive oil and ¼ teaspoon salt. Bake at 400° for 20 minutes or until crisp - **POINTS value: 2.**) **salad greens,** 2 cups, topped with 2 tablespoons Homemade Green Goddess Dip (page 12)	**Orange-Dijon Chicken, page 103,** 1 serving **cooked wild rice,** ½ cup **steamed broccoli,** 1 cup	**grilled peeled shrimp,** 6 ounces **Pesto Pasta Toss** (Toss ¾ cup hot cooked angel hair pasta with 2 teaspoons commercial pesto. Sprinkle with salt and pepper to taste - **POINTS value: 4.**) **sautéed spinach,** 1 cup	
SNACK	**peach-passion fruit fat-free yogurt smoothie,** 1 (7-ounce) container	**Quick Cocoa** (Stir 2 tablespoons fat-free chocolate syrup into 1 cup fat-free milk; microwave at HIGH 2 minutes or until hot. Top with 1 tablespoon frozen fat-free whipped topping, thawed - **POINTS value: 3.**)	**Chocolate-Raspberry Sundae** (Top ¾ cup vanilla light ice cream with ¼ cup raspberries and 2 tablespoons each of fat-free chocolate syrup and frozen fat-free whipped topping, thawed - **POINTS value: 5.**)	
POINTS VALUE	*POINTS* value for the day: 27	*POINTS* value for the day: 28	*POINTS* value for the day: 29	

General Recipe Index

POINTS® Value Recipe Index

VEGETABLE COOKING CHART

Vegetable	Servings	Preparation	Cooking Instructions
Asparagus	3 to 4 per pound	Snap off tough ends. Remove scales, if desired.	To steam: Cook, covered, on a rack above boiling water 2 to 3 minutes. To boil: Cook, covered, in a small amount of boiling water 2 to 3 minutes or until crisp-tender.
Broccoli	3 to 4 per pound	Remove outer leaves and tough ends of lower stalks. Wash; cut into spears.	To steam: Cook, covered, on a rack above boiling water 5 to 7 minutes or until crisp-tender.
Carrots	4 per pound	Scrape; remove ends, and rinse. Leave tiny carrots whole; slice large carrots.	To steam: Cook, covered, on a rack above boiling water 8 to 10 minutes or until crisp-tender. To boil: Cook, covered, in a small amount of boiling water 8 to 10 minutes or until crisp-tender.
Cauliflower	4 per medium head	Remove outer leaves and stalk. Wash. Break into florets.	To steam: Cook, covered, on a rack above boiling water 5 to 7 minutes or until crisp-tender.
Corn	4 per 4 large ears	Remove husks and silks. Leave corn on the cob, or cut off kernels.	Cook, covered, in boiling water to cover 8 to 10 minutes (on cob) or in a small amount of boiling water 4 to 6 minutes (kernels).
Green beans	4 per pound	Wash; trim ends, and remove strings. Cut into 1½-inch pieces.	To steam: Cook, covered, on a rack above boiling water 5 to 7 minutes. To boil: Cook, covered, in a small amount of boiling water 5 to 7 minutes or until crisp-tender.
Potatoes	3 to 4 per pound	Scrub; peel, if desired. Leave whole, slice, or cut into chunks.	To boil: Cook, covered, in boiling water to cover 30 to 40 minutes (whole) or 15 to 20 minutes (slices or chunks). To bake: Bake at 400° for 1 hour or until done.
Snow peas	4 per pound	Wash; trim ends, and remove tough strings.	To steam: Cook, covered, on a rack above boiling water 2 to 3 minutes. Or sauté in cooking spray or 1 teaspoon oil over medium-high heat 3 to 4 minutes or until crisp-tender.
Squash, summer	3 to 4 per pound	Wash; trim ends, and slice or chop.	To steam: Cook, covered, on a rack above boiling water 6 to 8 minutes. To boil: Cook, covered, in a small amount of boiling water 6 to 8 minutes or until crisp-tender.
Squash, winter (including acorn, butternut, and buttercup)	2 per pound	Rinse; cut in half, and remove all seeds. Leave in halves to bake, or peel and cube to boil.	To boil: Cook cubes, covered, in boiling water 20 to 25 minutes. To bake: Place halves, cut sides down, in a shallow baking dish; add ½ inch water. Bake, uncovered, at 375° for 30 minutes. Turn and season, or fill; bake 20 to 30 minutes or until tender.